IPT's ROTATING EQUIPMENT TRAINING MANUAL
Machinery Reliability & Condition Monitoring

by

BRUCE M. BASARABA and JAMES A. ARCHER

Published by

IPT PUBLISHING AND TRAINING LTD.
BOX 9590, EDMONTON, ALBERTA, CANADA T6E 5X2

www.iptbooks.com
E-mail: info@iptbooks.com
Phone (780) 962-4548   Fax (780) 962-4819
Toll Free 1-888-808-6763

Printed in Canada by
Elite Lithographers, Edmonton, Alberta

IPT's Rotating Equipment Training Manual

First Printing, August 1995
Second Printing, July 1998
Third Printing, August 2002
Sixth Printing March 2013
Seventh Printing April 2019

ISBN 13: 978-0-920855-28-7   ISBN 10: 0-920855-28-8
Copyright © 1995 by IPT Publishing &Training Ltd.

Acknowledgements

The authors and publisher wish to express their appreciation to the following for assistance in developing this publication:

Illustrations:
Cassandra Strumecki, Ted Leach and Michael Doyle.

Body text and illustration co-ordination:
A sincere thank you to Ian Holmes (Holmes Consulting) and Cindy Joly (Finelines Marketing) for their work in organizing this book into its present format, and restructuring the questions and answer book.

Proofreading:
A special thank you is extended to the following for their many hours proofreading this book:
Robert Beaune: B.SC. Mech. Eng., M.ED., Journeyman Millwright, Training Consultant.
and Alvin Nixon: Electrical Engineering Technologist, Journeyman Industrial Mechanic, Senior Electrical Specialist.

Metric Content

This publication is primarily designed for Canada and the United States. Both countries have adopted and use the Metric system, however the degree of use is not consistent in either country, or in certain types of industries. The application of Metric units to vibration analysis, equipment balancing, fluid analysis and performance monitoring for rotating equipment varies as some evaluations and measurements are identified using either one system or the other, and the individuals performing specific evaluations and measurements will have their own preferences. Therefore both Metric and Imperial are shown when practical.

About the Authors

Bruce Basaraba (B.Ed., M.A., Journeyman Millwright) and **James Archer** (HNC Mechanical Engineering, Mining Mechanical Engineer's Certificate, Journeyman Millwright) have a combined total of 60 years in the industrial maintenance and management fields. This combined experience includes working as journeyman millwrights, maintenance management and supervision, and teaching rotating equipment design, installation and maintenance in the millwright trade.

TABLE OF CONTENTS

i

TABLE OF CONTENTS

TABLE OF CONTENTS

TABLE OF CONTENTS

TABLE OF CONTENTS

TABLE OF CONTENTS

TABLE OF CONTENTS

TABLE OF CONTENTS

SECTION ONE

MAINTENANCE AND RELIABILITY

2 MAINTENANCE AND RELIABILITY

Rotating Equipment Maintenance Problems

The maintenance department of any industrial plant develops gradually, over a period of time. The maintenance department must be an integral support team which works with various departments within the plant in order to aid in accomplishing the primary objectives of the organization.

Rotating equipment maintenance constitutes a very high percentage of the plant's overall operating costs. In North America it is not unusual to see companies spending up to 50% of their total operating budget on what is referred to as maintenance. Performing planned and cost-effective maintenance on rotating equipment therefore is important, and more emphasis and planning towards having well managed, cost-effective and reliable maintenance programs in place has to be considered in the company's long range planning.

Maintenance problems are usually caused by: normal wear and tear, careless or untrained operations and maintenance personnel, improper lubrication or incorrect lubrication selection, and failure to make small repairs and adjustments which become catastrophic failures.

Additional maintenance problems are caused by: incorrect equipment or component design, excessive loads and speeds, incorrect alignment practices, excessive amounts of vibration, using low quality replacement parts such as bearings, seals and fasteners, and an unwillingness by management to place meaningful priorities on the maintenance functions.

Note: Other causes of maintenance problems could be listed, but one thing is abundantly clear; rotating equipment maintenance costs money and failure to perform corrective maintenance on equipment eventually costs the company far more over the long term.

Rotating Equipment Maintenance Problems (cont'd)

Current research in North America indicated the following cost related statistics concerning rotating equipment maintenance and reliability:

- Over 25% of bearings used in rotating equipment fail prematurely due primarily to faulty installation and/or poor lubrication practices.

- Over 70% of the failures experienced in plant and industrial hydraulic systems are caused by contaminated hydraulic fluids.

- Inconsistent and poor lubrication procedures are one of the principle causes of machinery breakdown.

- The average construction/contracting company spends between 25 - 45% of its operating budget on mobile equipment maintenance. This value is for parts and labor, not for fuels, lube or depreciation.

In order to reduce these trends and high costs, management and employees must consider changing their view of what the maintenance function is to be. Programs must be developed which provide effective maintenance practices and are seen as "investments", rather than costs. Once this change in thinking takes place, and is put into practice with both management and employee support, long-term maintenance expenditures can be reduced.

The recommended method for ensuring that a reliable maintenance program works in a particular environment is to have the people in that environment develop the program. Rather than just copy a maintenance program from someone else, develop it to respond to the in-plant equipment maintenance needs and ensure the program is satisfactory for the company's objectives.

Rotating Equipment Maintenance Problems (cont'd)

Note: Approximately one third of all maintenance dollars are wasted because the money is spent on "reaction" instead of "proactive" and "prevention" activities. This is mostly due to inefficiencies in maintenance programs which probably do the right things, but at the wrong time and often for the wrong reasons.

Maintenance Program Objectives

The primary objectives of any maintenance program's activities include:

1. To ensure that the equipment operates safely and relatively trouble-free for long periods of time.

2. To maximize the availability of machinery and equipment necessary to meet the planned production and operational objectives.

3. To consistently maintain the plant equipment in order to minimize wear and premature deterioration.

4. To make the equipment reliable so it can be counted on to perform to set standards and conditions.

Maintenance Improvement and Reliability Program (MIRP)

The following ten steps outline a plan when a company is considering developing an effective Maintenance Improvement and Reliability Program (MIRP).

Step 1: Begin by initiating a "total maintenance" approach. Production and maintenance must collectively work together. The maintenance department has to be viewed as being an integral part of the organization.

Step 2: Establish a clear vision by having the employees and management identify the problems, then specify the goals and objectives that must be set in order to achieve success.

MIRP Program (cont'd)

Step 3: Analyze the organization. Will the organization, as a whole, support the type of improvements required? If not, consider changing the organizational structure and/or redesign the system to meet the identified needs. Review the production and operational policies and procedures, as they may not be suited to the maintenance improvement and reliability program.

Step 4: Begin to develop an "action plan." Identify what is going to be attempted, who is to be involved, what are the resources required, etc. Action plans take on many different forms, but it is important that the plan contain inputs drawn from the reviews and analysis rather than from complaints.

Step 5: Assess the condition of the equipment and facilities. Be objective in the assessment. Determine which equipment requires immediate attention.

Step 6: Select the appropriate maintenance program. Is a computerized maintenance system needed? What technique will be employed, - reactive, preventive or predictive maintenance? Determine the order maintenance activities will be carried out, first, then second, etc.? What type of reporting system will be used to track and record the data collected when measuring the performance of each piece of equipment?

Step 7: Measure equipment condition. When measuring for equipment condition which method(s) will be considered: vibration analysis; fluid analysis; non-destructive testing; or performance monitoring methods?

MIRP Program (cont'd)

Step 8: Prepare the maintenance personnel. As the maintenance program activities and methods are implemented ensure that the maintenance personnel are trained to understand the program and why the activities and methods are performed. Without this step no type of maintenance improvement and reliability program will succeed.

Step 9: Monitor equipment and machinery effectiveness to the detail the maintenance program requires. Monitor for performance, reliability and quality. Over time, the recorded information can be used to evaluate the machinery and equipment condition and situation. This is an on-going activity of any quality maintenance program.

Step 10: Initiate periodic reviews. Equipment and machinery effectiveness is based on scheduled predictive and preventive maintenance activities.

The review of these activities may indicate common problems and trends which identify any design or operational changes required. Include engineering, maintenance and production personnel in these periodic reviews. Ensure that action plans develop from these review sessions, not just complaints.

Maintenance Programs
Methods of Maintenance

There are three ways to perform maintenance: preventive, predictive, and reactive or "breakdown" maintenance.

Preventive Maintenance Programs: Normally involve the routine scheduling of maintenance activities. The schedule is based on past experience and the manufacturer's recommendations. The activities of the preventive maintenance program are usually based on periodic sampling and inspections. An unskilled preventive maintenance team may leave the machine in a worse condition after the planned shutdown.

Preventive Maintenance Programs (cont'd)

Sufficient spare parts and available maintenance personnel are allocated when overhauls and shutdowns are scheduled. Often there continues to be "unplanned" losses, albeit, less than when no form of maintenance program is in place. Many repairs are often initiated before components reach their maximum working life, which results in a great deal of unnecessary expense.

Predictive Maintenance Programs: This is a systematic method of monitoring the plant's rotating equipment performance and is carried out on a regularly scheduled basis to determine the equipment condition. Predictive maintenance utilizes information from past and current performance records to objectively predict mechanical problems.

Predictions based on the analysis of the information form the basis for corrective actions to be taken.

Note: Unlike breakdown maintenance and preventive maintenance, predictive maintenance is an active condition monitoring approach rather than a reaction or time based approach to maintenance.

To run efficiently in modern industries, the production machinery must operate near or at the design capacity with minimum downtime. The specific purpose of a quality predictive maintenance program is to minimize unscheduled machinery failures, reduce maintenance costs and loss of production. To accomplish these objectives a program is required which will:

1. Regularly monitor the mechanical condition of all critical production equipment.
2. Identify outstanding problems.

From this program, the severity of each problem is quantified, and scheduled maintenance procedures are performed to prevent failures.

Predictive Maintenance Programs (cont'd)

Predictive maintenance programs evolved from preventive maintenance programs. Preventive maintenance programs for rotating equipment are generally based on periodic sampling and inspecting. Most preventive maintenance programs have established schedules for periodic inspections of identified equipment which is critical to the operation.

Predictive maintenance programs reduce the frequency and severity of emergency repairs and can increase equipment life. This system and the data gathered regarding performance and condition form the basis for predictive maintenance programs.

In a predictive maintenance program the specific maintenance tasks are based on actual need. This approach reduces the amount of unnecessary repairs, unexpected failures and downtime as repairs are often now done, and maintenance intervals therefore, should be extended.

Reactive (Breakdown) Maintenance Programs:

This type of maintenance program occurs by default if problems aren't detected and corrected prior to absolute failure. Typically, reactive or breakdown maintenance is the most expensive of the three maintenance methods. Reactive maintenance may, however, be justified for certain "non vital" machinery, or for machinery where lifetime and cost of failure does not justify a more planned approach to maintenance, as preventive or predictive maintenance programs are.

Predictive Maintenance Program Benefits

Setting up an effective predictive maintenance program will provide many of the following benefits:

- improved operator safety
- reduced environmental hazards
- increased production
- increased machinery availability
- provide for scheduled rather than unscheduled downtime
- reduced risk of catastrophic failures
- minimize unnecessary repairs and repair time
- reduce spare part inventories
- improve product quality
- optimize maintenance department size
- better utilization of maintenance personnel

Machinery Condition Monitoring

In previous machinery and equipment maintenance, a machine was often permitted to operate until complete failure occurred. Actual machinery condition monitoring was quite simple, as there was no real sophisticated method for measuring machine condition, nor did management or the employees concern themselves with a more proactive approach to maintenance.

The maintenance plan was to periodically tear down and overhaul the machine as assurance against failure.

Four techniques were commonly used in the past to monitor the machinery condition and these techniques continue to be used, although each technique has become more sophisticated. The techniques described "sense" the condition of the machine.

1. Any increases or decreases in temperature (touch and smell).
2. Any increases or decreases in vibration (touch).

Machinery Condition Monitoring (cont'd)

3. Any change in noise or sound from the machine (listen).

4. Any visual or observed changes and problems (sight).

Each technique helps in determining to what extent a mechanical fault exists and if it is progressing. The corrective action is often based on "feel", sound, or appearance.

Temperature

Higher temperature often indicates that a bearing is acting abnormally. High temperature can be detrimental to the bearing, the lubricant, and the shaft and seals. This is evident when the machine has continued to operate for extended periods when the bearing or lubrication temperatures have been in excess of 260°F (125°C).

Causes of high bearing and lubrication temperatures include insufficient or excessive lubrication, contaminated lubricants, overloading, bearing damage, faulty installation, insufficient bearing clearances, and improper or failed seals.

It is necessary to check the temperature of bearings periodically, both at the bearing itself and at other locations on the machine where high temperatures could be cause for concern. Any significant change in temperature is usually a good indication that a problem exists, especially if the operating conditions of the machine have not been altered.

Bearing temperatures can be determined roughly by hand feel, as shown in illustration #1, or by routinely and accurately checked with a surface thermometer. A permanently installed heat sensor may also be installed on or near critical parts of the machine.

Overheating is often first detected by smell resulting from hot plastics or oil.

Machinery Condition Monitoring (cont'd)

Vibration

Another method commonly used to "feel" the condition of a machine is to determine how much vibration exists at the machine. By touching the bearing, as shown in illustration #1, high temperature and vibrations are felt. The amount of vibration present is difficult to measure this way, but one may be able to compare the vibration felt today to how it felt yesterday, or several weeks ago.

Vibration can be more accurately measured by using tools such as vibration meters, analyzers, or monitors. Illustration #2 demonstrates the use of a simple vibration meter. The probe is placed on, or near the bearing and a vibration reading is given on the meter. The amount of vibration measured is used to determine the severity of the vibration and the condition of the machine.

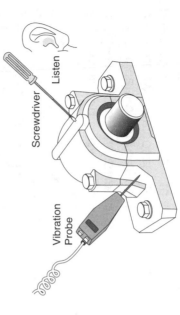

Illustration #1 — Detecting Bearing Temperature

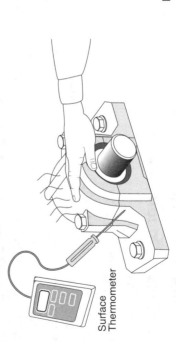

Illustration #2 - Detecting Bearing Vibration and Noise

Machinery Condition Monitoring (cont'd)

Listening

One method used in industry to identify irregularities on machinery and equipment is to listen for changes in sounds emitted from machines while operating under conditions of normal loads and speeds. One can do this by placing a screwdriver blade on the bearing housing and being safely positioned so the ear contacts the screwdriver handle. The ear is listening to the internal sounds coming from the bearing. Abnormal noises may be detected and traced to a specific component of the machine by experienced maintenance personnel.

More sophisticated methods are used to listen to bearings as well. A stethoscope can be used to listen to the internal sounds of the bearing parts. Microphones can be held over the machine or mounted at critical points to measure the sound amplitude being emitted.

Sound measurements can be used to determine the severity of the problem. Sound and vibration are closely associated when determining irregularities in running machinery.

Grinding, squeaking and other irregular sounds can point to worn bearings. The squeaking noise is often caused by inadequate lubrication. Insufficient bearing clearances can make a metallic tone. Indentations in the outer ring raceway will produce smooth, clear tones, and ring damage caused by shock loads or hammer blows lead to sounds varying in frequency according to the operating speed of the machine. Intermittent noises probably indicate damage to certain spots on the rolling members. Contamination in the bearing produces a rough grinding sound. Damaged bearings produce irregular and loud noises. Good bearings sound smoother, fewer irregular sounds, less grinding sounds, and more of a constant humming sound.

Machinery Condition Monitoring (cont'd)

Sight

Maintenance personnel, as shown in illustration #3, can simply look at equipment to see if there is anything out of the ordinary happening. Check for any apparent oil leaks or grease leaks around seal areas, or if any of the bearing housings are loose, cracked or improperly assembled.

Check the lubricant. Discoloration or darkening of the oil is usually a good indication that the lubricant is either contaminated or worn out. It is also very important to check whether or not there is sufficient lubricant.

Is the lubricant the proper one for the application? Check whether the air vent is free of obstructions.

Take a small sample of used oil and compare it with new oil. If it is cloudy in appearance, water has more than likely mixed with it, therefore, the oil must be replaced.

Dark or thick oil is a sure sign of contamination or that the oil has started to carbonize. Overheating may have caused this problem.

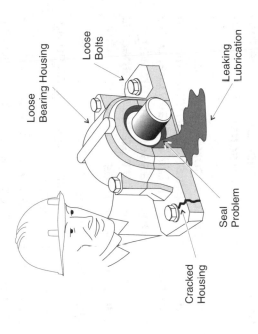

Illustration #3 — **Detecting Bearing Problems Visually**

Corrective Maintenance

Corrective maintenance work should be planned and scheduled, unless true emergencies unexpectedly arise. Planning involves identifying all resources necessary to repair the machinery. This identification of resources may include:

- tradesman man-hours worked
- available materials/replacement parts
- required special tools and equipment
- availability of contract personnel
- location of mechanical drawings
- supply of assembly/disassembly guidelines
- safety orientation
- installation and setting procedures
- sequence of tasks and time durations
- work schedules and shift rotations
- job cost estimates
- safety and environmental regulations and permits

Corrective Maintenance/Planning

- arrangements for restrooms, lunchrooms, lockers, etc.

Note: The maintenance planner responsible for planning and scheduling the corrective maintenance work must have direct access to records which contain past maintenance history, information on equipment design, bill of materials, parts list, assembly/disassembly drawings, and current inventory status for specific parts and assemblies.

Maintenance Planning

There are three basic areas of planning administered by maintenance planners.

Long-Range Planning: These plans for maintenance requirements are allied with, and dependent on, long-range sales and production forecasts. Planners work with management to outline what is needed in the way of decisions in order to reach certain goals in five to twenty years.

Maintenance Planning (cont'd)

Short and Mid-Range Planning: These plans project from one to five years into the future. Plans are developed under the direct supervision of the managers responsible for defined maintenance and production activities. Maintenance and operating budgets, equipment overhaul requirements and the activities identified through the predictive maintenance program are involved in both short and mid-range planning.

Immediate Planning: This type of maintenance planning may be referred to as "day-to-day" maintenance planning. This type of planning is done on a pre-programmed routine and is carried out by the maintenance teams. These plans are generated from the inspections, observations and performance measurements regularly performed as part of the predictive maintenance program.

These plans are primarily concerned with action oriented maintenance activities for to-day, tomorrow, and the following week.

Maintenance Planning: Using the Critical Path Method (CPM)

Illustration #4 and table #1 outline a method for developing a maintenance plan and schedule for performing major maintenance work on large projects. The critical path method (CPM) utilizes a system, not unlike a flow chart, for representing the inter-relationships between specific job activities of the project. The maintenance planner or project manager will find this method extremely useful for planning and controlling machinery and equipment installations, modifications, overhauls, facility expansions, new construction and start-up testing and commissioning.

Interpreting CPM
(see illustration #4, table #1)

1. Circles on the chart represent "nodes", which is the point marking the beginning or completion of a task in the project.

2. Arrows represent the work required to be performed between the nodes which must be completed before the following event may occur. The duration in time for the specific work is indicated as well. Time may be measured in hours, days, weeks, months, or years.

Direct relationships are established for the phases of progression of the total project through the arrow diagram. This requires plotting the nodes and jobs, analyzing the relationship between each, estimating the elapsed time, and establishing calendar dates for each node. Determining the longest elapsed time throughout the diagram defines the "critical path" from the beginning of the project to its completion.

Illustration #4 demonstrates a simplified example of a critical path for performing a turbine overhaul. *(Note: example only)*. The arrow diagram, as illustrated, identifies the relationships between the start and finish times for each job.

For example, Job 3 - 4, "inspect, clean control lines", has been estimated to require four days. Because of its relationship to other jobs, the job cannot be started before day 14, and must be started by day 56, leaving a 42 day float. The earliest finishing time is day 13 and the latest finishing time would be day 60. Table #1 demonstrates this analysis.

Note: CPM is not a technique for establishing maintenance time requirements for the individual elements of each job, but it offers a proven method for piecing the times of each specific job together to determine the total time required to successfully complete the project.

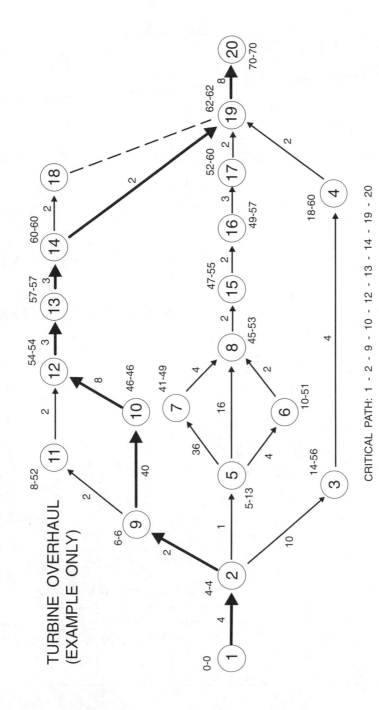

TURBINE OVERHAUL
(EXAMPLE ONLY)

CRITICAL PATH: 1 - 2 - 9 - 10 - 12 - 13 - 14 - 19 - 20

Illustration #4 - Critical Path Method

Maintenance Planning/CPM

Work Segment Number	WORK DESCRIPTION	Estimated Jobtime	Earliest Start Time	Latest Start Time	Earliest Finish Time	Latest Finish Time	Float	Critical Work
1-2	Check Stand - by Unit No:	4	0	0	4	4	0	4
2-3	Check Rebuild Calibrate gauges	10	4	4	14	14	0	
2-5	Dismantle Unit No: _Casing	1	4	4	5	5	0	
2-9	Dismantle Unit No: _Rotor	2	4	4	6	6	0	2
3-4	Inspect,Clean Control Lines	4	14	56	18	60	42	
4-19	Replace Control Gages	2	18	60	20	62	42	
5-6	Lubrication System : Overhaul	4	5	13	9	17	8	
5-7	Rebuild Unit No. _Impeller	36	5	13	41	49	7	
5-8	Clean, Inspect Unit No._ Casing	4	5	13	9	17	18	
6-8	Install, Fit Unit No:_Bearings	2	10	51	11	53	42	
7-8	Balance Unit No: _Impeller	4	41	49	45	53	4	
8-15	Reinstall Impeller Unit No: _	2	45	53	47	55	8	
9-10	Rebuild Unit No: _Rotor	40	6	6	46	46	0	40
9-11	Check, Dress Rotor Bearings	2	6	6	8	8	0	
10-12	Balance Unit No: _Rotor	8	46	46	54	54	0	8
11-12	Fit Unit No:_Seals, Bearings	2	8	52	10	54	44	
12-13	Reinstall Rotor Unit No:	3	54	54	57	57	0	3
13-14	Reinstall Unit No:_Casings	3	57	57	60	60	0	3
14-18	Test Unit No:	2	60	60	62	62	0	
14-19	Check Clearances Unit No:	2	60	60	62	62	0	2
15-16	Check Bearings Pump No:	2	47	55	49	57	8	
16-17	Reinstall Pump No:	3	49	57	52	60	8	
17-19	Install Shaft Seal, Packing	2	52	60	54	62	8	
19-20	Final Adjustment Tests	8	62	62	70	70	0	8

Table #1 - Planning and Sequencing Activities

(CPM) Critical Path Method (cont'd)

Note: Computer software is a must for planning and scheduling work functions and maintenance routines. Project management software often includes a model similar to the critical path method identified in this handbook. There are examples of this type of modern software which can be directly integrated with computerized predictive maintenance programs as well.

Maintenance Planning: PERT (Program Evaluation Review Technique)

The Program Evaluation Review Technique (PERT) is similar to CPM in that the elements of a program are also shown by the arrow diagram. The CPM chart's arrow diagram, node and job become PERT's network, event and activity, respectively.

Other differences involve the estimate of time for the completion of the activity (estimates of optimistic, most likely, and pessimistic elapsed times for each activity).

CPM identifies the tasks that will delay the completion date if they are not completed on time.

Both CPM and PERT lead to basic improvements in the depth of planning accomplished, resulting in better time estimates, and improved control of the project through earlier detection or logging of uncompleted events.

Implementation Concerns of a Predictive Maintenance Program:

● Implementation will require the company to invest in both equipment and manpower. If the program is to be successful, management must endorse the program as well as commit the necessary resources to keep the program operational for the long-term.

Predictive Maintenance: Concerns (cont'd)

- Predictive maintenance programs have failed because management may have agreed to providing initial resources to start the program, but operational resources to keep the program running were not fully secured to provide for on-going training and consulting support to modify or update the program. Insufficient support for providing on-going resources like these can lead to failure.

- It is imperative that viable communication links are established among the production personnel, maintenance crews, and the various predictive maintenance teams.

Predictive Maintenance Concerns

Lack of effective communication linkages or opportunities for feedback and discussion among the active participants will lead to misinformation and render the program ineffective.

Corporate and plant management have to "buy into" the objectives of the predictive maintenance program. Top level managers lead by example, if they are supporters of the program it will prosper. An impetus to endorse and support the program will filter down the organizational ranks and will help to make the program successful.

The predictive maintenance program can be organized into the "team concept." By having all the team members working together, with each member offering expertise, support and cooperation to other team members, the goals and objectives of the program can be more easily achieved.

Predictive Maintenance: Concerns (cont'd)

It may be found that too much is expected too early from a predictive maintenance program. Research and experience indicates that it may take a minimum of two years from program inception to begin to see benefits.

It is easy to become overwhelmed by the volume of technical information and data collected in the beginning stages of the predictive maintenance program. Many of the outstanding problems will be identified and corrected immediately. No attempt should be made to discontinue the program because many serious faults were initially corrected. Experience suggests that problems and faults associated with mechanical failures in rotating equipment are always going to exist. Sooner or later the problems resurface, but some form of objective prediction, may often avoid serious disasters or greatly reduce the seriousness of the problem.

Predictive Maintenance Program Applications

Predictive maintenance programs can be developed and implemented for a variety of industries, each having specific process and manufacturing machinery and rotating equipment.

Four methods for measuring the performance and reliability of rotating equipment will be discussed throughout this handbook. Each method mentioned is a "direct" method of measurement for determining the machinery condition. The results of these measurements are used in the predictive maintenance program. Abnormal measurements can indicate the severity level of the problem and help to predict the causes of failure. Problems detected and identified early can mean the difference between a simple repair or adjustment, or a complete overhaul of the machine.

Predictive Maintenance Program

Predictive Maintenance Program Applications (cont'd)

The four methods used for measuring the performance and reliability of rotating equipment and machinery are:

1. Vibration and Noise Measurements.

2. Non-Destructive Testing and Inspection.

3. Fluid Analysis.

4. Performance Measurement and Evaluation.

Illustration #5 identifies each of the four methods commonly used in modern day quality predictive maintenance programs for determining machinery performance and reliability.

Predictive Maintenance Program

1. Vibration and Noise Measurement: Involves measuring vibration and noise levels near the rotating equipment's bearings or other critical components. The vibration checks can be completed at locations on housings or supports near machinery components, such as: rotating shafts, bearings, gears, sheaves/pulleys, and hubs.

The basic characteristic of machinery vibration and noise is that all rotating equipment and associated components suffering from mechanical faults, begin to deteriorate and produce increased levels of vibration and noise at frequencies related to the speed of rotation (RPM).

These increased levels of vibration and noise can be accurately monitored to provide advance warning when mechanical faults exist which in turn could cause serious breakdowns or failures. See Sections Two and Three for more detail.

Predictive Maintenance Program

Applications (cont'd)

Vibration measurement, or as some commonly say, vibration analysis, has become one of the most recognized methods for measuring machinery performance and reliability. Vibration analysis is generally included in most quality predictive maintenance programs.

2. Non-Destructive Testing (NDT) and Inspection:

This method used for checking machinery condition has in the past been designated a specialty field. Various methods now are available for trained maintenance personnel to perform non-destructive tests on a wide range of rotating equipment and plant machinery parts.

Techniques commonly used for performing non-destructive tests include:

- visual (direct and remote)
- ultrasonic
- eddy current
- radiography (x-ray)
- liquid dye penetrants
- magnetic particle inspections

Non-destructive testing methods are used to identify and quantify internal and external faults to specific parts of rotating equipment and machinery. This includes: shafting, gearing, couplings, bearings, threaded fasteners, impellers, blading, rolls, bearing housings, casings, covers and machinery frame and support systems. Cracks, imperfections, forging irregularities, oxidation, corrosion, erosion, porosity, bad welds, and general deterioration may be detected by using one of the non-destructive methods identified. See Section Six for more detail.

FLUID ANALYSIS

- VISUAL TESTING
- SPECTROSCOPY
- FERROGRAPHY

NON-DESTRUCTIVE TESTING

- LIQUID PENETRATION INSPECTION
- MAGNETIC PARTICLE INSPECTION
- VISUAL (DIRECT AND REMOTE)
- ULTRASONIC INSPECTION
- EDDY CURRENT
- RADIOGRAPHY (X-RAY)

PREDICTIVE MAINTENANCE

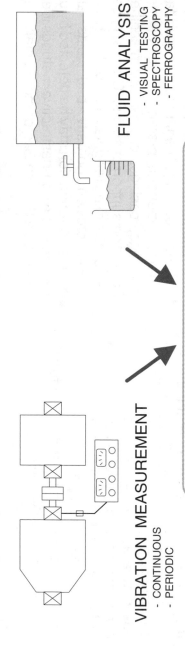

VIBRATION MEASUREMENT

- CONTINUOUS
- PERIODIC

MACHINE PERFORMANCE EVALUATION

VOLTS

AMPS

OHMS

PRESSURE   VELOCITY

TEMPERATURE   VACUUM

Illustration #5 — Monitoring Machine Condition

Predictive Maintenance Program
Applications (cont'd)

Non-destructive testing is performed on a routine basis or as a one time only test, depending on the circumstance. The objective is to identify faults within the component prior to further deterioration or disintegration. Inspect the test results and decide as to what the most appropriate corrective action will be.

3. Fluid Analysis: Expert analysis of fluids, such as lubricants and coolants, are normally performed periodically on critical and expensive machines. For example, lubrication fluid, such as oil, is supplied to critical areas on a machine, such as bearings, seals, gears or chain drives. By performing an analysis of the oil one may be able to determine whether concentrated areas of heavy wear exist at some particular part.

Fluid analysis involves the study of lubricating oils, hydraulic fluids, greases, fuels, coolants, and flushing fluids. These fluids travel unhindered throughout the component's sections. For example, if an oil or grease lubricated bearing begins to wear, metal from the bearing will begin to appear in the lubricant.

There are many methods for performing fluid analysis. The oil filter collects debris which can be recovered and analyzed. While the machine is operating, an oil sample is safely drawn, disclosing various foreign particles suspended during fluid circulation. Magnetic plugs, strategically located in areas of the lube system, collect/attract ferrous materials which may have originated from ferrous components within the machine. See Section Five for more detail.

Predictive Maintenance Program Applications (cont'd)

Other techniques for analyzing fluids include:

a. Spectroscopy: Which involves burning oil or hydraulic fluid samples to determine the quantity of metal particles in a given sample size.

b. Ferrography: A technique for not only determining the type of metal contaminant found in the lubricant, but how the contaminant was generated; by corrosion, impact damage, or sliding wear.

4. Machinery Performance Measurement and Evaluation: This method of monitoring machinery condition is done while the machine is operating at specific speeds and loads. This method consists of collecting, either on demand or continuously, performance data information, such as: temperatures, pressures, flows, voltage, amperage, resistance, vacuum, RPM, and surges.

This data is then compared to the normal settings for specific loads and speeds as recommended by the manufacturer of the machine.

After the performance data has been collected, an evaluation report is prepared which identifies which performance ratings are hinting that possible machine failure is about to occur. Generally, this method of machine condition monitoring requires several types of testing equipment. Additionally, trained maintenance personnel are needed to perform most of the tests. Evaluating the test results may take another level of trained personnel to perform. See Section Eight for more detail.

Measuring Machinery Performance Review

Periodically measuring machinery performance and reliability provides an early warning system for identifying impending changes in machinery condition.

Measuring Machinery Performance Review (cont'd)

Any of the four methods described can be used for measuring the performance and reliability of rotating equipment and plant machinery. The information gathered is used to determine whether the equipment is in good operating condition or if serious problems and faults exist.

After the mechanical problems and faults have been identified, appropriate corrective actions must be considered. The technical data collected during the testing activities will serve to form many of the corrective action decisions made. In doing these activities, one has primarily followed the principle steps of a predictive maintenance program. The instrumentation used to collect the data and the knowledge and experience required to analyze the data and to make predictions are key elements to the overall success of the predictive maintenance program.

Measuring Machinery Performance Conclusion

After the predictive maintenance program has been established, it is accepted that the information collected to form many of the predictions will come from several sources. The predictive maintenance program is made up of statistical data accumulated from vibration and noise measurements, non-destructive testing and inspections, fluid analysis, and machine performance measuring and evaluations. Not often can one method stand alone, and it is to the company's benefit to incorporate all of these methods for detecting machinery condition. Vibration measurement and analysis is the foundation to build a rotating equipment predictive maintenance program on, but non-destructive testing and inspection, fluid analysis, and performance measurement and evaluation are excellent support systems to have on hand for further quantifying machinery condition.

SECTION ONE - QUESTIONS
Maintenance and Reliability

1. Rotating equipment maintenance constitutes a very high percentage of a plant's overall operating costs.

   ☐ true   ☐ false

2. List four primary causes of maintenance problems:

   Answer: _____

3. Programs must be developed which provide effective maintenance practices, and which are seen as:

   ☐ costs rather than investments
   ☐ investments rather than costs
   ☐ customer satisfiers rather than true requirements

4. The recommended method for ensuring that a reliable maintenance program works in a particular environment is to have employees help develop the program.

   ☐ true   ☐ false

5. Identify the four primary objectives of an effective maintenance program.

   Answer: _____

6. Step One of the "Maintenance Improvement and Reliability Program" (MIRP) is to initiate a "total maintenance approach." Explain what this means.

   Answer: _____

7. Step Two of the "Maintenance Improvement and Reliability Program" (MIRP) is establishing a "clear vision." Explain what this means.

   Answer: _____

8. Step Three of the "Maintenance Improvement and Reliability Program" (MIRP) is "analyze the organization." Explain what this means.

   Answer: _____

9. Identify Step Four and Step Five of the "Maintenance Improvement and Reliability Program" (MIRP).

   Answer: _____

10. Step Six of the "Maintenance Improvement and Reliability Program" (MIRP) asks which maintenance program technique will be appropriate? What are the three techniques?

Answer: _____

11. Which four measurement techniques are referred to in Step Seven of the "Maintenance Improvement and Reliability Program" (MIRP)?

Answer: _____

12. Can the "Maintenance Improvement and Reliability Program" (MIRP) succeed without properly preparing the maintenance personnel? Refer to Step Eight of MIRP.

☐ yes   ☐ no

Provide an explanation to your response.

Answer: _____

13. Step Nine of the "Maintenance Improvement and Reliability Program" (MIRP) requires monitoring equipment and machinery effectiveness. Explain what purpose monitoring serves.

Answer: _____

14. Step Ten of the "Maintenance Improvement and Reliability Program" (MIRP) requires initiating "periodic reviews." What purpose do these periodic reviews serve?

Answer: _____

15. Which type of maintenance program normally involves routine scheduling of maintenance activities and the schedule is mainly based on past experience and manufacturer recommendations?

☐ preventive   ☐ predictive
☐ reactive

16. Which type of maintenance program uses a systematic method of monitoring and trending the plant's equipment performance?

☐ preventive   ☐ predictive
☐ reactive

17. _____ maintenance programs reduce the frequency and severity of emergency repairs and can increase equipment life.

☐ preventive   ☐ predictive
☐ reactive

18. Which type of maintenance program bases specific maintenance tasks on actual need?

☐ preventive ☐ predictive
☐ reactive

19. Which type of maintenance program occurs by default if problems are not detected and corrected prior to absolute failure?

☐ preventive ☐ predictive
☐ reactive

20. Identify four techniques which are commonly employed for "sensing" the condition of a machine.

Answer: _____

21. What causes high bearing and lubrication temperatures?

☐ insufficient bearing clearances
☐ faulty installation
☐ insufficient or excessive lubrication amounts
☐ all of the above

22. A method used to "feel" the condition of a machine is for determining how much _____ exists at the machine.

☐ noise ☐ vibration
☐ oil pressure ☐ resistance

23. The amount of vibration measured is used for determining the _____ of the vibration.

☐ frequency ☐ amplitude
☐ phase ☐ severity

24. What device can be held over a machine or even mounted on a machine to measure sound amplitude?

☐ stethoscope ☐ microphone
☐ oscilloscope ☐ proximity probe

25. Discoloration or darkening of a lubricating oil is usually an indication that the lube is:

☐ normal and proper color
☐ high quality and synthetic
☐ contaminated or worn out

26. What are three basic areas of planning administered by maintenance planners?

Answer: _____

27. The "Critical Path Method" (CPM) utilizes a system for representing the inter-relationships between specific job activities of a maintenance project.

☐ true ☐ false

28. "Critical Path Method" (CPM) is a technique for establishing time requirements for the individual elements of each job.

    ☐ true   ☐ false

29. List three main concerns which should be considered when implementing a predictive maintenance program.

    Answer: _____

30. It may be found that too much is expected too early from a predictive maintenance program.

    ☐ true   ☐ false

31. Increased levels of vibration and noise can be accurately monitored to provide advance warnings when serious mechanical faults exist in rotating machinery.

    ☐ true   ☐ false

32. Vibration analysis is not one of the more recognized methods for measuring machinery performance and reliability.

    ☐ true   ☐ false

33. Non-destructive testing methods are used to identify and quantify internal and external faults to specific parts of rotating equipment and machinery.

    ☐ true   ☐ false

34. By performing an analysis of a lubricant one may be able to determine whether any areas of heavy wear exist in the machine.

    ☐ true   ☐ false

35. Machinery performance measurement and evaluation is a method of monitoring machine condition while the machine is operating at specific speeds and loads.

    ☐ true   ☐ false

36. Periodically measuring machinery performance and reliability:

    ☐ is only done on critical machines and equipment
    ☐ is too time consuming and costly to do
    ☐ is unrealistic in today's high production demand operations
    ☐ provides an early warning system for identifying changes in machinery condition

SECTION TWO
VIBRATION ANALYSIS

Introduction To Vibration Analysis

Using vibration measurements is one of the best methods available for detecting and controlling the mechanical condition of rotating equipment. The basic characteristics of machinery vibration will be discussed in this section.

Vibration analysis is the process of performing vibration measurements and interpreting the collected data. This process of "direct measurement" is used to determine the the mechanical condition of a machine, locate specific faults and provide information for planning corrective action.

What Is Vibration?

Vibration is defined as the motion of a machine or machine part back and forth from its normal center position or position of rest. This motion may be described as being the "rhythmic oscillation" of a machine or one of its parts.

A force which is changing in direction or magnitude is necessary to cause vibration. Since all machines have slight imperfections causing these forces, there is some vibration present.

One method commonly used to demonstrate machine vibration is to simply suspend a weighted coiled spring from a fixed point, as shown in illustration #6. Machines have properties similar to the actions displayed by the weighted spring. If the weight is lifted (force) from its normal neutral position (position of rest) and then released, the weight will travel through its neutral position to a lower and upper limit of travel. This demonstration illustrates the reciprocal motion of a weighted spring but more graphically, the action of the weighted spring simulates machinery vibration.

Vibration Amplitude

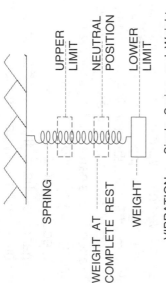

SPRING

UPPER
LIMIT

NEUTRAL
POSITION

WEIGHT AT
COMPLETE REST

LOWER
LIMIT

WEIGHT

VIBRATION :   Single Spring and Weight
in Suspension

Illustration #6 - Suspended Weight

Vibration amplitude is a measure of the amount of the vibration in a machine. The characteristics for measuring the amount of vibration are displacement, velocity and acceleration. Each of these vibration measurement characteristics may be expressed in Imperial or Metric units.

The vibration amplitude associated with each corresponding vibration frequency determines the severity of the vibration.

The greater the vibration amplitude, the more severe the vibration. Amplitude measurement readings are taken with vibration measurement instruments. The instrument will have an amplitude meter, scaled to indicate the amount of vibration present.

Vibration Facts

- It is natural for machines to vibrate and make noise. Vibration and noise are closely associated in definition and description. Machines that are operating in the best condition possible will have some vibration and noise.

- When machinery vibration and noise increase, some mechanical fault may be identifying itself. Machinery vibration and noise do not increase in amplitude for no reason. Some force is causing the vibration and noise.

Vibration Facts (cont'd)

It is possible to detect and identify a mechanical fault by performing vibration and/or noise measurements and noting the characteristics. Each mechanical fault or defect within rotating equipment generates its own characteristic vibration and noise pattern.

Machinery Properties

It was mentioned that machinery vibration could be compared to the actions of a suspended weighted spring. By applying forces to the weight, simply a lift or pull, one simulates machinery vibration. A basic understanding of how spring/mass units react to vibration forces can assist in recognizing and solving many vibration problems found on rotating equipment.

All machines have three properties which combine to ultimately determine how the machine will respond to the forces which cause vibration.

The three machine properties and their representative symbols are:

- stiffness - (K)
- mass - (m)
- damping - (C)

Stiffness (K) is the measure of the force required to bend or deflect a machine part or a structural member a measurable distance.

Mass (m) is a measure of the weight of the system or unit divided by acceleration. The force affected by the mass of the system is an "inertia force", whereby inertia is defined as the tendency of an object at rest to remain at rest, or the tendency of an object in motion to remain in motion. The greater an object's mass, the greater the forces required to accelerate or decelerate it.

Machine Properties (cont'd)

Damping (C) may be interpreted as being the tendency to slow down (reduce velocity) the vibratory motion of a system. Damping removes energy from the system.

Note: The above mentioned machine properties represent forces inherent to every rotating machine or structure which tend to resist vibration.

Excitation Forces

Excitation Forces = K + m + C

= Stiffness + Mass + Damping

The exciting force is in equilibrium with the restraining forces of stiffness, mass and damping. The amount of vibration resulting from the exciting force will depend on the combined effect of stiffness, mass and damping properties present.

The restraining forces, stiffness, mass and damping do not work together. The restraining forces of inertia and stiffness are 180 degrees out-of-phase, thereby canceling one another. Damping is proportional to velocity.

The effect frequency has on the magnitude of the restraining forces must be considered. Stiffness is proportional only to displacement, therefore, the stiffness force is not affected to any great degree by the frequency of the exciting force. The stiffness force remains relatively constant regardless of frequency.

The inertia force is proportional to vibration acceleration. Acceleration is proportional to frequency squared. The inertia force increases with the square of the exciting force frequency.

Excitation Forces (cont'd)

As indicated in illustration #7, where the relationship between frequency and the magnitude of stiffness and inertia forces are shown, there will be a particular frequency when the stiffness and inertia forces become equal in magnitude.

The restraining forces of stiffness and inertia are out-of-phase by 180°, and will completely cancel one another if the stiffness force equals the inertia. When this occurs, the system essentially loses the restraining forces of stiffness and inertia. As a result, for a given exciting force, the system will exhibit a much higher amplitude at this particular frequency with only the damping force keeping the system in control. This point is known as the resonant frequency of the system.

Vibration Causes

It is generally concluded that mechanical troubles found in rotating equipment create the necessary forces to produce vibration.

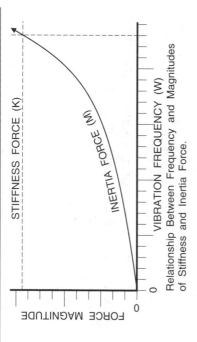

Relationship Between Frequency and Magnitudes of Stiffness and Inertia Force.

Illustration #7 — Frequency, Stiffness and Inertia

The cause of vibration must be a force which is changing either its direction or amount. The characteristics of a vibration are determined by the manner in which the force is generated and this is the reason why each cause of vibration has its own unique characteristics.

Vibration Causes (cont'd)

Some of the common mechanical troubles which have been known to produce vibration in rotating equipment are:

- Unbalance of Rotating Parts
- Shaft/Coupling Misalignment
- Worn or Damaged Bearings
- Bent/Bowed Shafts
- Mechanical Looseness
- Worn or Damaged Gears
- Faulty Drive Belts, Worn Sheaves
- Worn Drive Chains and Sprockets
- Load and Torque Variations
- Electromagnetic Forces
- Aerodynamic Forces
- Hydraulic Forces
- Rubbing
- Resonance

Vibration Characteristics

The characteristics of vibration measurements yield information regarding the machine's condition and any mechanical faults.

Plotting the distance a vibrating body travels against time provides measurable characteristics of the vibration. Referring to the weight suspended on the spring, as noted in illustration #8, the characteristics of the vibration are plotted as movement of the weight against time.

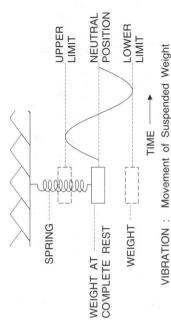

VIBRATION : Movement of Suspended Weight Plotted against Time

Illustration #8 — Vibration Over Time

Vibration Characteristics (cont'd)

There are five measurable characteristics of vibration. The tradesperson and the rotating equipment technician should familiarize themselves with these characteristics since they are essential to accurate vibration analysis.

The five vibration characteristics are:

1. Frequency
2. Displacement
3. Velocity
4. Acceleration
5. Phase

1. Vibration Frequency: The amount of time required to complete one cycle of vibration is called the "period of vibration." If a period of one second is required to complete one cycle of vibration, the vibration is said to have a frequency of 60 cycles per minute.

Frequency in vibration analysis is given in intervals of time, usually in units of cycles per minute (CPM), or cycles per second (Hertz - Hz). Refer to illustration #9.

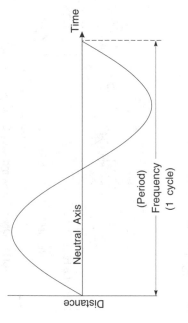

Illustration #9 — Frequency

Note: The forces which cause vibration, through the rotating motion of a machine's part, and as a result, the vibration produced, will be dependent upon the rotating speed of the part which is at fault. Knowing the frequency of vibration assists in identifying the part which is causing the problem.

Vibration Characteristics (cont'd)

Vibration amplitude is a measure of the amount of the vibration in a machine. Vibration amplitude readings are expressed in terms or units of displacement, velocity and acceleration. Each of these units are actual characteristics of vibration and can be expressed in Metric or Imperial units.

The vibration amplitude associated with corresponding vibration frequencies determine the severity of the vibration in the rotating machinery. The greater the vibration amplitude, the more severe the vibration is.

2. Vibration Displacement: The total distance traveled by the vibrating part, from one extreme limit of travel to the other extreme limit of travel is referred to as "peak-to-peak displacement." Refer to illustration #10. Displacement is normally expressed in "mils", where 1 mil equals one-thousandth of an inch (0.001 inch).

In metric units, displacement is expressed in "microns", where 1 micron equals one millionth of a meter (0.000001 meter), or one-thousandth of a millimeter (0.001 millimeter). It is recommended that displacement measurements be taken on rotating equipment which is subjected to low frequency vibrations and where stress conditions should be considered. Rigid machinery parts and components are often classed as having brittleness properties. Brittleness is the tendency of a material to fracture or break when subjected to stresses. Stress limits can be exceeded by flexing of the machine parts and this is important where brittle castings are of concern.

Note: A low frequency vibration is identified in this book as being below 600 cycles/minute (10 Hz).

Vibration Characteristics (cont'd)

3. *Vibration Velocity:* Vibration velocity is a measurement of the maximum speed of the vibrating part as the vibration crosses the neutral axis. Since the vibrating weight, as noted in illustrations #7 and #8, is moving up and down, it must be moving at some speed. The speed of the moving weight is constantly changing. At the upper limit of travel the speed is zero because the weight must come to a stop before it can travel in the opposite direction. The weight rapidly accelerates from the upper limit to the neutral axis, then decelerates to the lower limit. The greatest speed is reached at the neutral axis. Refer to illustration #11.

The velocity of a vibration is a measurable characteristic, but since vibration velocity is constantly changing throughout the cycle, the highest, or "peak" velocity is normally selected for measurement.

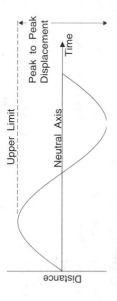

Illustration #10 - Displacement

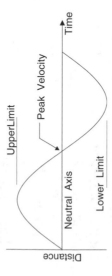

Illustration #11 - Peak Velocity

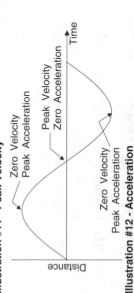

Illustration #12 - Acceleration

VIBRATION ANALYSIS

Vibration Characteristics (cont'd)

Vibration velocity is expressed in units of inches per second or millimeters per second.

The speed of the vibration movement is constantly changing from 0.000 in/sec (mm/sec) at the upper and lower limits of travel extremes to a maximum speed at the neutral axis (peak velocity).

Note: The peak velocity of a vibrating part is dependent upon the distance the part moves (displacement) and how often this occurs (frequency). Vibration velocity, therefore, is a function of both displacement and frequency. Vibration velocity is a direct measurement of vibration used to determine the severity of the vibration (amplitude).

Fatigue failure is also a function of both the amount of movement (displacement) and the number of times the movement occurs (frequency). Therefore, fatigue failure from vibration is a direct function of velocity.

Vibration Characteristics

Since most machinery failure results from fatigue, velocity provides the best indication of severity of a given vibration in most cases. For this reason, unfiltered vibration velocity readings provide the best indication of overall machinery condition at frequencies from 600 to 60,000 CPM.

4. *Vibration Acceleration:* The velocity of a vibrating part is zero at the extreme limits of travel, then the part accelerates to pick up speed as it travels towards the neutral axis. Vibration acceleration is the measurement of the rate of change of velocity. It is another important characteristic of vibration, as it is an indication of the amount of force being applied to machinery parts.

As shown in illustration #12, the acceleration of the machine part is maximum at the extreme limit of travel where the velocity is zero. As the velocity of the part increases, the acceleration of the part decreases. At the neutral axis, the velocity is maximum and the acceleration is zero.

Vibration Characteristics (cont'd)

As the part travels through the neutral axis, the movement decelerates upon reaching the opposite extreme limit of travel.

Vibration acceleration (peak) is measured in "g's" peak, where one "g" is the acceleration produced by the force of gravity at the surface of the earth.

One "g" equals 32.1739 feet/sec/sec or 9.81 meters/sec/sec.

Note: Vibration acceleration measurements are related to vibrating forces being applied to the machine. Relatively large forces (high vibration acceleration) can occur at very high frequencies, even though displacement and velocity readings are relatively low.

When vibration frequencies are above 60,000 cycles/minute it is recommended to use vibration acceleration measurements.

Illustration #13 indicates four vibration characteristics plotted on a distance - time motion plot.

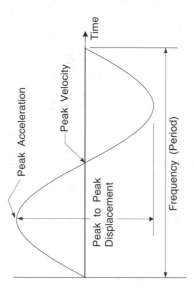

Illustration #13 - Characteristics of Vibration.

Vibration Characteristics (cont'd)

Table #2 gives a quick reference for identifying vibration amplitude characteristics.

Note: Vibration displacement, velocity and acceleration are all related to each other. Vibration frequency characteristics help to determine the cause(s) of the vibratory forces.

VIBRATION AMPLITUDE CHARACTERISTICS			
Amplitude: Measure of "Severity" of Vibration			
Amplitude	Unit		Recommended Frequency Range
	Imperial	Metric	
Displacement (Peak to Peak)	mil (0.001in)	micron 0.001mm	0 - 600 CPM
Velocity (Peak)	inches/sec	mm/sec	600 - 60,000 CPM
Acceleration (Peak)	g's	g's	60,000 + CPM

Table #2 - Vibration Amplitude Characteristics

Vibration Characteristics (cont'd)

5. Phase: Another characteristic of vibration is "phase." Phase angle measurements provide an effective method for comparing one vibration motion with another or to determine how one machine part is vibrating relative to another machine part.

Phase is defined as being the position of a vibrating part at a given instant with reference to a fixed point or another machinery part.

Illustration #14 indicates one method for describing phase. Two weighted springs (weight #1 & weight #2) are rising and falling (vibrating) at the same frequency and displacement; however weight #1 is at the upper limit of travel at the exact same instant weight #2 is at the lower limit of travel. Phase is used to express this comparison. One complete cycle of motion of weights #1 and #2, starting at the exact same instant, is plotted to represent their phase relationship.

The points of peak-to-peak displacement for each weight are separated by 180 degrees. To conclude, weights #1 and #2 are vibrating 180 degrees out-of-phase.

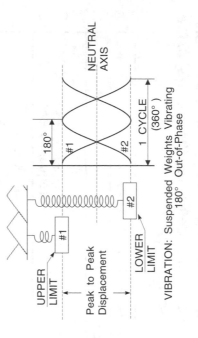

VIBRATION: Suspended Weights Vibrating 180° Out-of-Phase

Illustration #14 - 180° Out-of-Phase Vibration

Vibration Characteristics (cont'd)

Illustration #15 identifies weight #1 and #2 being 90 degrees out-of-phase. Weight #1 is at the upper limit at the exact same instant weight #2 is at the neutral position moving towards the upper limit of travel.

Illustration #16 identifies weight #1 and #2 being in-phase or zero degrees out-of-phase. Each weight is at the upper limit of travel at the exact same instant.

Phase readings are expressed in degrees (0 - 360 degrees), where one complete cycle (frequency of vibration) equals 360 degrees. A "stroboscopic light" or oscilloscope is used to determine phase relationships of vibrating parts. Phase measurements can be used to identify specific machinery faults and for balancing the rotating components of a machine (dynamic balancing).

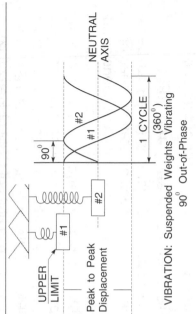

Illustration #15 - 90° Out-of-Phase Vibrations

VIBRATION: Suspended Weights Vibrating 90° Out-of-Phase

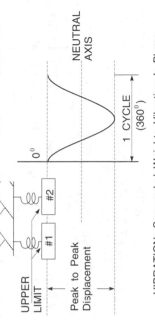

VIBRATION: Suspended Weights Vibrating In-Phase

Illustration #16 - In-Phase Vibrations

Vibration Characteristics/Frequency

Vibration Characteristics (cont'd)

Vibration displacement, velocity, and acceleration characteristics can be expressed as vector diagrams illustrated on "Polar Graph" paper. This method is used for determining both the position and amount of unbalance. Illustration #17 shows how a vibration velocity measurement is plotted as a vector quantity on polar graph paper. The scale selected is at the discretion of the technician.

Note: Methods for balancing rotating machinery components will be further discussed in Section Four of this book.

Vibration Frequency and RPM

The frequency of vibration (CPM) can be expressed in multiples of rotation speed of the machine. Machine vibration frequencies primarily tend to occur at direct multiples or sub-multiples of the machine's rotating speed (RPM). Frequency of vibration is referenced as being one times RPM, two times RPM, 1/2 times RPM, 37% of RPM, etc., rather than in units of CPM or Hertz (Hz).

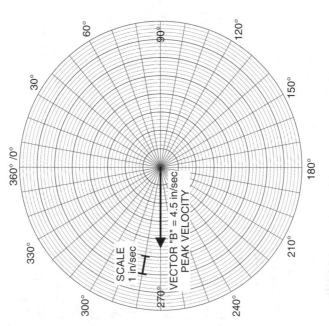

EXAMPLE VECTOR "B":
VIBRATION VELOCITY (PEAK) = 4.5 in/sec

Illustration #17 - Polar Graph

VIBRATION ANALYSIS

Vibration Frequency and RPM (cont'd)

Vibration frequency examples are as follows:

a. 1 x RPM: The frequency of vibration is the same as the machine's RPM.

b. 2 x RPM: The frequency of vibration is twice the machine's RPM.

c. 1/2 x RPM: The frequency of vibration is one-half the machine's RPM.

d. 0.37 x RPM: The frequency of vibration is thirty seven percent of the machine's RPM.

Frequency Characteristics

Synchronous Vibration: Synchronous vibration occurs at a frequency which is some direct multiple or integer fraction of the machine's rotation speed. For example: 1 x RPM; 2 x RPM; 3 x RPM; 4 x RPM; 1/2 x RPM; and 1/3 x RPM. These examples of vibration frequency are "locked in" with the machine's RPM.

Asynchronous Vibration: Asynchronous vibration, also referred to as non-synchronous, is when vibration components are not an integer multiple of rotating frequency.

Natural Frequency: Natural frequency is defined as being the frequency at which a machine, machine part or structural member vibrates due to its physical length, diameter, weight, material and construction (flexibility).

Resonance

Resonance is defined as an amplified vibration caused by excitation forces which correspond in frequency to the natural frequency of the machine part or structural member. Resonance magnifies the amplitude of vibrations in systems which are undamped.

Resonance, as it corresponds to machine parts and structural members, could be described as being similar in action to a spring system. Any part of the machine or structure that can be deflected by a force and has the ability to return to its original shape or position, once the force has been removed, has spring like characteristics.

Resonance (cont'd)

Stiffness properties in the machine part or structural member affect the amount the part will deflect when a known force is applied.

Illustrations #18A and #18B identify two units which are regarded as being spring systems. In #18A the pillow blocks flex like a spring, and in #18B the machine base flexes. The shaft supported between two bearings has spring characteristics, as does the machine's base, both being anchored permanently to concrete blocks.

Note: Machine parts and structural members that deflect by pivoting about a friction joint, such as a hinged mechanism, are not classed as being spring-like systems. The machine part or structural member must flex and have the ability to return to its original shape or position.

The machine part or structural member which has spring-like characteristics has its own natural frequency of vibration.

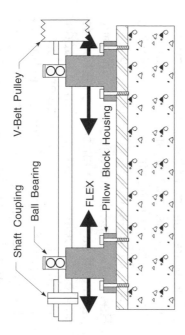

Illustration #18A — Spring System (Pillow Blocks)

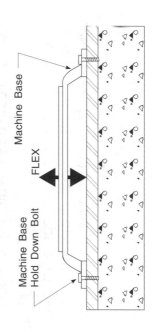

Illustration #18B — Spring System (Machine Base)

Resonance (cont'd)

The piping system located in a process plant is, essentially, long springs having resonant frequencies which are determined by pipe length, weight, type of material, distance between supports/hangars and stiffness of supports and hangars. Fluid in the pipe system will lower the natural frequency because of the added weight. The fluid serves to dampen vibration as well.

Resonance and Damping

Note: As a frequency comparison, observe the actions of a piano, guitar, or other stringed instrument. The higher frequency strings are shorter in length; smaller in diameter; and stretched tighter than others.

When a guitar string or tuning fork is struck, each vibrates at its natural frequency. The sound will eventually fade and die out as the vibration stops.

The property that causes vibration to decrease is called damping. Increasing the damping effect serves to reduce the time it takes for the vibration to stop. When a guitar player's finger touches the vibrating guitar string, the vibration stops quickly.

Vibration may be controlled through use of damping. Shock absorbers on each wheel of an automobile provide damping action, preventing the vehicle from uncontrollable bounce on rough roadways. Mechanical and structural systems exhibit some amount of damping action and if one can increase the damping, the time required to decrease the vibration is reduced.

Critical Speed

Critical Speed is defined as being a type of resonance which occurs when a shaft or rotating machine component revolves at a speed close to its natural frequency.

Critical Speed (cont'd)

For example: the critical speed of an exhaust fan may occur when its rotational speed is equal to the natural frequency of the fan and rotor assembly. If the rotating speed of the fan was 1760 RPM and its natural frequency was 1800 CPM, the critical speed of the exhaust fan is approximately 1800 RPM.

The vibration amplitude rises at a much higher rate through the machine's critical speed. The vibration amplitude smoothes out as the machine RPM passes beyond the critical speed. It is important to operate rotating equipment at speeds well above or below their critical speed, or damage may result to the equipment and surroundings.

Most tradespeople and technicians who specialize in rotating equipment design and maintenance are very conscious of keeping their machinery operating at speeds outside of the critical speed range.

Note: Resonance at the natural frequency of a machine's part is usually referred to as the first critical speed. Resonance can occur at a higher speed again, called the second critical speed, the next highest speed, called the third critical speed, and so on.

For the same vibration force input, the vibration amplitude, measured in displacement at the higher critical speeds (second and third) is less than when measured at the first critical speed. The velocity of the vibrating machine part is normally less at the second and third critical speeds, since the frequency of vibration is higher.

Note: Higher critical speeds do not necessarily always occur at a full integer multiple of the natural frequency, such as two, three, or four times the natural frequency.

Measuring Vibration Amplitude

The displacement, velocity and acceleration characteristics of vibration are measurements of vibration amplitude, used to determine the severity of vibration. Vibration amplitude is the indicator used for determining just how bad or good the rotating equipment is in operation.

To determine the severity (amplitude) of vibration, one must measure vibration in terms of either displacement, velocity, or acceleration. However, the question is, which parameter should be selected?

The three vibration characteristics, displacement, velocity, and acceleration are interrelated. When displacement and frequency values are known, velocity (peak) can be calculated. These calculations serve to represent the important relationship between vibration amplitude measurements associated with displacement, velocity and acceleration.

Note: In practice, the tradesperson or technician will not have to perform these types of calculations on the job, but it is of interest to rotating equipment maintenance personnel to understand the relationships between vibration characteristics.

To Calculate Velocity (peak):

$$V = 52.3 \times D \times F \times 10^{-6}$$

Where:

V = velocity (peak) in inches/second

D = displacement (peak-to-peak) in mils

F = frequency in CPM

Note: (Metric) To find velocity (peak) in millimeters/second, The displacement (D) has to be expressed in "microns."

When displacement and frequency are known, acceleration (peak) can be determined by using the following calculation:

Measuring Amplitude (cont'd)

To Calculate Acceleration (peak):

g (peak) = 14.2 x D (F/1000)^2 x 10^{-3}

Where:

g = acceleration (peak) due to gravity
D = displacement (peak-to-peak) in mils
F = frequency in CPM

Note: (Metric) To find vibration acceleration (peak) where displacement (D) is measured in microns, use the following equation:

g (peak) = 5.6 x D (F/1000)^2 x 10^{-4}

Selecting the Best Vibration Indicator

It must be determined whether vibration displacement, velocity, or acceleration is the best indicator of vibration severity.

The severity of vibration in a machine part can be compared to a person applying a bending action (displacement) to a piece of wire and how many times the wire is bent (frequency).

Repeated bending eventually causes the wire to break. Repeated cycles of vibration acted on a machine part or structural member will fatigue the part as well.

Vibration velocity is a function of displacement and frequency. The measure of vibration velocity is a direct measure of vibration severity.

Vibration velocity (peak) provides the best overall indicator for determining machine condition.

When vibration displacement is used to determine vibration severity, it is necessary to know the frequency of vibration.

Vibration severity charts are available for cross-referencing vibration displacement or acceleration with vibration frequency to conclude the severity of vibration in the machine. Refer to illustrations #19 and #20.

Selecting the Best Vibration Indicator (cont'd)

Note: The guidelines offered in illustrations #19 and #20 apply to machines such as: electric motors; fans; blowers; pumps; and gearboxes. With these applications, the vibration amplitude does not directly affect the quality or overall finish of a product.

The amplitude readings are taken on/near the support bearings or structure of the machine.

When using illustration #19 note that the left side of the table indicates displacement (peak-to-peak) readings in mils. A displacement reading, for example, of 2.0 mils occurring at a frequency of 1800 CPM is in the "slightly rough" range of the severity chart.

The same reading at a frequency of 10,000 CPM would indicate that the severity of vibration is in the "very rough" range.

The diagonal lines on illustration #19 which divide the zones of severity are constant velocity lines.

The velocity scale is represented on the lower right side of illustration #19 (inches/sec-peak). A peak velocity reading of 0.09 inches/sec is in the "fair" range regardless of the frequency of vibration (100 - 100,000 CPM).

When using illustration #20, note that the left side of the table indicates vibration acceleration (peak) in "g's." An acceleration reading of 0.1g at the frequency of 60,000 CPM is in the "very smooth" region of the severity chart. A peak velocity reading of 0.09 inches/sec is in the "fair" range regardless of the frequency of vibration.

Note, on Illustration #19, a peak velocity reading of 0.09 inch/second indicated that the machine operated in the "fair" range as well.

Selecting the Best Vibration Indicator (cont'd)

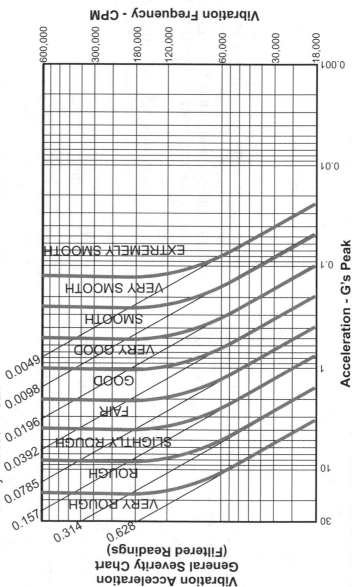

Illustration #19 - Vibration Indicators

Selecting the Best Vibration Indicator (cont'd)

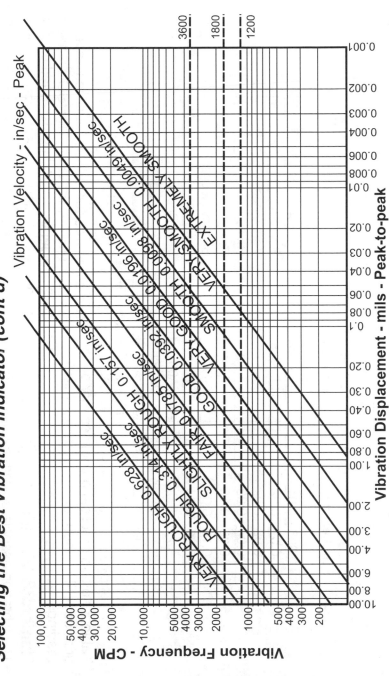

Vibration Velocity - in/sec - Peak

EXTREMELY SMOOTH

VERY SMOOTH 0.0049 in/sec

SMOOTH 0.0098 in/sec

VERY GOOD 0.0196 in/sec

GOOD 0.0392 in/sec

FAIR 0.0785 in/sec

SLIGHTLY ROUGH 0.157 in/sec

ROUGH 0.314 in/sec

VERY ROUGH 0.628 in/sec

Vibration Frequency - CPM

100,000
50,000
40,000
30,000
20,000
10,000
5000
4000
3000
2000
1000
500
400
300
200

3600
1800
1200

Vibration Displacement - mils - Peak-to-peak

0.001
0.002
0.003
0.004
0.006
0.008
0.01
0.02
0.03
0.04
0.06
0.08
0.1
0.20
0.30
0.40
0.60
0.80
1.00
2.00
3.00
4.00
6.00
8.00
10.00

Illustration #20 - Vibration Indicators

VIBRATION VELOCITY (PEAK)		
Velocity (Imperial & Metric)		Range
inches/second	mm/second	
0 - 0.005	0 - 0.1	Extremely Smooth
0.005 - 0.01	0.1 - 0.25	Very smooth
0.01 - 0.02	0.25 - 0.5	Smooth
0.02 - 0.04	0.5 - 1	Very Good
0.04 - 0.08	1 - 2	Good
0.08 - 0.16	2 - 4	Fair
0.16 - 0.32	4 - 8	Slightly Rough
0.32 - 0.64	8 - 16	Rough
Above 0.64	Above 16	Very Rough
Note: if vibration velocity is 0.30 inches/second (8 mm/sec) or greater, locate the cause and correct.		

Table #3 - Vibration Tolerances

Table #3 offers practical guidelines of vibration severity when using velocity (peak) readings.

Numerous Vibration Frequencies

The vibration associated with rotating equipment machinery is usually complex, consisting of many frequencies.

The standards for judging vibration severity are published by the ISO. The ISO Standard 2372 is a general standard designed primarily for shop testing and acceptance and a more specific standard designed for vibration evaluation of in-place machinery.

VIBRATION ANALYSIS

Numerous Vibration Frequencies (cont'd)

The ISO standard contains criteria for judging machine condition from casing velocity measured at a specified location at each bearing. This standard, as shown in illustration #21, applies to machines operating within a speed range from 600 - 12,000 RPM (10 - 200 Hz) and specifies a measurement limited to a frequency band of 600 - 60,000 CPM (10 - 1000 Hz).

NOTE: ISO Standard 2372 requires true "rms" (root mean square) amplitude measurement. This distinguishes between flexible-support and rigid-support, and recognizes that a support system may be rigid in one direction and flexible in the other. As in rotor dynamics, a flexible support is defined as a support with its first natural frequency below the main frequency of excitation (shaft rotating speed).

Numerous Vibration Frequencies   55

A rigid-support is one in which the first natural frequency of the support structure is higher than the main excitation frequency.

ISO Standards also recognize that the machine casing vibrations can be transmitted from the environment and are not applicable when the transmitted excitation is greater than one-third of the operating value.

Another chart used for judging machinery vibration severity is shown in illustration #22. This chart is referred to as a "vibration nomogram." Vibration frequency is located upper scale, vibration amplitude, acceleration, velocity and displacement are located on the three lower scales.

To use the chart, plot the vibration frequency and amplitude in one of the three measurements (acceleration, velocity or displacement), and connect the plotted points.

Numerous Vibration Frequencies (cont'd)

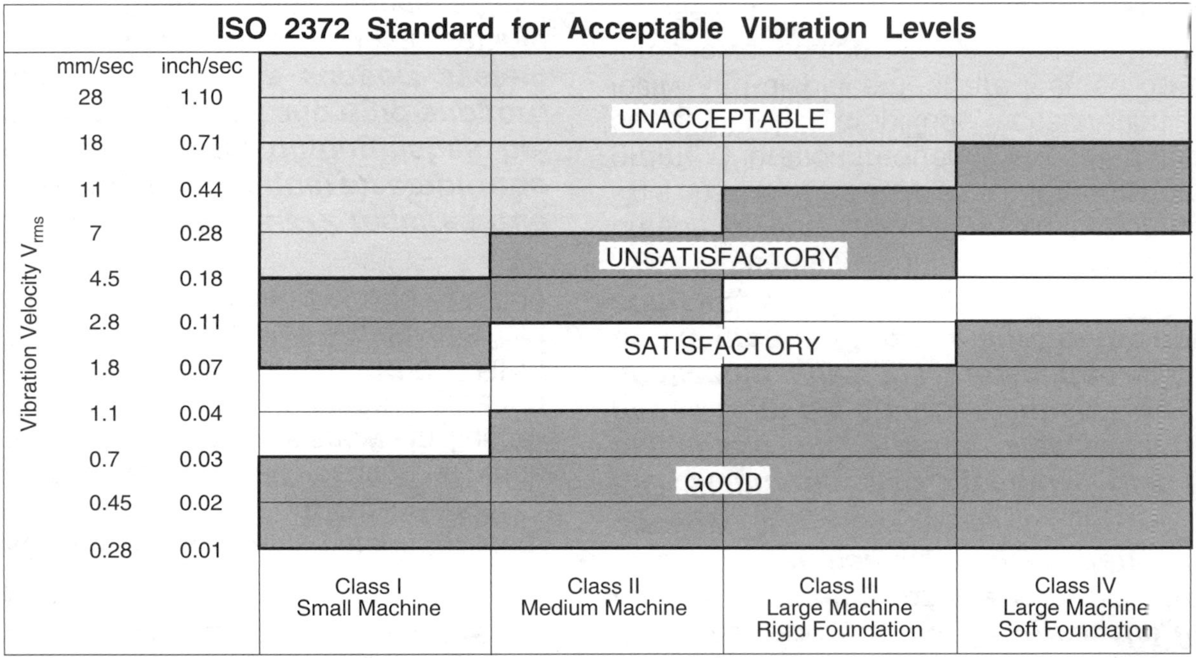

Illustration #21 - ISO Standards for Vibration Severity

Numerous Vibration Frequencies
(cont'd)

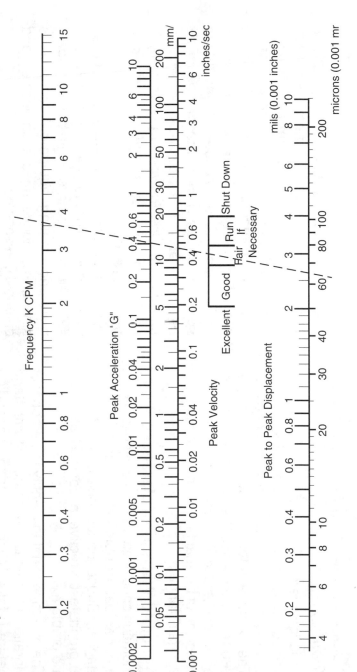

Illustration #22 - Vibration Nomogram

Numerous Vibration Frequencies (cont'd)

To judge overall machinery condition the line should continue through the portion of the chart which indicates machinery condition. The example is for a vibration frequency at 3600 CPM and a peak velocity measurement of .43 inches/sec. (11 mm/sec.). The overall condition of the machine in this example is in the "fair" range.

Absolute Vibration Tolerances

Vibration checks are primarily used to detect mechanical troubles/faults during early stages. Subsequently, one can determine appropriate corrective actions to eliminate the problem.

The objective is not to identify the amount of vibration a particular machine will withstand before it fails, but to determine impending problems early enough to avoid unnecessary failures.

Research indicates that it is very difficult to provide absolute vibration tolerances for any given type of rotating equipment. There are many similar characteristics that lead to machinery failure, but there are also many unique circumstances which occur at unexpected times which serve to cause a machine or one of its parts to fail. The development of mechanical failure, induced by vibration, is far too complex for applying fixed vibration tolerances.

Practical guidelines for vibration severity, as indicated in illustrations #19, #20, #21, and #22, and table #3 are available for tradesmen and rotating equipment technicians having experience in vibration analysis and diagnostic assessments.

Absolute Vibration Tolerances (cont'd)

The values shown in table #3, and illustrations #21 and #22 service typical rotating equipment, such as; electric motors, fans, pumps, and blowers. The vibration amplitude experienced in this equipment usually does not directly affect the quality or finish of the product being handled.

The vibration tolerances suggested may not apply for machines such as crushers, rolling or grinding mills, or for precision machinery. Crushers and mills inherently have high amplitudes of vibration, while precision machines, such as cylindrical grinders, have low amplitudes of vibration.

Maintenance records and the tradesman's work experience with the equipment may often conclude an assessment of the machinery condition.

Vibration amplitude associated with precision machines can adversely affect the quality of the finished product.

Table #4 indicates a reference guide to vibration tolerances recommended for precision tools. Associating absolute vibration tolerances to precision machine tools is less complex than attempting to do this for general rotating equipment.

The reason being, the vibration tolerances are based on the machine's ability to make a product which must meet specified size limitations, or surface finish tolerances. The values identified in table #4 represent the vibration amounts for which acceptable products have been made on the machine.

Absolute Vibration Tolerances (cont'd)

Vibration Tolerances for Precision Machines		
	Tolerance Range Displacement (Peak to Peak)	
Machine Type	mils 1mil = 0.001 inch	microns 1 micron = 0.001 mm
Lathe (Metal)	0.20 - 1.00	5.0 - 25
Boring Machine	0.06 - 0.10	1.5 - 2.5
Grinders:		
- centerless	0.04 - 0.10	1.0 - 2.5
- surface	0.03 - 0.20	0.8 - 5.0
- cylindrical	0.03 - 0.10	0.8 - 2.5
- thread	0.01 - 0.06	0.3 - 1.5
Note: unfiltered readings only		

Table #4 - Vibration Tolerances for Precision Machines

Vibration tolerances may vary depending on the material used to make the product, its hardness, size and desired finish.

The quality of the size and finish required, when compared to the machine's normal pattern of vibration, will reveal the acceptable levels of vibration for a particular machine.

Absolute Vibration Tolerances (cont'd)

When the quality of size and finish first begins to deteriorate, an unacceptable amount of vibration amplitude is indicated. It usually is the responsibility of the tradesperson or the rotating equipment specialist to maintain the preciseness of the precision machine tools. They may find a need to modify the absolute vibration tolerance for a particular machine and this modification would be based on experience and product quality.

The initial values for vibration tolerances shown in table #4 serve to act as a guideline only. The values may be modified to suit the tolerances required for the precision machines in a given plant.

Sound

Everything that moves makes sound. Vibrations (low or high frequency) have their own characteristic effect on the total amount of sound (noise) produced.

With various rotating equipment installations, a multitude of noise generating sources are present. Physical factors such as room size, piping design, wall materials, air movement, mechanical drives and proximity of equipment to one another serve to contribute to the overall noise levels associated with the area.

Each piece of rotating equipment operating under existing surroundings and at designed loads and speed will produce a characteristic "normal" sound. Tradespeople, rotating equipment technicians and plant operators quickly learn to recognize characteristic noises and are aware of changes to the normal sounds.

Usually when a noise change is heard, the machine should be checked immediately to determine where the sound change is originating from.

Sound (cont'd)

Public concern over the issue of noise in the workplace and consistent noise-induced problems in the community has grown over the past two decades in North America. Federal, state and provincial regulations govern the maximum noise amounts a worker can be subjected to on the worksite.

Rotating equipment manufacturers are more conscious of how much noise their product produces. Organizations purchasing rotating equipment now specify how much permissible noise they will accept from the equipment. Communities have established restrictions to how much noise they will tolerate, whether the noise originates from traffic, industries or music.

Sound Sources

Sound, when transmitted in the atmosphere, is described as being variations in air pressure. Sound is in "wave" forms. The movement of individual particles is longitudinal, or back and forth. Energy is required to set up the sound waves.

Sound can be visualized as originating at a point source and radiating from the point in all directions, that is if there is no interference. The sphere of the wave motion is increased as the waves move outward, but the total energy of the wave over the surface of the sphere is unchanged. Over any small area on the sphere, the energy diminishes rapidly as the sphere grows in size. Thus, the greater the distance from the originating source, the less the intensity of the sound. This varies inversely as the square of the distance from the point source.

Sound (cont'd)

There is also a slight reduction in noise intensity because of friction of one air particle upon another as the sound wave progresses. In the sound wave, the air particles do not change their normal positions, one with the other.

The air particles simply move back and forth, pushing each other. This back and forth motion works to build areas of pressure above atmosphere and adjacent areas of pressure below atmosphere. These variations in pressure are very small, but sufficient for discernment by the ear and sound measuring instruments.

Note: Sound waves can be reflected to new directions or bounced back. Two or more sound waves, originating from separate sources, will combine in complex forms, depending on their individual frequency and amplitude.

Causes of Sound

Sound waves can be generated by:

Vibration of Solid Structures: Solid structures, such as beams, walls, and machines which vibrate move the air above and below atmospheric pressure. This is the air which is in contact with the structure.

Movement of Air Over Solid Structures: Sound can be generated by continuous air movement over solid structures such as beams, walls, pipes and machines. The structure does not vibrate, but moving air, in and around the structure, creating high and low pressure zones, generate the sounds. Flow of air through ported screens or ventilation grills also produces sound.

Turbulent Air Mixing: Sound may come from turbulent mixing of fast moving air with slow moving air. No solid structure is involved. The high velocity air mixing with slow moving air often creates very loud and distinguishable sound.

Sound Characteristics (speed)

The speed, or the velocity sound waves radiate outward from the source is referred to as the "propagation velocity", or more commonly, "the speed of sound." The speed of sound in air at the standard temperature of 75°F (24°C) is a constant value of 1135 feet/second (346 meters/second); this value is considered the standard measurement for the speed of sound.

Refer to illustration #23 to identify how the velocity of sound varies with temperature.

Note: The velocity of sound is a constant which is independent of sound amplitude. Do not compare the velocity of sound with vibration velocity. Vibration velocity is a measure of vibration amplitude.

Sound Characteristics (amplitude)

Sound amplitude is defined as a measure of how far the air pressure rises above atmospheric pressure and then falls below atmospheric pressure.

The maximum amount by which the pressure differs from atmospheric pressure is called the "pressure amplitude of sound".

The pressure amplitude of sound is usually expressed in units of "microbars." One microbar equals one millionth of a bar and one bar represents almost one atmosphere, 100 kPa or 14.5 PSI. The pressure amplitude of sound may also be expressed in units of "dynes per square centimeter." One dyne per square centimeter equals one microbar.

The faintest sound the human ear hears is approximately 0.0002 microbars. This sound pressure amplitude is referred to as "acute threshold of hearing." The loudest sound the human ear tolerates is approximately 2000 microbars. this sound pressure amplitude is referred to as "threshold of pain."

Note: Do not confuse sound amplitude with the amplitude used for vibration measurement.

Sound Characteristics (cont'd)

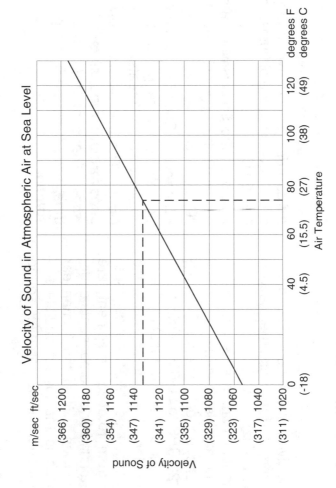

Illustration #23 - Air Temperature and Sound Intensity

Sound Characteristics (cont'd)

Sound frequency is defined as being the number of complete cycles of rise and falls in pressure in a given time period. Sound frequency is expressed in cycles per second (CPS), or Hertz (Hz).

Frequency is important in all sound measurements. The audible spectrum, called the "audio-frequency range", extends from approximately 20 CPS to 20,000 CPS. Some sounds are pleasant, others irritable, therefore, less popular. The difference is in the combination of sounds. Most sounds, especially ones from rotating equipment, are made up of a number of components of different frequencies. What the human ear hears as pitch is the lowest audible frequency component in a complex sound wave.

For a more complete understanding of sound problems, not only should the magnitude of the sound be measured, but so should the sound frequency.

Sound frequencies associated with human hearing fall into three distinct categories:

Infrasonic: Sounds which are at frequencies below the range of human hearing, less than 20 CPS.

Audio-sonic: Sounds which are at frequencies within the range of human hearing, 20 to 20,000 CPS.

Ultrasonic: Sounds which are at frequencies above the range of human hearing, 20,000 CPS and greater.

Note: The audio-sonic sounds are the ones industry must always be concerned with. These sounds, over a period of time, will affect the hearing of plant personnel.

Sound Characteristics
(frequency and wavelength)

Sound frequency is inversely proportional to wavelength. High frequency sounds have short wavelengths and low frequency sounds have relatively long wavelengths.

Determining the frequency of sound and knowing the sound wavelength is important for identifying the source of the sound, just as vibration frequency assists one to locate the machine's vibration problem. The frequency at which a machine vibrates determines the frequency of the noise being emitted. For example, a machine vibrating at a frequency of 3600 CPM generates a sound frequency of 3600 CPM.

Characteristic disturbing noises generated by rotating equipment often help to define which method is most appropriate for controlling the noise. The noise generated by vibration which is relatively low will usually indicate no mechanical problem exists.

The noise is inherent to the machine. To reduce disturbing noises, acoustic enclosures may have to be installed to restrict or absorb the noise. Insulating the machine, its piping and support system with proven sound insulation materials will work to confine the noise as well.

Sound Measurement

Sound amplitude, or pressure functions are measured using the logarithmic decibel (dB) scale which is considered the most convenient method for such measurements. It is inconvenient to measure the sound amplitude in microbars. The human ear responds to a wide range of sound pressure amplitudes, ranging from 0.0002 to 2000 microbars, or a ratio of 10 million to one. Therefore, it is simpler to use the decibel scale for measuring sound amplitude. Using microbars proves to be a rather long linear range.

Sound Measurement (cont'd)

The sound pressure level (SPL) in decibels is defined in the equation:

$$dB = 20 \log_{10} \frac{(sound\ pressure)}{SRP}$$

Where:

Sound Pressure: is the sound amplitude of interest in microbars.

Standard Reference Pressure (SRP): is a set value of the weakest sound that can be heard by a person with very good hearing in a quiet location.

It represents a pressure variation of 0.0002 microbars (0.0002 dynes/centimeter squared), therefore, the standard reference pressure is 0.0002 microbars.

Note: With the above equation it is possible to calculate sound pressure level (SPL) if the sound pressure in microbars or dynes is known, or the sound pressure in microbars can be calculated if the SPL is known.

Noise measurement and engineering calculations are generally referenced in the decibel unit.

Typical Sound Pressure Levels

From the SPL (Sound Pressure Level) equation it is concluded that the acute threshold of hearing becomes 0 dB and the threshold of pain is 140 dB. The decibel scale from 0 to 140 dB is a convenient method for understanding SPL, much easier than working from the 0.0002 to 2000 microbar scale.

The logarithmic dB scale best represents the human ear's response to sound changes. Under controlled testing conditions, the ear can detect a 1 dB change, whereas it is unlikely the ear would note the change from 500 to 510 microbars. Table #5 identifies the decibel levels to which the human ear responds.

Typical Sound Pressure Levels

Illustration #24 provides examples of noise levels typical to home and industry. Each of the identified sounds can vary in sound level as many factors serve to alter the sound measurement.

For example, the distance between the microphone and the sound source will significantly affect the sound measurement level.

SOUND INTENSITY AND THE HUMAN EAR	
Change in Sound Intensity	**Human Ear Response**
1 dB	Detect change under controlled conditions
3 dB - 5 dB	Noticeable difference in loudness
6 dB	Significant increase in loudness
10 dB	Appears almost twice as loud to the human ear
10 dB - 20 dB	Unbelievably louder
Example: a 6 dB change in sound intensity will be a significant increase in loudness or a 10 dB change in sound intensity is 3.162 x sound pressure, or almost twice as loud as the original sound heard.	

Table #5 -Sound Intensity

Sound Pressure Levels

Typical Sound Pressure Levels (cont'd)

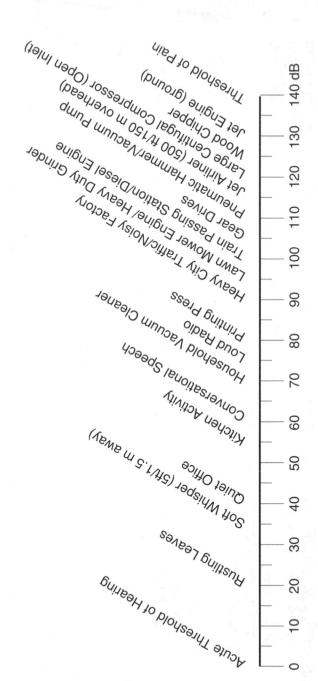

Illustration #24 - Sound Thresholds

Sound Fields

There are three types of sound fields and each have an effect on the sound pressure levels measured. A single sound source sends out uniform sound waves which radiate in all directions. Industrial noise is usually associated with more than one sound source, thus the sound waves themselves become more complex.

Types of Sound Fields

Near Field: Sound waves coming from more than one source, as shown in illustration #25, begin to form interference patterns at points close to each source. At these points the sound pressure level can be greater, or less, than at points away from them. This region around the sources where the interference patterns are most pronounced is called the "near field." This pattern extends outwardly in all directions from the vibrating force.

Generally, the higher the sound frequency, the smaller the "near field" region will be.

Far Field: The region beyond the near field is called the "far field." The sound waves are relatively free of interference. The measured sound pressure levels will not vary significantly when the microphone location is changed slightly, but the sound pressure level will decline when the microphone is moved further from the vibration source. Refer to illustration #25.

Reverberant Field: When sound waves meet a solid surface, they reflect, therefore, a third field, called the "reverberant field" is created. This field is most significant near the reflecting surface and interference patterns, similar to the near field, are generated back from the surface. The closer the reflecting surface is to the sound source, and the larger its surface size is, the greater the "reverberant field" becomes. See illustration #25.

Sound Fields

Note: When possible, it is recommended to take noise measurements in the far field region. The sound measurements will be more consistent and the location of the microphone less critical.

Directional Noise

Noise sources do not radiate the same amount of noise level in all directions. If more noise is radiated in one direction than another, the noises are considered as "directional noise" sources. It is important to note that most types of rotating equipment would be considered directional noise sources.

Noise and Machinery Condition Relationship

Research indicates that it is difficult to provide information on inherent or normal noise levels for specific rotating equipment. There are many references available which identify typical noise levels for selected pieces of rotating equipment, but to identify specific noise levels for each machine is difficult.

Factors which make it difficult to establish specific noise levels for machinery are:

- the type of immediate surroundings
- machine location within the building
- machine proximity to other machines

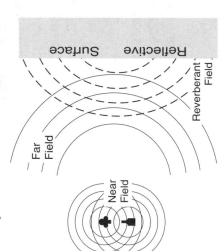

Illustration #25 - Three Types of Noise Fields

Noise and Machinery Condition Relationship (cont'd)

- type of building materials used
- design/type of machine foundation and support structure
- machinery operational loads and speeds
- effects of noise reverberation and frequency
- type of power transmission components used

Establishing standard noise level measurements for specific types of machinery is practically impossible. Therefore, noise level measurements taken to detect machinery condition must be based on recording noise increases in the "normal" noise level. The normal noise level for each machine is best established when it has been first commissioned.

Note: When measuring noise levels for predictive maintenance, be attentive to increases in noise levels of two or more

decibels. This is the signal that mechanical trouble is developing.

Acceptable Noise Level Facts

- Tasks involving exactness and sustained worker concentration are significantly effected by bothersome noise, or by high noise levels.
- Long term jobs requiring constant vigilance are especially susceptible to noise levels.
- Noise is more than likely going to cause a higher rate of work related errors and accidents than an actual reduction in total production.
- Moderate noise can cause the pupil to dilate, effecting the eye's ability to focus.
- Loud sounds are usually more annoying than sounds of similar description, but not as loud.
- High frequency sounds are usually more annoying (above 2000 CPS) than are lower frequency sounds of the same sound pressure level.

Acceptable Levels/Measurements

Acceptable Noise Level Facts (cont'd)

- Hearing, particularly in the higher sound frequencies, deteriorates with age.

- Loud noises and high frequency noises interfere with normal communication.

- As noise levels increase, the worker's attention span lessens.

- Noise is more likely to lead to increased errors in work if the noise continues to be above 85-90 dB.

- Ear protection is recommended for continuous exposure to sound pressure levels above 85-90 dB.

- Exposure to intense noise may produce hearing damage. Some of the hearing loss may be temporary, with partial or complete recovery in time. Some damage may be permanent. The amount of hearing damage depends on: the loudness of the noise; the length of time; and the frequency.

Vibration and Noise Measurements

Instruments for measuring machinery noise and vibration can be classed in three categories:

1. vibration meters
2. vibration monitors
3. vibration analyzers.

Note: SPL Meters (Sound Pressure Level) are used to measure machinery noise only.

1. Vibration Meters: A typical vibration meter is a small portable instrument, often called a "hand-held" instrument, used primarily to take routine, periodic vibration checks on rotating equipment. The readings determine the "overall" vibration level. There are meters available that have the capacity to measure vibration and noise levels.

Some vibration meters have FFT capabilities. FFT refers to "Fast Fourier Transform" which is a calculation method for converting a time waveform into a series of discrete components of frequency and amplitude.

Vibration Measurements (cont'd)

Illustration #26 identifies one type of portable vibration meter which has the capacity to take overall vibration level readings. This meter has an amplitude scale and is capable of measuring peak-to-peak displacement, as well as peak velocity.

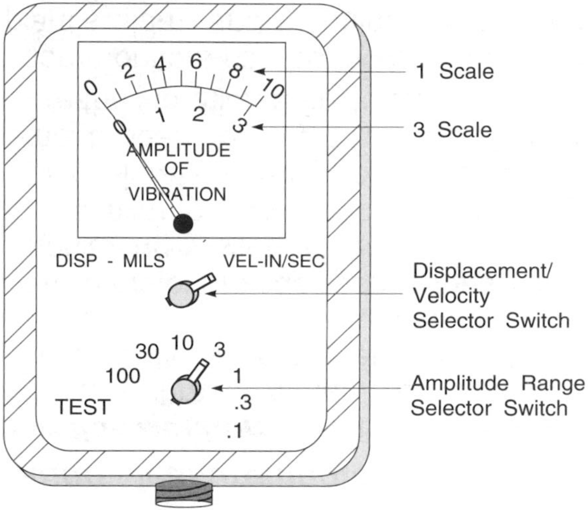

Illustration #27 identifies a type of vibration/sound meter which has the capacity to take overall vibration level readings, as well as decibel readings of the rotating equipment. This meter has an amplitude scale and the technician can select peak-to-peak displacement or peak velocity to measure the vibration amplitude.

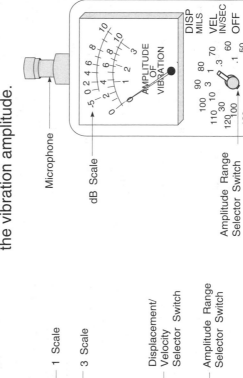

Illustration #27 - Vibration and Sound Level Meter

Illustration #26 - Vibration Meter

Vibration Measurements (cont'd)

2. Vibration Monitor: The vibration monitor is similar to a vibration meter. The difference is that the monitor is permanently installed in either a control room or instrumentation station. The monitor provides continuous vibration monitoring. Vibration monitors have features similar to the vibration meter. They monitor for vibration, using peak-to-peak displacement, peak velocity or acceleration to measure the vibration amplitude.

Vibration monitors can be incorporated into the plant's alarm and machinery shutdown system. When preset vibration levels have been reached or surpassed, the vibration monitor will activate an alarm system to warn plant personnel that a serious vibration problem is occurring at one of the machines.

The vibration monitor can also be linked with the plant's system for shutting down machinery when vibration levels exceed the preset values for a particular machine.

This type of installation can reduce catastrophic machine failure, help prevent accidents to plant personnel and inform the predictive maintenance team when machinery is experiencing serious vibration problems.

3. Vibration Analyzer: The vibration analyzer instrument is more complex in features and operation than either the meter or the monitor. The vibration analyzer is used to specifically identify machinery vibration problems by measuring and comparing vibration and noise characteristics, i.e.; amplitude, frequency and phase.

The vibration analyzer contains a tunable filter which separates individual frequencies of complex rotating equipment noises and vibrations. Depending on the manufacturer and the design of the equipment, there are many types of filter. They include *Fixed Band Width* (good for high frequencies) and *Percentage* filters.

VIBRATION ANALYSIS

Vibration Measurements (cont'd)

The vibration analyzer may include a "stroboscopic" light which synchronizes with the frequency of the noise or vibration or can be set to flash at any rate within its range.

The stroboscopic light (strobe) is used for analyzing machinery problems and for performing "in-place" dynamic balancing of rotating parts. Illustrations #28 and #29 show two types of vibration analyzers.

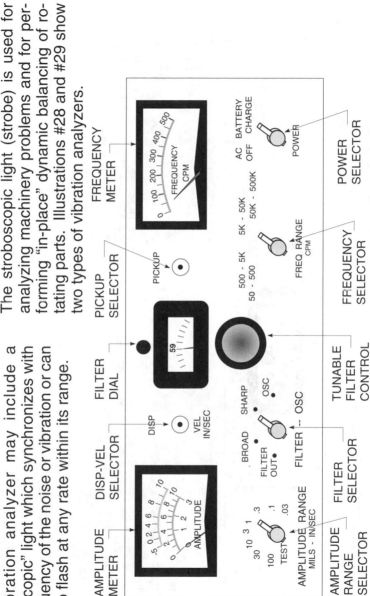

Illustration #28 - Vibration Analyzer

Vibration Measurements (cont'd)

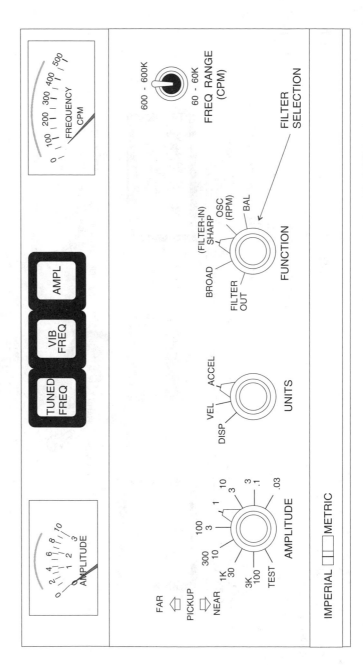

Illustration #29 - Basic Analyzer Controls

Vibration Measurements (cont'd)

FFT Analyzers have become popular as primary diagnostic instruments for analyzing machinery condition. They employ a mathematical procedure to compute the frequency-domain equivalent of a time-domain signal.

FFT Analyzers, are fast, flexible, have an easily interpreted graphic display, and are replacing vibration analyzers where frequencies were identified and the amplitude of each was measured with a manually tuned filter - a tedious, time consuming, and often inaccurate process. FFT Analyzers have averaging provisions for statistically accurate

data which can be used for comparison. They are also capable of producing a graphic display called a "Waterfall Spectrum", shown in illustration #30, where one spectrum is stacked on top of another to observe what is happening during transition periods, such as runup or coastdown.

FFT Analyzers can zoom into a part of a spectrum, as in illustration #31, to help sort out a complex spectrum with closely spaced components. The magnified section of a high frequency spectrum gives improved resolution results. This is a valuable feature for gear, bearing and electric motor analysis.

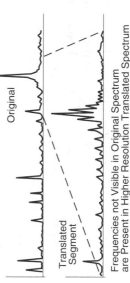

Original

Translated
Segment

Frequencies not Visible in Original Spectrum
are Present in Higher Resolution Translated Spectrum

Illustration #31 - Magnified High Frequency Spectrum

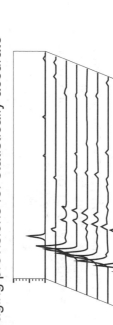

Illustration #30 - Waterfall Spectrum

Transducers - Proximity Probes

A transducer is defined as being a sensing device which converts one type of energy into another type of energy. For vibration measurements, the transducer is the instrument which converts the mechanical vibrations into electrical signals. For noise measurements, the transducer is a microphone. The microphone converts sound pressure oscillations into electrical signals.

Note: There are various types and designs of transducer instruments available for measuring both vibration and noise. The transducer is essential to the process, as it is the "pickup" used to collect the vibration and noise measurements.

Types of Transducers

Proximity Probes: The proximity probe is a non-contact pickup for collecting vibration signals.

It is used extensively in applications where shaft vibration measurements are monitored to detect when seal and bearing clearances are in danger. This is the basic function of the proximity probe, or as it is sometimes called, the "non-contact" pickup.

Illustration #32 identifies a type of proximity probe installed to sense relative motion between the shaft and bearing of the machine.

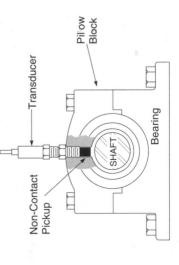

Illustration #32 - Proximity Pickup (Non-Contact)

Transducers - Proximity Probes (cont'd)

The proximity probe shown in illustration #32 is used for measuring shaft displacement relative to bearing housing or casing in either mils or microns. This pickup is used with either portable vibration analyzers or with permanently installed vibration monitors.

The proximity probe differs in operation from other vibration and acceleration measurement transducers. This proximity probe is not a "self generating" device. It requires electrical power from a signal transmitter. A high frequency AC signal is sent to the tip of the pickup which produces a magnetic field at the pickup tip. The metallic conductivity of the shaft, in close proximity, absorbs energy from the magnetic field, subsequently, producing a consistent, measurable signal which is proportional to the relative distance between the pickup and the shaft.

The instantaneous amplitude changes of the signal are detected as an AC signal being proportional to the peak-to-peak displacement of the shaft.

Illustration #33 shows a typical pickup tip for an installed proximity probe. It is installed in the machine, usually on or near a bearing support housing, with the pickup tip in close proximity to the rotating shaft. The distance between the shaft and the tip is commonly referred to as the "gap." The gap setting depends on what type of proximity probe is being used.

Other factors which determine gap settings are shaft materials and what type of equipment is the probe being installed too. Typical gap settings are in the range of 0.020 to 0.100 inch (0.50 to 2.54 millimeters).

Transducers/Proximity Probes

Transducers - Proximity Probes (cont'd)

NON-CONTACT
PICKUP

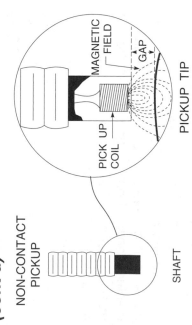

SHAFT

PICKUP TIP

Illustration #33 - Non Contact Pickup Operation

To facilitate installation and calibration of a proximity probe, the pickup gap is indicated by a gap meter located on the vibration analyzer or monitor. *The gap reading can be taken while the shaft is rotating, commonly referred to as being the "mean gap", or while the shaft is at rest, referred to as the "static gap."*

The gap meter provides the means for calibrating the proximity probe when conventional methods for verifying the gap distance are not easy or possible.

Mounting The Proximity Probe

It is preferred that proximity probes be mounted in rigid holders for accurate adjustment capabilities and easy removal during machine operation. Mounting the probe internal to the machine is also acceptable when machine design has room and is safe for pickup adjustment and removal during machine operation. Some designs prevent internal installation of pickup holders.

The pickup may have a threaded body for installation into tapped holes, while other styles may be inserted into a fitted hole and permanently located with set screws or epoxy grout. The signal cable is usually protected with armored covering to shield against abrasion and moisture contamination.

Transducers - Proximity Probes (cont'd)

For field applications where there is no provision for mounting the pickup in a tapped or fitted hole on the bearing, the pickup must be mounted using a rigid holder or bracket setup. When brackets are used they must be held rigid to the machine. Brackets and holders must be kept as short as possible and have bulk to minimize any vibrations of the mounting itself.

Disadvantages of Proximity Probes

- Must avoid excessive shaft runout caused by either mechanical or electrical faults.

- It may be sensitive to various shaft materials which could affect its accuracy.

- In order to function, the proximity probe requires an external power source.

- Installing on certain machinery configurations may prove impractical.

- Limited frequency response: generally less than 30,000 CPM (500 Hz).

Velocity Transducers

The typical velocity transducer is a mechanical instrument with simple internal moving parts which provide the necessary vibration signals. It consists of a suspended coil of wire supported by relatively stiff springs. The wire coil is surrounded by a permanent magnet which produces a magnetic field surrounding the coil. Refer to illustration #34.

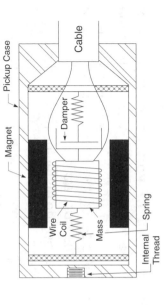

Illustration #34 - Construction of a Typical Moving Coil or Sensitivity Type Velocity Transducer

Velocity Transducers (cont'd)

When performing a vibration measurement, the velocity pickup is either attached to or held against the vibrating part. The permanent magnet being firmly attached inside the transducer case follows the vibration motion. The coil of wire, acting as the conductor and supported by the stiff springs, remains stationary. The relative motion between the magnetic field and the coiled conductor is the same as the motion of a part relative to a fixed point in space. The voltage generated by the pickup is directly proportional to the relative motion.

Note: The operation of the velocity transducer relies on the law of physics which states, "when a conductor is moved through a magnetic field, or if a magnetic field is moved past a conductor, a voltage will be induced into the conductor."

The amount of voltage is dependent upon: the length of the conductor in the coil; strength of the magnetic field; and the velocity of the magnetic field as it passes the conductor.

To conclude, the faster the motion, the larger the voltage. The voltage output of the velocity pickup is proportional to the velocity of the vibration. When the velocity of the vibrating machine part increases or decreases, the voltage generated either increases or decreases proportionally.

The sensitivity of the velocity transducer is only constant over a specified vibration frequency range. The pickup sensitivity decreases at low frequencies because at these low frequencies, below 600 CPM, the pickup coil does not remain in the stationary position with respect to the permanent magnet.

Velocity Transducers (cont'd)

Amplitude sensitivity errors are evident when using a velocity transducer at frequencies below 600 CPM due to the fact that the natural frequency of the spring-magnet assembly is normally from 8 - 10 Hz. The instrument will indicate a value less than the actual amplitude of vibration being measured.

Mounting The Velocity Transducer

The velocity transducer, as with other vibration pickups, is sensitive to vibrations occurring in the direction in which the pickup is placed. The velocity pickup can be placed in any position. This does not affect the pickup's normal operation or overall sensitivity.

Note: When a bracket, probe, or clamp is mounted between the velocity pickup and the machine part's surface (point to be measured), spring-like characteristics are generated.

This tends to amplify the true vibration at certain vibration frequencies, therefore, the accuracy of the vibration measurements are lowered.

One of the most reliable and secure mounting practices for the velocity transducer is to fasten it directly to a threaded stud. After the pickup is threaded onto the stud, the pickup's flat surface should sit square to the mating surface of the machine part. The stud length is measured to exact length to avoid bottoming the stud into the end cap and avoid unnecessary damage to the transducer. Refer to illustration #35.

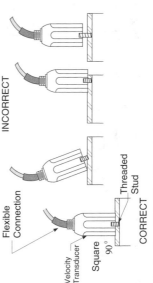

Illustration #35 - Stud Mounted Transducer

Velocity Transducers (cont'd)

Illustration #36 shows the velocity transducer mounted to a stud coming from an externally mounted bracket from the machine.

Note: *Erroneous readings may result from the use of this type of bracket because of the cantilever position. The bracket should be made rigid enough to avoid flexing or another type of mounting should be used.*

Hand Held Transducer without Probe

The velocity transducer can be used simply by holding it flat and square on the machine part. When holding it against curved or irregular surfaces, keep in mind that the transducer is designed to pickup vibrations only in the direction parallel to its axis. If the transducer is held unsteady, the direction of axis shifts, therefore the readings will vary.

Note: *Apply enough hand pressure to prevent the velocity pickup from wandering on the machine part's surface.*

If a tingling sensation is felt, apply more hand pressure because high vibration frequencies are present.

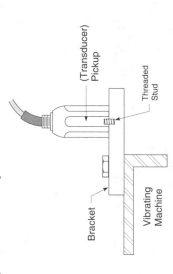

Bracket

(Transducer) Pickup

Threaded Stud

Vibrating Machine

Illustration #36 - Stud Mounted Transducer on Bracket

Hand Held Transducer with Probe

The velocity transducer is threaded on its end cap to accept a standard size stud or probe end. The probe is convenient for reaching into difficult points on the machine to measure the vibration at that point. The probe is made of light-weight material, such as aluminum, and is slightly pointed where contact is made with the machine.

Velocity Transducers (cont'd)

Hand held probe lengths vary. The longer it is more caution should be used when vibration frequencies exceed 15,000 CPM. The accuracy of the vibration readings become less reliable. Shorter length probes, or larger diameter probes should be used at vibration frequencies above 15,000 CPM.

Illustration #37 identifies a relatively long probe attached to a velocity transducer. Any unsteadiness in holding the probe, or application of unequal pressure will result in errors of the vibration measurements.

Magnetic Pickup Holder

A magnet can be attached to the end cap of the velocity transducer and this provides another option for placing the transducer on or near a machine part. The surface should be reasonably flat and free of paint, dirt or grease to ensure that the magnet holds the transducer firmly in place.

If the magnet is allowed to rock, the vibration pickup axis changes direction, therefore resulting in erroneous readings. See illustration #38.

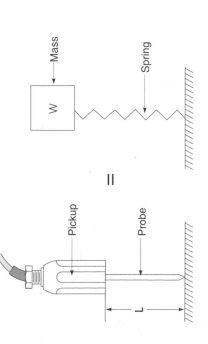

Illustration #37 - Vibration Pickup

Magnetic Pickup Holder

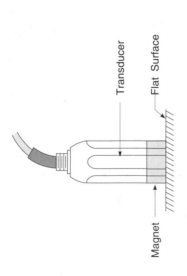

Illustration #38 - Magnetic Pickup Holder

Shaft Stick

There may be times when it is necessary to determine the actual vibration of a shaft in order to compare with the amount of vibration coming from the bearing housing. Proximity probes are useful for this type of measurement, as the non-contact pickup is attached firmly into the rigid bearing housing.

Another method for taking vibration readings directly from the machine's shaft is by using a shaft stick, as shown in illustration #39. The shaft stick is made of hardwood and one end is curved to accommodate the shaft curvature. The opposite end has a threaded stud which is threaded into the transducer.

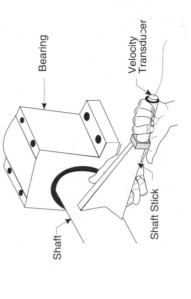

Illustration #39 - Shaft Stick

Velocity Transducers (cont'd)

In order to use shaft sticks the shaft must be reasonably smooth and free of obstructions. If the stick is applied to rough surfaces, erroneous readings result. *Take extra caution in order to avoid locations on the shaft where keys, keyways, screws, etc. are found.*

When using the shaft stick on machinery operating at 3600 RPM or more, try to be quick, and don't hold the stick against the shaft until the stick burns from excessive friction. Apply a thin coating of medium weight lube oil or grease to the shaft stick's contact surface to help reduce friction. It is recommended that the shaft stick be not used when machinery RPM exceeds 10,000.

Use both hands to firmly grip the shaft stick and attached transducer. Prevent the shaft stick from "walking" up or down the rotating shaft and use enough hand pressure to prevent any chatter.

To maintain steady pressure is important, as the overall accuracy of the vibration readings is greatly affected.

Shaft Rider

The shaft stick is used for periodic vibration checks, while the shaft rider is preferred when it is desirable to continually monitor shaft vibration. See illustration #40.

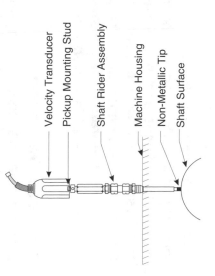

Velocity Transducer
Pickup Mounting Stud
Shaft Rider Assembly
Machine Housing
Non-Metallic Tip
Shaft Surface

Illustration #40 - Shaft Rider

Velocity Transducers (cont'd)

The shaft rider is permanently mounted into the machine's bearing housing and a spring loaded probe is held firmly against the shaft's surface. The non-metallic tip accurately follows the shaft motion. The velocity transducer is mounted by a threaded stud to the shaft rider. The transducer senses the shaft motion and transmits the signal to the vibration monitor.

Note: The shaft rider attachment is preferred for use on large rotor units, such as turbines, generators, and rotary or axial compressors. For these units, it is desirable to obtain measures of absolute shaft vibration in order to determine machine condition and for performing in-place dynamic balancing.

Note: Both the shaft rider and the shaft stick can provide high vibration readings due to shaft run-out, bent shaft or shaft surface damage.

Note: The shaft stick and the shaft rider are both very accurate attachments for determining consistent and reliable vibration measurements on most rotating equipment. Both attachments get close to the sources of vibration, at the shaft and in or near the shaft's support bearings.

Accelerometer Transducer

The accelerometer transducer is a self-generating instrument with an output proportional to the vibration acceleration. The accelerometer is especially suited for those exceptionally high vibration frequencies. Any machinery parts, such as gears, and anti-friction bearings can be analyzed by using the accelerometer. Rotating equipment, such as gas turbines and centrifugal compressors, which require continuous vibration monitoring, are best fitted with permanent accelerometers on the bearing housings.

Accelerometer Transducer (cont'd)

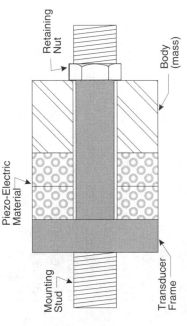

Piezo-Electric
Material

Retaining
Nut

Body
(mass)

Mounting
Stud

Transducer
Frame

Illustration #41 - Typical Accelerometer Transducer

The typical accelerometer is similar in operation to the velocity transducer. However, in the accelerometer, the coil as found in the vibration transducer, is replaced with sensitive material that has the characteristic of being able to produce an electrical charge whenever a force, such as vibration, is applied to it. The greater the amount of force applied to the material, the greater the amount of electrical charge generated.

The material contained in the accelerometer is "piezo - electric"; a crystal substance similar to that used in record players, where vibration on the needle is converted into a pulsating electric signal. See illustration #41. The signal produced by the accelerometer transducer is integrated by an electronic circuit into vibration amplitude. The accelerometer's output is expressed in "picocoulombs per g." The unit "g" is the standard unit of acceleration produced by the force of gravity at the surface of the earth. One "g" equals 32.1739 feet/second/second, or 9.81 meters/second/second.

Mounting an accelerometer transducer to the machine's part is more critical than mounting the velocity transducer. The reason is because of the accelerometer's sensitivity to high frequency vibration.

Accelerometer Transducer (cont'd)

It is often difficult to determine the best location in order to achieve the most meaningful vibration measurements.

It is recommended to use similar mounting procedures as described for the velocity transducers.

Accelerometer Mounting Recommendations

• Apply a thin coating of grease lubricant to the mounting stud.

• Do not use excessive force when tightening the accelerometer pickup to the machine part. Excessive torque may distort or damage the instrument. Insufficient torque permits a loose mount which may cause large output errors at high frequencies.

When using mounting jigs/brackets, to hold the accelerometer, make them quite rigid, but as lightweight as possible.

• Avoid using long spring-like structural members for any mounting brackets. See illustration #36.

• For maximum damping, use cast type mounting brackets or fabricated mounts.

The accelerometer may be mounted against any flat surface by:

• Screwing directly into the machine casing.

• Screwing into the mounting bracket.

• Mounting on metallic surfaces with magnetic holders.

• Mounting on metallic or non-metallic surfaces by adhesive bonding.

VIBRATION ANALYSIS

Microphones

Microphones are used to convert air pressure oscillations (sound) into mechanical movements (vibration). The majority of microphones used for measuring sound amplitude use some type of diaphragm. The diaphragm vibration is converted into an electrical signal.

In the microphone depicted in illustration #42, the diaphragm is coupled to an element which generates an electrical current when stressed by the vibration of the diaphragm. The microphone, unlike the vibration transducers which only sense vibrations in the direction pointed, are a multi-directional instrument. It is sensitive to sounds coming from all directions.

Note: When positioning the microphone, care should be taken to consider the possible sound fields which are present. The near, far and reverberant sound fields effect the noise levels being measured. See pages 71 and 72 for a further explanation.

The presence of the operator taking the noise level measurements, if he is near the microphone, may affect the measured results by two or more decibels. The operator should be positioned with the microphone held well out in front with the apparent noise source either to the far right or left. Refer to illustration #43.

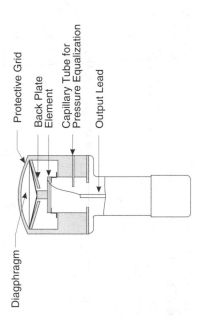

Protective Grid
Back Plate
Element
Capillary Tube for Pressure Equalization
Output Lead
Diagphragm

Illustration #42 - Microphone

Microphones (cont'd)

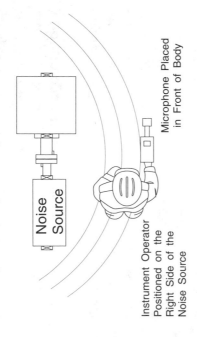

Instrument Operator
Positioned on the
Right Side of the
Noise Source

Microphone Placed
in Front of Body

Noise Source

Illustration #43 - Noise Source

Vibration Pickup Positions

Obtaining vibration amplitude measurements in three directions is important to assist the vibration technician distinguish between a variety of mechanical problems. Refer to illustration #44.

It is recommended that the vibration pickup be placed on, or as near possible, to the machine's bearings because it is through the bearings that the vibration forces are commonly transmitted.

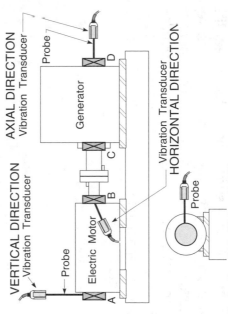

VERTICAL DIRECTION
Vibration Transducer — Probe

AXIAL DIRECTION
Vibration Transducer — Probe

Generator

Electric Motor

Vibration Transducer
HORIZONTAL DIRECTION — Probe

A B C D

Illustration #44 - Pickup Positions

Vibration Pickup Positions (cont'd)

The vibration pickup measures only the vibration occurring in the direction in which the pickup is being pointed. Therefore, it is necessary to record the position of the pickup for all the vibration readings taken. The vibration readings are recorded as measured in horizontal, vertical and axial directions at each bearing point on the machine train.

Note: It is usually only necessary to take one axial reading for machinery which is coupled as a driver and driven unit together.

Vertical and horizontal vibration readings are taken with the pickup perpendicular to the machine's shaft centerline. These readings are referred to as "radial" vibration measurements.

Axial vibration readings are taken with the pickup placed on the machine parallel to the machine's centerline. Ensure that the pickup is placed on or near the machine's bearing.

Note: Each particular brand and model of vibration meter, vibration monitor, and vibration analyzer will have its own unique features and operating procedures. Before one begins to take vibration amplitude readings carefully read the manufacturer's instruction handbook which should outline in detail the operating procedures. The person who is taking the vibration amplitude and/or noise level readings must first comprehend basic principles of vibration and noise analysis, as well as the characteristics and causes of vibration and know the most appropriate methods for correcting the problems.

Amplitude vs. Frequency Readings

Vibration amplitude versus vibration frequency data can be obtained and recorded several ways. The basic vibration analyzer, as shown in illustration #28, uses a manually tuned filter. The filter is tuned by hand in order to scan all the vibration frequencies.

Amplitude vs. Frequency (cont'd)

Significant vibration amplitude, in displacement, velocity or acceleration, and corresponding frequencies are identified by carefully observing the analyzer's amplitude and frequency meter. Usually the data is manually recorded on a data sheet, similar to the one shown in illustration #45.

The data sheet has a section where the vibration technician can sketch the machine which is to be analyzed. The sketch should include the bearing points (referenced) where the vibration measurements are taken from. The data sheet can be filed for future reference.

The noted bearing points clearly identify where all vibration readings were taken from and this will identify the location for any future readings.

When the vibration analysis data is being manually recorded, consider the following points:

• Measure and record the overall or filter out amplitude and corresponding frequency at each measurement point in all three positions (vertical, horizontal, axial).

• Where it is likely to encounter vibration frequencies below 600 CPM, it is recommended that the vibration technician consider using displacement for determining the amplitude of vibration in "filter-in" and the appropriate pickup.

• The "filter-out" amplitude readings reveal the extent of the vibration problem, as well as provide a basis for comparison with "filter-in" amplitude readings. All "filter-out" readings should be measured in velocity.

"Filter-out" readings are often referred to as "overall vibration."

VIBRATION ANALYSIS

DATA SHEET

DATE:

☐ NOISE ☐ VIBRATION ANALYSIS OF: _____

FOR: _____

VIBRATION ANALYZER TYPE: _____

PERFORMED BY: _____

LEGEND:
→ PICKUP POINT
✕ PLAIN BEARING
⊗ ANTI-FRICTION BEARING
─‖─ COUPLING

TEST CONDITIONS:

PICKUP		NOISE		FILTER OUT					FILTER IN					
				DISPLACEMENT			VELOCITY							
POINT	POS.	dB(C)	CPM	mils	micron	CPM	in/sec	mm/sec	CPM					
	H													
	V													
	A													
	H													
	V													
	A													
	H													
	V													
	A													

Illustration #45 - Noise/Vibration Data Sheet

Amplitude vs. Frequency (cont'd)

- Velocity measurement is the most preferred unit for determining the amplitude of vibration in "filter-out." Many organizations continue to solely use velocity readings in frequencies ranging from 0 to 60,000 CPM for all "filter-in" readings. When high vibration frequencies are encountered, over 60,000 CPM, consider using acceleration for measuring the amplitude of vibration in "filter-in."

- Dominant frequency readings usually direct attention to the mechanical problem source.

- Conclusions should not only be based on "filter-out" vibration amplitude readings.

- "Filter-in" vibration amplitude readings are obtained at each frequency range of the analyzer. By scanning each frequency range with the tunable filter, vibration frequencies can be located.

- After the dominant vibration frequency has been located, adjust the tunable filter to locate the peak amplitude reading on the analyzer's amplitude meter.

- Record the peak amplitude of vibration for the frequency at all bearing points in three positions (vertical, horizontal, axial).

- Proceed to scan for the next most dominant frequency with the tunable filter and again record the peak vibration amplitude and corresponding frequency for each bearing point in all three positions.

- Continue the filter-scanning procedure until all significant vibration frequencies have been located and their corresponding vibration amplitudes recorded. Illustration #46 shows a completed data sheet which has been developed by using the scanning method.

DATA SHEET

DATE: 28 AUG 2002

☐ NOISE ☒ VIBRATION   ANALYSIS OF: _#12 I.D.FAN_

FOR: _Determine cause of vibration amplitude increase_

VIBRATION ANALYZER TYPE: _____

PERFORMED BY: _T.J._

LEGEND:

PICKUP POINT ——►   PLAIN BEARING ✕

ANTI-FRICTION BEARING ⊗   COUPLING ⊣⊢

TEST CONDITIONS:

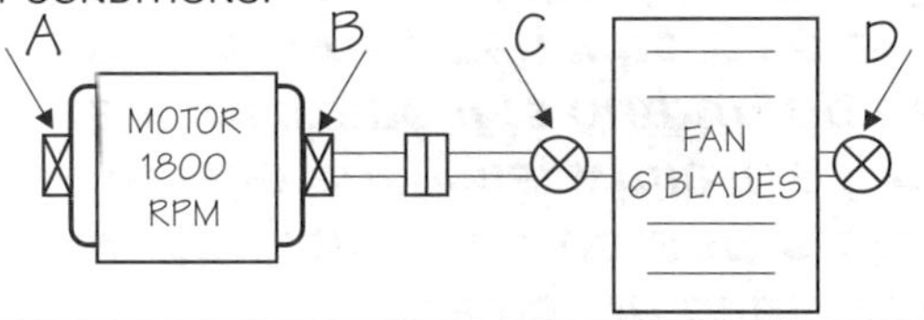

(A) MOTOR 1800 RPM — (B) — (C) — FAN 6 BLADES — (D)

PICKUP		NOISE		FILTER OUT						VEL	FILTER IN	
				DISPLACEMENT			VELOCITY					
POINT	POS.	dB(C)	CPM	mils	micron	CPM	in/sec	mm/sec	CPM	VEL 1800	VEL 3600	VEL 5400
A	H			3.0		1800	.62		1800	0.5	0.10	0.09
	V			1.6		1800	.31		1800	0.25	0.11	0.04
	A			0.8		1800	.10		1800	0.07	0.04	0.01
B	H			4.5		1800	.41		1800	0.32	0.10	0.04
	V			2.7		1800	.30		1800	0.19	0.09	0.04
	A			1.2		1800	.15		1800	0.13	0.02	0.01
C	H			2.9		1800	.51		1800	0.22	0.10	0.02
	V			1.5		1800	.39		1800	0.14	0.09	0.02
	A			1.4		1800	.19		1800	0.11	0.04	0.01
D	H			1.1		1800	.11		1800	0.10	0.04	0.02
	V			0.80		1800	.09		1800	0.07	0.04	0.03
	A			0.85		1800	.08		1800	0.05	0.02	0.01

Illustration #46 - Data Sheet Example

"X - Y" Plotter

Various manufacturers of vibration analyzers design their equipment with provisions for connecting an external "x - y" plotter/coordinate recorder for making graphic "signatures" of vibration amplitude versus vibration frequency. See illustration #47.

FFT Analyzer Recordings

FFT Analyzers have the capability of storing many signatures of vibration, based on vibration amplitude versus vibration frequency. The stored data can be downloaded into a computer and various graphic spectrums can be produced to present the signatures of vibration.

There are several manufacturers of vibration analysis equipment who have built their equipment with filters that automatically scan all frequencies in a preselected range, and provide a printout of amplitude vs. time or amplitude vs. frequency as shown in illustration #48.

The vibration technician has only to hold the vibration pickup on the bearing point, in the three positions, and the analyzer automatically scans all the frequencies and records the corresponding amplitude of vibration. Data collection is automatic. This operation usually only takes a few seconds and then a message on the analyzer would tell the operator to move to the next bearing point on the route.

Note: Data collection is typically a different process than performing a field analysis, even though the instrument used may be the same. In data collection, the instrument records and stores the data for later analysis, while in a field analysis, the instrument is outputting the data to a printer or screen where an on-the-job visual analysis of the data is performed. Vibration meters and analyzers can store data used during field analysis and call it up later on a computer.

VIBRATION ANALYSIS

FFT Recording (cont'd)

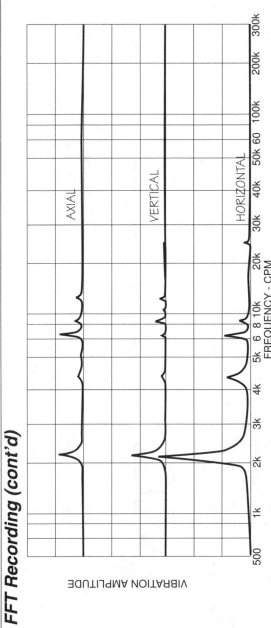

MACHINE	FRESH AIR FAN	AMPLITUDE FILTER OUT	0.36 IN/SEC (HORIZ)
MACHINE LOCATION	LOWER LEVEL	AMPLITUDE RANGE	0.3 IN/SEC (PEAK)
OPERATING CONDITIONS			

	2200 RPM	FILTER IN	X SHARP		BROAD
	30% DAMPER	TYPE PICKUP	X VEL	ACCEL	N/C
		MEASURE POSITION	C	H	V	A
		DATE	15 Jul 2003	BY	RLF

SKETCH

2200 RPM — C, D

1750 RPM — A, B

Illustration #47 - Plotter Output

FFT Recording (cont'd)

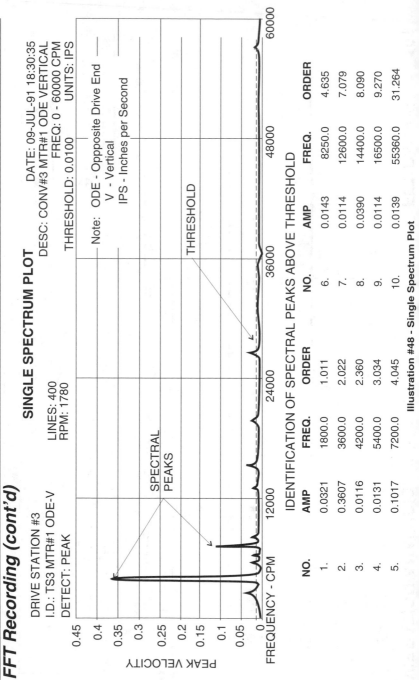

SINGLE SPECTRUM PLOT

DRIVE STATION #3
I.D.: TS3 MTR#1 ODE-V
DETECT: PEAK

LINES: 400
RPM: 1780

DATE: 09-JUL-91 18:30:35
DESC: CONV#3 MTR#1 ODE VERTICAL
FREQ: 0 - 60000 CPM
THRESHOLD: 0.0100   UNITS: IPS

Note: ODE - Oppposite Drive End
         V - Vertical
         IPS - Inches per Second

IDENTIFICATION OF SPECTRAL PEAKS ABOVE THRESHOLD

NO.	AMP	FREQ.	ORDER	NO.	AMP	FREQ.	ORDER
1.	0.0321	1800.0	1.011	6.	0.0143	8250.0	4.635
2.	0.3607	3600.0	2.022	7.	0.0114	12600.0	7.079
3.	0.0116	4200.0	2.360	8.	0.0390	14400.0	8.090
4.	0.0131	5400.0	3.034	9.	0.0114	16500.0	9.270
5.	0.1017	7200.0	4.045	10.	0.0139	55360.0	31.264

Illustration #48 - Single Spectrum Plot

FFT Recording(cont'd)

		VIBRATION AMPLITUDE MEASUREMENTS					
		Unit	Date	Prev.Val	Last Val	%Chg	Alrm
DRIVE STATION #3	Conveyor Station #3						
TS3	MTR#1 ODE-H	IPS	09-JUL-91	0.17832	0.04455	150	A2
TS3	MTR#1 ODE-V	IPS	09-JUL-91	0.10421	0.3853	270	A2
TS3	MTR#1 ODE-A	IPS	09-JUL-91	0.0549	0.2079	279	A1
TS3	MTR#1 DE-H	IPS	09-JUL-91	0.12468	0.4351	249	A2
TS3	MTR#1 DE-V	IPS	09-JUL-91	0.10505	0.122	16	—
TS3	GRBOX#1 ODE-H	IPS	09-JUL-91	0.11289	0.1041	8	—
TS3	GRBOX#1 ODE-V	IPS	09-JUL-91	0.10189	0.3519	245	A2
TS3	GRBOX#1 ODE-A	IPS	09-JUL-91	0.0941	0.4571	386	A2
TS3	GRBOX#1 DE-H	IPS	09-JUL-91	0.09316	0.2679	188	A1
TS3	GRBOX#1 DE-V	IPS	09-JUL-91	0.08245	0.2941	257	A1
TS3	MRT#2 ODE-H	IPS	09-JUL-91	0.07901	0.3356	325	A1
TS3	MTR#2 ODE-V	IPS	09-JUL-91	0.12645	0.1751	38	—
TS3	MTR#2 ODE-A	IPS	09-JUL-91	0.05462	0.3119	471	A1
TS3	MTR#2 DE-H	IPS	09-JUL-91	0.08552	0.2213	159	A1
TS3	MTR#2 DE-V	IPS	09-JUL-91	0.06296	0.1195	90	—
TS3	GRBOX#2 ODE-H	IPS	09-JUL-91	0.08901	0.1627	83	—
TS3	GRBOX#2 ODE-V	IPS	09-JUL-91	0.12375	0.2167	75	A1
TS3	GRBOX#2 ODE-A	IPS	09-JUL-91	0.15169	0.2129	40	A1
TS3	GRBOX#2 DE-H	IPS	09-JUL-91	0.12489	0.2074	66	A1
TS3	GRBOX#2 DE-V	IPS	09-JUL-91	0.06372	0.08879	39	—

Note: DE - Drive End   ODE - Opposite Drive End   H - Horizontal   V - Vertical   A - Axial

Table #6 - Vibration Amplitude Measurements

FFT Recording (cont'd)

Once the route has been completed, the operator would probably have to down-load the recorded information into a computer where the data would be stored for future analysis.

There are many types of software available which interpret the vibration amplitude and frequencies. The software can show a variety of spectrums, graphs, and databases which clearly identify the corresponding vibration amplitude for each scanned frequency. Illustration #48 identifies one example where vibration spectrums have been recorded automatically, where the filter goes through a large range of frequencies in a very short period of time and the spectrums are printed out on a plotter.

Table #6 indicates an example of a database for the various pieces of equipment which have been analyzed and are part of the route for a conveyor system.

The measurements are an "overall" or "filter out" velocity measurement.

Real-Time Spectrum Analysis

One of the most common methods for analyzing vibration and noise amplitude versus frequency data is by using "real-time" spectrum analysis. Not all vibration and noise analysis situations have steady and predictable vibration and noise patterns. Some machinery operates under continually varying conditions of speed, load, etc. Random vibrations, extraneous vibrations, often sporadic, result from inconsistencies in things like flow, pressure, voltage, amperage, resistance, turbulencies, etc. *A single signature of vibration may not truly measure the machine's vibration problems. The short, random vibration measurement checks of amplitude versus frequency are not sufficient for machinery operating in fluctuating operating conditions.*

Real-Time Spectrum Analysis (cont'd)

The "real-time" spectrum analysis analyzes complex vibration and noise much faster than conventional vibration analyzers which use manually tuned filters. It can also analyze many more points than the traditional analyzer. The number of machines being monitored for vibration keep on expanding with more and more points being analyzed for vibration amplitude and frequency.

The "real-time" analyzer provides an instantaneous and continuous updated display of vibration amplitude versus frequency spectrums or as time wave forms which can be displayed as the vibration is occurring. The "real-time" spectrum analyzer can include a built-in strip chart. The strip chart provides an instant hard copy of the vibration signature. This is useful for quick analysis and for comparison and interpretation purposes.

Data Interpretation

After the vibration amplitude and frequency data has been collected, the next step is to compare the vibration readings with the characteristics of vibration typical of various types of mechanical problems. Note that the essential feature in the comparison process is the vibration frequency. The comparison by vibration frequency is made on the basis of the machine's RPM or the specific speeds of the machine's parts and components.

Table #7 outlines the vibration frequencies usually encountered when performing machinery vibration analysis. The vibration technician performing the analysis should know and understand the various vibration frequencies which are identified as being predominant.

This frequency data assists the identification of the most likely cause(s) of vibration. The frequencies identified in table #7 are referenced in terms of machinery RPM.

Data Interpretation (cont'd)

	Vibration Frequencies and the Likely Causes	
Frequency in Terms of RPM	Most Likely Cause	Other Possible Causes and Remarks
1 x RPM	Unbalance	1) Eccentric journals, gears or pulleys 2) Misaligned or bent shaft - if high axial vibration 3) Bad belts - if at RPM of belt 4) Resonance 5) Reciprocating forces 6) Electrical problems
2 x RPM	Mechanical looseness	1) Misalignment - if high axial vibration 2) Reciprocating forces 3) Resonance 4) Bad belts - if 2 x RPM of belt
3 x RPM	Misalignment	Usually a combination of misalignment and excessive axial clearances (looseness)
Less than 1 x RPM	Oil Whirl (less than 1/2 RPM)	1) Bad drive belts 2) Background vibration 3) Sub-harmonic resonance 4) "Beat" vibration
Synchronous (AC line frequency - 60 Hz)	Electrical problems	Common electrical problems including broken rotor bars, eccentric rotor, unbalanced phases in poly-phase systems, unequal air-gap.
2 x Sync. frequency (120 Hz)	Torque pulses	Rare as a problem unless resonance is excited.

Table #7A - Vibration Frequencies

Vibration Frequencies and the Likely Causes

Frequency in Terms of RPM	Most Likely Cause	Other Possible Causes and Remarks
Many times RPM (Harmonically related freq.)	Bad gears Aerodynamic forces Hydraulic forces Mechanical looseness Reciprocating forces	Gear teeth times RPM of bad gear Number of fan blades times RPM Number of impeller vanes times RPM May occur at 2, 3, 4 and sometimes higher harmonics if severe looseness
High frequency (not harmonically related)	Bad anti-friction bearings	1) Bearing vibration may be unsteady - amplitude and frequency 2) Cavitation, recirculation and flow turbulence cause random high frequency vibration 3) Improper lubrication of journal bearings (friction excited vibration) 4) Rubbing

Table #7B -Vibration Frequencies (continued)

Data Interpretation (cont'd)

	Vibration Identification			
Cause	Amplitude	Frequency	Phase	Remarks
Unbalance	Proportional to unbalance Largest in radial direction	1 x RPM	Single reference mark	Most common cause of vibration.
Misalignment couplings or bearings and bent shaft	Large in axial direction 50% or more of radial vibration	1 x RPM usual 2 & 3 x RPM sometimes	Single double or triple	Best found by appearance of large axial vibration. Use dial indicators or other method for positive diagnosis. If sleeve bearing machine and no coupling misalignment, balance the rotor.
Bad bearings anti-friction type	Unsteady - use the velocity measurement if possible	Very high - several times RPM	Erratic	Bearing responsible most likely the one nearest point of largest high-frequency vibration.
Eccentric journals	Usually not large	1 x RPM	Single mark	If on gears largest vibration is on line with gear centers. If on motor or generator vibration disappears when power is turned off. If on pump or blower attempt to balance.
Bad gears or gear noise	Low - use the velocity measurement if possible	Very high gear teeth times RPM	Erratic	Look for tooth wear, gear eccentricity and backlash, gear misalignment. cracked and/or broken tooth, gear hunting problems.

Table #8A - Data Interpretation

Vibration Identification

Cause	Amplitude	Frequency	Phase	Remarks
Mechanical looseness		2 x RPM	Two reference marks Slightly erratic	Usually accompanied by unbalance and/or misalignment.
Bad drive belts	Erratic or pulsing	1, 2, 3 & 4 x RPM of belts	1 or 2 depending on frequency. Usually unsteady.	Strobe light best tool to freeze faulty belt.
Electrical	Disappears when power is turned off	1 x RPM or 1 or 2 x synchronous frequency	Single or rotating double mark	If vibration amplitude drops off instantly when power is turned off cause is electrical.
Aerodynamic hydraulic forces		1 x RPM or number of blades on fan or impeller x RPM		Rare as cause of trouble except in cases of resonance.
Reciprocating forces		1, 2 and higher orders x RPM		Inherent in reciprocating machines can only be reduced by design changes or isolation.

Table #8B - Data Interpretation (continued)

Data Interpretation (cont'd)

The vibration identification chart, as shown in table #8, lists the most common causes of vibration encountered, along with characteristic vibration amplitude, frequency and phase features for each vibration cause.

Note: The "remarks" column of table #8 provides helpful information to be considered when attempting to pinpoint mechanical problems and vibration sources.

Tables #7 and #8 serve as useful references to assist in the interpretation of the data collected from the performed vibration analysis. The causes of vibration identified at each frequency provide a basis to start from. Many years of vibration analysis experience contributed to the development of these tables. Maintenance personnel should learn more about their own machinery and corresponding vibrations. They can also make their own identification charts, based on vibration frequencies commonly recorded on the machinery they routinely analyze.

Tables #9A, #9B, and #9C provide a list of the most common problems encountered in and around modern rotating equipment. A relative probability number is shown and this indicates which problem is most likely in a given set of circumstances.

Where no number rating appears, this indicates that the problem will not exhibit the amplitude or frequency characteristics shown.

Note: The number rating provided for each mechanical problem represents a percentage value. Number 10 indicates the fault will always show the characteristic vibration frequency (100%). The number 5 indicates that 50% of the time the characteristic indicated for a specific fault will occur.

Tables #10A, #10B, and #10C provide appropriate remarks for the likely causes of vibration found on tables #9A, #9B and #9C.

Vibration Causes and Probability Rating (Part 1 of 3)

Vibration Cause	Predominant Frequencies											Predominant Amplitude									
												Direction			Phase No. of Ref. Marks	Prob. Location					
	0 – 40%	40 – 50%	50–100%	1 × RPM	2 × RPM	Higher Multiples	0.5 × RPM	0.25 × RPM	Lower Multiples	Odd Frequency	Very High Freq.	Horizontal	Vertical	Axial		Rotor/Shaft	Bearings	Casing	Foundation	Piping	Coupling
UNBALANCE																					
Initial unbalance				10								5	4	1	1	9	1				1
Shaft bow, loose parts				10								5	4	1	1	9	1				1
MISALIGNMENT																					
Shaft misalignment		8		4	5	1						3	2	5	1,2,3	8	1	1			
LOOSENESS																					
Mechanical looseness					8	1						5	4	1	2,*		3	2	2	2	
Clearances in excess	1								1			5	4	1	*	7	1	1			1
DISTORTION																					
Foundation	1	2	5	2					1		1	5	4	1	*	3	1	1	1		
Casing	1	1	1	8	1						1	5	4	1	*	9	1	1			
Seal rubbing	1	1	1	2	1	1			1	1		4	3	3	*	8	1	1			
Rotor rubbing (axial)	2	2	2	3	1	1			1	1		4	3	3	*	7	1	2			
Piping forces	2			4	5	1						3	2	5	1,2	3	4	3			
BAD BEARINGS																					
Eccentricity	1	1	1	8	2							5	4	1	1	9	1				
Radial bearing damage	1	9	9	4	2						2	4	3	3	*	7	2	1			
Thrust bearing damage	9	9	9	9	9							3	2	5	*	6	2	2			
Bearing excited vibration	10	10	10								1	5	4	1	*	5	2	2	1		

Table #9A - Data interpretation

Vibration Causes and Probability Rating (Part 2 of 3)

| | Predominant Frequencies | | | | | | | | | | | Predominant Amplitude | | | | | | | | | |
| | | | | | | | | | | | | Direction | | | | Prob. Location | | | | | |
	0 - 40%	40 - 50%	50 - 100%	1 x RPM	2 x RPM	Higher Multiples	0.5 x RPM	0.25 x RPM	Lower Multiples	Odd Frequency	Very High Freq.	Horizontal	Vertical	Axial	Phase No. of Ref. Marks	Rotor/Shaft	Bearings	Casing	Foundation	Piping	Coupling
GEARS																					
Gear Inaccuracies						2				2	6	5	3	2	*	8	1	1			
COUPLINGS																					
Coupling Inaccuracies					1	8	1					4	2	3	*	7	2	1		'	
CRITICALS																					
Critical Speed				10								5	4	1	C	6	4				
Rotor & Bearing System				10								5	4	1	C	7	3				
Coupling Critical				10								4	2	4	C	1	1				
Overhang Critical				10								5	4	1	C	7	1				
RESONANCE																					
Resonant Vibration				10								4	4	2	*	2	1	2	3	2	
Sub-Harmonic Resonance							10	10	10			3	3	4	R	2	2	2	2	2	
Harmonic Resonance					10	10						4	4	2	R	2	1	1	3	3	
Casing Resonance				8	1		1					5	4	1	R		4	4	1	1	
Support Resonance				8	1		1					5	4	1	R		2	5	2	1	
Foundation Resonance				8	1		1					4	3	3	R		1	4	4	1	
Torsional Resonance				4	2	2				2		4	3	3	R	1	4	4	4		1

Table #9B - Data Interpretation (continued)

Vibration Causes and Probability Rating (Part 3 of 3)

	Predominant Frequencies											Direction				Predominant Amplitude — Prob. Location					
	0 - 40%	40 - 50%	50 - 100%	1 x RPM	2 x RPM	Higher Multiples	0.5 x RPM	0.25 x RPM	Lower Multiples	Odd Frequency	Very High Freq.	Horizontal	Vertical	Axial	Phase No. of Ref. Marks	Rotor/Shaft	Bearings	Casing	Foundation	Piping	Coupling
OTHER CAUSES																					
Bad Drive Belts			10	10	10							4	3	3	1,2,*	5	3	1	1		
Reciprocating Forces			3	5	2							3	6	1	*	5	3	1	1		
Aero/Hydro Forces			2	6							2	5	4	1	1,M	4	3	2	1		
Friction Induced Forces	8		1									5	4	1	*	8	2				
Oil Whirl		10										5	4	1	*	8	2				
Resonant Whirl		10										5	4	1	*	2	2	2	2	2	
Dry Whirl											10	4	3	3	*	4	2	2	1		1
ELECTRICAL																					
Out-of-round Rotor				10								5	4	1	1, RDM	9	1				
Misaligned Rotor/Stator				10								4	3	3	RDM	8	2				
Stator Bore - Eliptical				10								5	4	1	RDM	8	2				
Defective Bar				10								5	4	1	RDM	9	1				
Bent Rotor Shaft				10								3	2	5	1	9	1				
Rotor not Elect.Centered				10								3	2	5	1	6	4				

LEGEND: Phase No., * - Eratic, C - Changing, M - Multiple, RDM - Rotating Double Mark, R - Rocking

Table #9C - Data Interpretation (continued)

Vibration Causes - Remarks (Part 1 of 3)

UNBALANCE	Most common cause of vibration whose amplitude is proportional to the amount of unbalance. May be aggravated by or may produce complications such as seal rubs, bearing failures or resonances (overhung rotors may show relatively high axial vibration).
MISALIGNMENT, LOOSENESS AND DISTORTION	Misalignment most commonly appears as a large axial vibration. High radial readings can be caused if large amounts of parallel misalignment exist and when a rotor is held rigid in the axial direction. Use dial indicators or other methods for positive diagnosis. May produce friction or deflection forces which can be severe. Looseness creates many problems. Small amount may allow violent vibration. Looseness in bearings may be mistaken for oil whirl. Usually accompanied by unbalance and/or misalignment. Distortion causes vibration indirectly by generating misalignment, causing uneven rubs or uneven bearing contact. Piping forces and foundation distortion often cause resonance problems. Rubs are characterized by the presence of many frequencies all over the spectrum.
BAD BEARINGS AND JOURNALS	In the case of anti-friction bearing failures, very high frequencies will be noted with the bearing responsible being the one at the point of the largest high frequency vibration. Journal eccentricity relating to gears appears largest in line with gear centers. On motors or generators vibration disappears when power is turned off. On pumps and blowers, improvement may be accomplished by balancing. Acceleration measurements are recommended when analyzing for anti-friction bearing failures. Measuring "shock" within anti-friction bearings is another method for anlyzing failures.

Table #10A - Vibration Causes - Remarks

	Vibration Causes - Remarks (Part 2 of 3)
GEARINGS AND COUPLINGS	Misalignment is the prime cause of gearing failures. Pitting, scuffing and fractures cause non-uniform results. Couplings are susceptible to both misalignment and torsional forces.
CRITICALS	For practical purposes, the terms "natural frequency", "resonance", and "critical speed" are synonymous. Minute unbalances cause large shaft deflections due to centrifugal force at critical speed. Differs from resonant vibration in that the shaft does not vibrate "back and forth" but rotates in an ever increasing bow, assuming equal radial damping. Shaft will bend rather than fail from fatigue as in the case of resonance. A critical may be improved by balancing. Resonance may be improved by internal damping.
RESONANCE	Resonance only amplifies vibrations from other sources. It cannot generate vibration but can create highly dangerous situations by amplifying normal vibration in rotating machines or from pulsations in piping. May cause rotor or bearing abnormalities such as resonant whirl. Torsional vibration is not normally noticed externally since motion is superimposed on the rotation similar to the action of a washing machine agitator. Failures may occur without warning unless gearing is involved resulting in noise. Torsional resonant frequencies coinciding with electrical frequencies can become very serious.

Table #10B - Vibration Causes - Remarks (continued)

	Vibration Causes - Remarks (Part 3 of 3)
MISCELLANEOUS BASIC CAUSES	Bad Belts - strobe light will freeze a faulty belt. Cure is matched belt sets, equal tension and correct alignment. Reciprocating Forces - inherent in reciprocating machines - can only be reduced by design changes or isolation. Aero-Hydro Forces - occur usually at no. of impeller blades x RPM. Random pulses may produce related resonance. Friction Whirl - sometimes called "hysteresis whirl" is rare but violent. Cause - rotor passes through critical; angle between unbalance and shaft "high spot" swings 180 degrees with friction damping also 180 degrees out of phase. Frequency of vibration always at actual rotor critical speed. Oil Whirl - caused by shaft being pushed around in bearing clearance by oil pressure wave. Frequency half shaft speed less 2% - 8% due to friction effects.
ELECTRICAL	Phase at synchronous frequency. Electrical causes of vibration will show up at 60 and 120 hz (1 and 2 x line frequency) and disappear quickly when power is turned off. A "slip-beat" vibration may occur at slip speed times number of poles. "Beat Frequency" relates to more than one machine operating at nearly the same speed. Mechanical defects may be detected with conventional indicating methods. Defective Bar - break bar connection, energize one phase with low voltage and turn rotor by hand. Current surge will indicate broken bar. Check air gaps.

Table #10C - Vibration Causes - Remarks (continued)

SECTION TWO - QUESTIONS
Vibration Analysis

1. *Vibration analysis is the process of performing vibration measurements and interpreting the collected data.*

   ☐ true   ☐ false

2. *Vibration is defined as:*

   ☐ an intense energy
   ☐ torsional load
   ☐ the motion of a machine or machine part, back and forth from its normal position of rest
   ☐ the movement of machine parts caused by centrifugal force

3. *Machines which operate in the best condition possible will have no vibration and noise.*

   ☐ true   ☐ false

4. *Machinery vibration and noise increases in amplitude for no apparent reason.*

   ☐ this is a false statement
   ☐ some force must be causing the vibration and noise
   ☐ it is natural to have increased noise and vibration in a machine, therefore there is no reason for alarm.

5. *All machines have three properties which combine to ultimately determine how the machine will respond to the forces which cause vibration. List these three properties and provide a brief explanation of each.*

   Answer: _____

6. *The cause of vibration must be a force which is changing either its direction or amount.*

   ☐ true   ☐ false

7. *The cause of vibration does not have to have its own unique characteristics.*

   ☐ true   ☐ false

8. *What is required to provide a measurable characteristic of vibration?*

   ☐ distance and time
   ☐ RPM and frequency
   ☐ displacement and velocity
   ☐ phase and time

9. *What are five common measurable characteristics of vibration?*

   Answer: _____

10. *The amount of time required to complete one cycle of vibration is called the:*

    ☐ severity of vibration
    ☐ amplitude of vibration
    ☐ period of vibration
    ☐ direct measurement of vibration

11. *What is the best vibration characteristic to measure, or consider, for equipment that is subjected to low frequent vibration?*

    ☐ Displacement
    ☐ Velocity
    ☐ Acceleration
    ☐ Phase

12. *The total distance travelled by the vibrating part, from one extreme limit of travel to the other extreme limit of travel, is referred to as "peak-to-peak displacement."*

    ☐ true   ☐ false

13. *Displacement (peak-to-peak) is expressed in units of:*
    Answer: _____

    _____

14. *Vibration velocity is constantly changing throughout the cycle of vibration.*

    ☐ true   ☐ false

15. *"Peak velocity" is normally selected for velocity measurements. Explain what this means.*
    Answer: _____

16. *"Peak velocity" is expressed in units of:*
    Answer: _____

    _____

17. *Vibration acceleration is the measurement of the rate of change of velocity.*

    ☐ true   ☐ false

18. *As the velocity of the vibrating part increases, the acceleration of the part decreases.*

    ☐ true   ☐ false

19. *Vibration acceleration (peak) is measured in units of:*

    ☐ "g's"
    ☐ "g's" per second
    ☐ inches or millimeters per second
    ☐ mils or microns

20. Another characteristic of vibration is phase. Phase is defined as:
- ☐ the total peak-to-peak distance a vibrating part moves
- ☐ the measurement of the maximum speed of the vibrating part
- ☐ the position of a vibrating part at a given instant with reference to a fixed point or another machine part
- ☐ the amount of time required to complete one cycle of vibration

21. Phase readings are expressed in _____.
- ☐ "g's"
- ☐ degrees
- ☐ cycles per minute (CPM)
- ☐ mils or microns

22. What instrument is used to determine phase relationships of vibrating parts?
- ☐ vibration transducer
- ☐ stroboscopic light
- ☐ accelerometer
- ☐ microphone

23. The frequency of vibration can be expressed in:
- ☐ multiples or sub-multiples of rotation speed
- ☐ cycles per minute (CPM) or cycles per second (CPS)
- ☐ hertz (Hz)
- ☐ all of the above

24. The following definition applies to which characteristic of vibration? "Amplified vibration caused by excitation forces which correspond in frequency to the natural frequency of the machine part or structural member."
- ☐ phase
- ☐ synchronous vibration
- ☐ asynchronous vibration
- ☐ resonance

25. The following definition applies to which characteristic of vibration. "A type of resonance which occurs when a shaft or rotating machine component revolves at a speed close to its natural frequency."
- ☐ critical speed
- ☐ flash angle
- ☐ vibration amplitude
- ☐ synchronous vibration

Vibration Analysis

26. Vibration amplitude is the indicator used for determining how bad or how good the rotating equipment is while in operation.

☐ true   ☐ false

27. The objective is not to identify the amount of vibration a particular machine will withstand before it fails, but to determine impending problems early enough to avoid unnecessary failures.

☐ true   ☐ false

28. Research indicates that it is quite easy to provide absolute vibration tolerances for any given type of rotating equipment.

☐ true   ☐ false

29. Vibration amplitude associated with precision machines normally does not adversely affect the quality of the finished product being produced by that machine.

☐ true   ☐ false

30. Which six physical factors contribute to the overall noise levels associated with machinery installations?

Answer: _____

31. Is it true that tradespeople, rotating equipment specialists, and plant operators learn to recognize characteristic noises from the machines and equipment they operate and maintain?

☐ yes   ☐ no

32. Sound, when transmitted in the atmosphere, is described as:

☐ air molecules in collision
☐ energy cycles
☐ being variations in air pressure
☐ being variations in the air density

33. Sound waves can be generated by:

Answer: _____

34. Sound amplitude is defined as:

Answer: _____

35. Which scale is the most common for expressing units of sound amplitude?

☐ decibel (dB)   ☐ hertz (Hz)
☐ microbars   ☐ microns

36. Identify what the acute threshold of hearing and the acute threshold of pain is in decibels.

Answer: _____

37. What are three types of sound fields?

Answer: _____

38. When possible, it is recommended to take noise measurements in the _____ field region.

Answer: _____

39. Noise level measurements taken to detect machinery condition must be based on recording noise increases in the "normal" noise level.

❏ true   ❏ false

40. Instruments for measuring machinery noise and vibration can be classed in three categories. These are:

Answer: _____

41. For vibration measurements, which device converts mechanical vibration into electrical signals?

❏ microphone
❏ stroboscopic light
❏ transducer
❏ voltmeter

42. Which instrument converts sound pressure oscillations into electrical signals?

❏ microphone
❏ transducer
❏ proximity probe
❏ filter

43. Which type of vibration transducer requires electric power from a signal transmitter?

❏ vibration transducer
❏ accelerometer
❏ proximity probe
❏ microphone

44. Which type of vibration transducer is considered to be a "non-contact" pickup?
    □ velocity transducer
    □ accelerometer
    □ shaft stick
    □ proximity probe

45. Amplitude errors are evident when using a velocity transducer at frequencies below 600 CPM.
    □ true   □ false

46. When a bracket, probe, or clamp is mounted between the velocity pickup and the machine part's surface, _____ characteristics are generated.
    □ torsional
    □ axial
    □ spring-like
    □ synchronous

47. What extra precaution should be taken when using a shaft stick on a high speed shaft?
    Answer: _____

48. The shaft rider type of vibration pickup is one of the least accurate attachments for determining consistent and reliable vibration measurements.
    □ true   □ false

49. Which type of vibration transducer uses a method called "piezo-electric" for converting vibration impulses into a pulsating electric signal?
    □ accelerometer
    □ velocity transducer
    □ proximity probe
    □ shaft rider

50. Identify three positions for placing the vibration pickup when taking a series of vibration measurements at a bearing point on a machine.
    Answer: _____

51. It is recommended that the vibration pickup be placed on, or as near possible, to the machine's bearings.
    □ true   □ false

52. The vibration pickup measures only the vibration occurring in the direction in which the pickup is placed.

☐ true   ☐ false

53. When encountering vibration frequencies below 600 CPM it is recommended to use _____ for determining the amplitude of vibration.

☐ velocity
☐ acceleration
☐ phase
☐ displacement

54. Which type of vibration amplitude readings are commonly referred to as the "overall vibration?"

☐ filter-in amplitude readings
☐ filter-out amplitude readings

55. When taking velocity measurements, the preferred amplitude reading is:

☐ filter-out   ☐ filter-in

56. When high vibration frequencies are encountered, over 60,000 CPM, consider using _____.

☐ velocity   ☐ acceleration
☐ displacement   ☐ phase

57. When taking acceleration measurements, the preferred amplitude reading is:

☐ filter-out   ☐ filter-in

58. FFT vibration analyzers have the capability of storing many signatures of vibration, based on vibration amplitude versus vibration frequency.

☐ true   ☐ false

59. The "real-time" vibration analyzer provides an instantaneous and continuous updated display of vibration amplitude versus vibration frequency.

☐ true   ☐ false

60. Is it possible to make reliable comparisons of the vibration readings taken from a machine with the characteristics of vibration which are typical for various types of mechanical problems?

☐ yes   ☐ no

61. The vibration frequency data collected assists in the identification of the most likely causes of vibration.

☐ true   ☐ false

62. *One of the most common causes of vibration is unbalance. Unbalance is usually identified at what frequency in terms of RPM?*

   ❑ 1 x RPM   ❑ 2 x RPM
   ❑ 3 x RPM   ❑ many times RPM

63. *Mechanical looseness is another cause of vibration. It is usually identified at what frequency in terms of RPM?*

   ❑ 1 x RPM   ❑ 2 x RPM
   ❑ 3 x RPM   ❑ many times RPM

64. *Misalignment, as another major cause of vibration, usually is quite evident when the vibration is recorded from which pickup position?*

   ❑ horizontal
   ❑ vertical
   ❑ axial

SECTION THREE

VIBRATION CAUSES

Vibration Causes - Introduction

This section will discuss several primary causes of vibration and the characteristics of vibration for each cause.

Finding the part of the rotating machine causing the vibration is accomplished by the analysis of the frequency and amplitude readings collected during the monitoring. The frequency of vibration is normally some multiple of the RPM of the part in trouble. Determining the problem with the part is the next step, and to accomplish this the characteristics of vibration for each type of problem need to be known.

The primary causes of vibration, and the prevailing characteristics discussed in this section are:

Vibration From Unbalance

Many vibration and balancing specialists suggest that machinery unbalance is the most common cause of vibration in rotating equipment. The vibration caused by unbalance occurs at a frequency equal to 1 x RPM of the unbalanced part.

Note: Unbalance is not the only problem that can cause vibration frequencies of 1 x RPM. Misalignment also causes high levels of vibration at 1 x RPM.

VIBRATION CAUSES

Vibration From Unbalance (cont'd)

The largest amplitude of vibration will be measured in the radial direction (vertical and horizontal), although unbalance of an over-hung rotor may be indicated by high amplitude readings in the axial direction as well, possibly as high as the radial readings.

The units used for measuring unbalance are varied. It may be stated that a machine is out-of-balance 5 mils. This usually means that the vibration amplitude is 5 mils and it has been determined that unbalance is causing the vibration. Unbalance units can also be measured in ounce-inches or gram-centimeters. To calculate these unbalance units multiply the amount of unbalance by the radius at which it is acting. For example, one ounce of unbalance at one inch radius will result in one ounce-inch of unbalance.

Causes Of Unbalance

There are many reasons that unbalance is present in a rotor. Several reasons are:

Deposit and Build-Up: Rotors used in material handling may become unbalanced due to the unequal build-up of deposits on the rotor and its parts. The gradual increase of build-up can lead to a serious problem when the build-up becomes uneven, as when deposits begin to break away. As the deposits break away the vibration increases and even more deposits break off. A serious unbalance within the rotating equipment results. During scheduled inspection it may be necessary to clean the parts where deposits are greater.

Corrosion and Wear: Rotors, such as fans, blowers and impellers are involved in material handling processes where they become subjected to abrasion, corrosion, and wear. The materials used in the rotor parts can deteriorate unevenly, therefore unbalance and vibration increases.

Vibration From Unbalance (cont'd)

To avoid corrosion and wear the rotor parts must be made from materials which offer long-term resistance to the corrosive or abrasive effects of the products being handled.

Eccentricity: Eccentricity exists when the true or geometric centerline of a part does not coincide with its rotating centerline. Either the part has been made off-center, or the center of rotation has been located off-center. Eccentricity may be caused by a mechanical defect (out of roundness), variations in electrical properties, or uneven heating (thermal bow). One example of eccentricity is shown in illustration #49.

Keys And Keyways: The key and keyway setup which locks the hub to the shaft of the machine is a source of unbalance. The lack of industry standards regarding their application and component balancing is one of the problems with key and keyways.

Unbalance

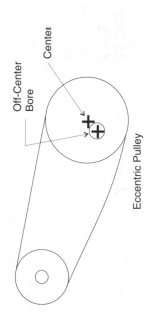

Off-Center Bore

Center

Eccentric Pulley

Illustration #49 - Example of Eccentricity

One manufacturer may balance their equipment with a full key, while another may not use any key.

For example, a pulley manufacturer may balance pulleys without a key, and an electric motor manufacturer balances motors without keys; when the motor and pulley are assembled with a key, unbalance usually results. Even if both manufacturers balanced their products with a full key, the assembled units would continue to be unbalanced.

VIBRATION CAUSES

Vibration From Unbalance (cont'd)

A mistake often made by installers of new motors, when mounting the motor coupling on the motor shaft, is cutting the key flush with the end of the coupling. This usually leaves several inches of keyway unfilled creating an imbalance. See illustration #50.

When a motor is balanced in the factory or a service facility the keyway is filled with a half-key in order to provide the proper balance. If a coupling is properly mounted the motor user should have installed a step key which has full-height in the coupling area and half-height in the portion of keyway not covered by the coupling. See illustration #51. An allowable method for coupling mounting is shown in illustration #52. A full height key is used to fill half of the keyway behind the coupling.

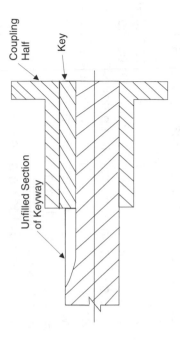

Illustration #50 - Unbalance Caused by Keyway

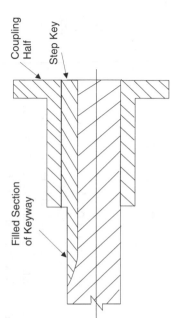

Illustration #51 - Correct Key Mounting

Vibration From Unbalance (cont'd)

Clearance Tolerances: Another problem is excessive clearance in the assembled machine parts. Illustration #53 shows the key and keyway assembly. If the bore in the hub is oversize beyond tolerance and a key and setscrew is used, the takeup in the clearance shifts the weight of the hub further to one side of the shaft's rotating centerline. This causes an eccentric situation.

Distortion: Two forces cause distortion of rotating parts and this ultimately effects the original balancing of the part. The two causes of distortion are stress and thermal forces. Both of these forces can change the shape of the part to alter the balance.

Rotating parts, ones which are fabricated by welding, can experience distortion due to the stresses formed from the welding operations. Stress relieving, during manufacture, corrects the distortion problems.

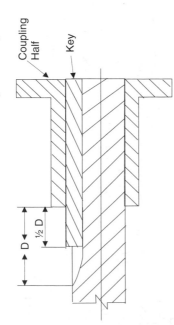

Illustration #52 - Allowable Key Assembly

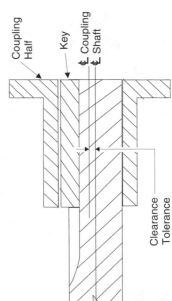

Illustration #53 - Excessive Clearances

Unbalance

VIBRATION CAUSES

Vibration From Unbalance (cont'd)

Distortion can affect parts which have been formed and shaped by extrusion, drawing, pressing, rolling or bending and have internal stresses. If the rotating parts are not stress relieved, they may distort slightly to take on new shapes.

Distortion which occurs with temperature change, is termed "thermal distortion." Metal and other materials expand when heated and contract when cooled. Most rotating parts have minor imperfections and are heated unevenly during operation. The parts may expand unevenly causing distortion. This thermal distortion is common on rotating equipment operating under inconsistent temperatures. For example; electric motors, fans, blowers, compressors (centrifugal and axial), turbines, centrifugal pumps, etc.

Where operating clearances and tolerances are important, thermal distortion conditions may require that rotating parts be balanced.

The balancing is best performed under normal operating conditions and temperatures, even though the parts were balanced originally, either at the manufacturer's plant or in-place when the machine was cold.

Casting Imperfections: Rotating parts which have been cast, such as impellers, sheaves and rotors, may contain imperfections such as blow holes or sand traps which result from the casting process. These are usually not detectable by visual inspection. If there is concern, X-ray or ultrasound testing of the part should be done before machining to try and determine the quality of the casting. Any voids created by either the blow hole or sand trap causes an unbalance situation. Dynamic balancing of the part is imperative, especially for parts operating at high speed (above 3600 RPM).

In summary, machinery unbalance is one of the most common causes of vibration. In most cases, the data collected from an unbalance condition indicates:

Vibration From Unbalance (cont'd)

a.   The vibration frequency is 1 x RPM of the unbalanced part.

b.   The amplitude is proportional to the amount of unbalance.

c.   The amplitude of vibration is usually larger in the radial directions of measurement, horizontal or vertical (for machines with horizontal shafts).

d.   Phase analysis normally shows stable phase readings.

e.   Phase will shift 90 degrees when the pickup is shifted 90 degrees.

Vibration From Misalignment

Shaft and coupling misalignment continue to be one of the main causes of vibration, probably second to unbalance. It is fortunate that this source of vibration can be easily corrected by applying some basic alignment practices. Most companies do not have definite standards as to what is considered proper alignment.

Unbalance/Misalignment

Alignment tolerances should depend on such factors as equipment classification, size, operating speeds, operating temperature, coupling type, bearing and seal type and how essential the machine is to the operation.

Types of Misalignment

The terms commonly used to describe the types of misalignment encountered between two rotating machines coupled together are:

Parallel Offset Misalignment: when the shaft centerlines are parallel to each other, but are offset from one another. This condition occurs horizontally and vertically. See illustration #54A.

Angular Misalignment: where the centerlines of the two shafts meet at an angle. This condition occurs horizontally and vertically. See illustration #54B.

Combinations of Parallel Offset and Angular Misalignment: See illustration #54C. Most machinery operates with a combination of both angular and parallel misalignment.

VIBRATION CAUSES

Vibration From Misalignment (cont'd)

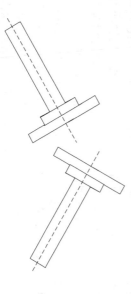

Illustration #54A - Parallel Offset Misalignment

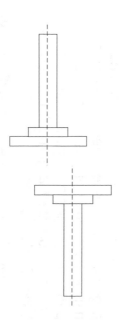

Illustration #54B - Angular Offset Misalignment

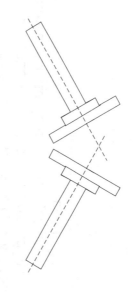

Illustration #54C - Combination Misalignment

There is a general misconception that flexible couplings do not require as strict alignment tolerance as rigid couplings. Misaligned flexible couplings continue to transmit torque and the vibration is not as severe, but the vibration can be high enough to cause excessive wear on bearings, seals, other internal parts and to the coupling itself. Depending on the application, it is recommended that flexible couplings be aligned as carefully and accurately as if they were rigid couplings. The more accurate the alignment, the lower the vibration.

Vibration From Misalignment (cont'd)

Another problem concerning shaft and coupling misalignment is the amount of tolerance allowed after the alignment job is completed. As well there are various conditions which must be considered before performing the alignment.   Checks must be made for soft legs, piping strain, thermal growth problems, bearing clearances, axial end play, shim amounts, coupling runout and hold down bolt clearances.

The recommended alignment methods include rim and face, crossdialing and laser alignment. It is recommended that maintenance personnel who are responsible for performing alignments, be familiar with each of the recognized alignment methods and associated practices.

The most common vibration amplitude, due to shaft and coupling misalignment, is at a vibration frequency of 1 x RPM.

Misalignment

However, where the misalignment is serious, the highest vibration amplitude may be measured at 2 x RPM or 3 x RPM.

Unfortunately, 1 x RPM is also the vibration frequency of other common vibration sources such as unbalance, bent shaft, eccentric armature, etc.

Misalignment, even with flexible couplings, results in two forces, axial and radial, which result in axial and radial vibration. Even if the coupling is flexible, when misalignment exists vibration will be found. The severity of vibration usually increases with increased misalignment. The significant characteristic of vibration caused by misalignment is that it will be in the radial and axial direction.

Axial vibration is usually the best indicator of misalignment. In general, whenever the axial amplitude of vibration is greater than one-half of the highest radial vibration (horizontal or vertical), then misalignment should be suspected as being the cause of vibration.

VIBRATION CAUSES

Vibration From Misalignment (cont'd)

Angular misalignment will primarily subject the shafts of the driver and driven machine to high amounts of axial vibration, see illustration #55A.

Illustration #55B demonstrates the shafts axial motion relative to the shaft's revolution in degrees.

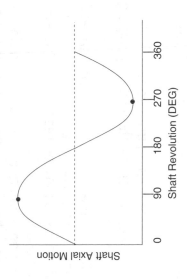

Illustration #55B - Angular Misalignment Effect

Note: Angular misalignment may be easier to picture if one thinks about one side of the coupling attached by a spring. A push/pull effect is what is actually occurring.

Illustrations #56A and #56B demonstrate how parallel offset misalignment produces a radial vibration at a vibration frequency of 2 x the shaft RPM.

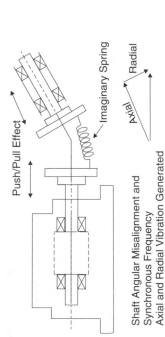

Push/Pull Effect

Imaginary Spring

Axial

Radial

Shaft Angular Misalignment and
Synchronous Frequency
Axial and Radial Vibration Generated

Illustration #55A - Axial Misalignment

Misalignment

Vibration From Misalignment (cont'd)

The vibration analysis data shown on each signature of vibration in illustration #57 is the result of misalignment. The predominant vibration is displayed at 1 x RPM in the axial direction. Note, there is significant vibration at 2 x RPM in the axial direction as well.

Note: Coupling and shaft misalignment does not always create high axial vibration. If axial vibration is high, first check to see if there are symptoms from other sources for the high axial vibration. Check for:

1. Resonance coming from some other part in the axial direction such as piping or a pedestal.

2. If flexible metal disc couplings with resilient metallic discs are used, one or more of the discs may be resonant in the axial direction.

3. A bent shaft acts very similar to angular misalignment, and the vibration characteristics this condition produces can contribute to high axial vibration also.

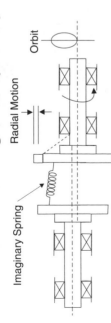

Shaft Offset Misalignment and
Twice Synchronous Frequency
Radial Vibration Generated

Illustration #56A - Parallel Offset Misalignment

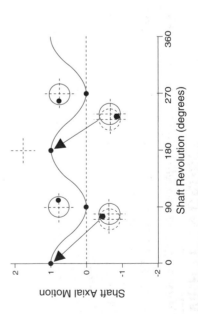

Illustration #56B - Parallel Offset Misalignment Effect

Vibration From Misalignment (cont'd)

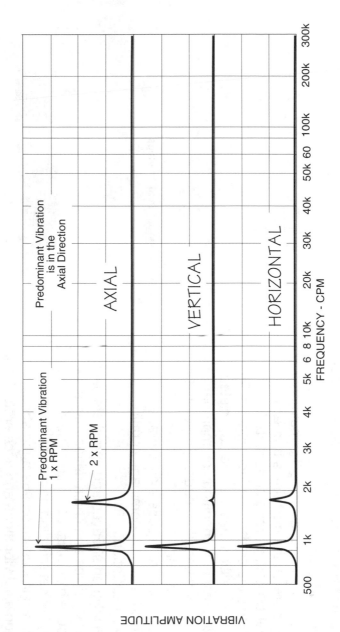

Illustration #57 - Vibration Analysis From Misalignment

Vibration From Misalignment (cont'd)

4. Misaligned bearings (antifriction and friction) are found where the main bearing bore on the machine's frame is either twisted, warped or deflected. This effects the shafts' bearing supports. This condition may also be associated with "soft leg" conditions or improperly shimmed base/foot pads. Proper installation and alignment of the bearings is necessary to reduce axial vibration which is the predominant vibration. See illustration #58.

5. Misaligned sheaves and sprockets used in "V" drives and chain drives may also cause high axial vibration. The angular and offset misalignment conditions shown in illustration #59 bring about high axial vibrations and accelerate the wear of sheaves, sprockets, chains and drive belts.

Misalignment

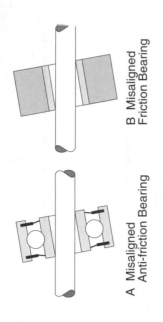

A Misaligned
Anti-friction Bearing

B Misaligned
Friction Bearing

Illustration #58 - Misaligned Bearings

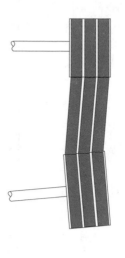

Illustration #59 - Misaligned V-Belt Pulleys

VIBRATION CAUSES

Vibration From Misalignment (cont'd)

Misalignment Sources

To reduce high vibration amplitude caused by misalignment, it is necessary to know what sources will cause misalignment and increased vibration of the coupled shafts.

Improper alignment methods used to attempt to correct the misalignment at the coupling.

Failure to perform preliminary alignment checks such as, "soft legs", dial indicator bar sag, coupling runout, and axial end-play.

Temperature increases, (thermal growth) of the machinery from startup to full operation.

Temperature growth of the machinery support structure and bases.

Strains from piping which tend to pull on the machinery, either axially or radially.

Improper alignment tools and equipment provided to do the alignment job may lead to unknowingly faulty alignments.

Internal coupling binding may cause increased vibration. Couplings, such as gear type, chain, and steel grid, may be somewhat misaligned and increased vibration is noted as the coupling begins to wear. The misalignment causes gradual binding or seizing, resulting in gradually increasing vibration due to the original misalignment. This could also occur if the coupling was poorly lubricated. Binding and seizing is accelerated by both misalignment and lubrication problems.

Machinery foundations may settle over time, causing deflections between bearings on the machinery. The imposed deflection causes bearing wear and higher amounts of vibration.

Vibration From Eccentric Forces

Eccentricity is another source of machinery vibration. This condition means that the rotating shafts' centerline is not in the same position as the rotor's geometric centerline. Illustrations #60, #61 and #62 provide several examples of eccentricity.

Vibration From Eccentric Forces (cont'd)

Note: Eccentricity, as shown in illustrations #60, #61 and #62 does not mean "out-of-round."

Eccentricity results in more weight on one side of the rotating centerline than on the other side. This condition is actually a form of unbalance and produces a vibration similar to unbalance at a frequency of 1 x RPM.

A common example of eccentricity exists when the bore of an antifriction bearing's inner race is not concentric with the inner race geometric centerline, as shown in illustration #60. This will produce an unbalance in the part mounted on the bearing. By balancing the rotor, the forces causing the vibration will be managed, and the vibration will be effectively reduced.

Eccentricity

Note: It is for this reason that balancing a rotor in its own bearings is recommended. Assure that the position of the bearing's inner race on the shaft does not change. This is because the eccentricity of the bearing race is compensated for by the correction weights mounted to the rotor. If this relationship were to change, then the condition would be worse than if no correction for unbalance or eccentricity were made.

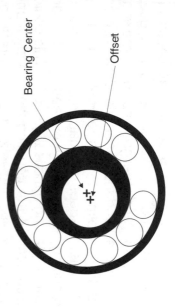

Bearing Center

Offset

Illustration #60 - Eccentric Bearing Mounting

VIBRATION CAUSES

Vibration From Eccentric Forces (cont'd)

There is one example where eccentricity cannot be corrected by routine balancing. The eccentric gear, shown in illustration #61, produces "reaction forces" because of the cam-like action against the mating gear. The greatest vibration will occur in the direction on a line though the centers of both gears, at a frequency equal to 1 x RPM of the eccentric gear.

This condition looks like unbalance, but is not.

Note: The clearance between the gear's bore and the matching shaft can also cause eccentricity problems. If the bore to shaft line-to-line contact made on the gear-cutting machine, and if the keyway was positioned so that tightening the set-screws produces line-to-line contact at another position, the shaft would be forced to rotate at a slightly different center than when the teeth were machined, therefore, the gear would not run true.

In the case of the eccentric motor armature, shown in illustration #62, the armature itself may be balanced in terms of rotor weight distribution. 1 x RPM force is generated between the armature and stator because of the varying magnetic attraction between the eccentric armature and poles. Increasing the magnetic field strength by increasing motor load may result in increased vibration.

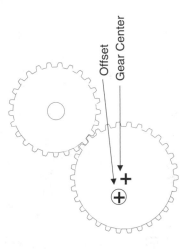

Offset

Gear Center

Illustration #61 - Eccentric Gear Condition

Vibration From Eccentric Forces (cont'd)

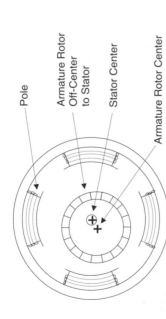

Pole

Armature Rotor
Off-Center
to Stator

Stator Center

Armature Rotor Center

Illustration #62 - Eccentric Motor Armature

One way to verify this eccentric condition is to measure the vibration with the electric motor operating under normal load and speed. Then turn the power off and observe what happens to the amplitude of vibration. If the amplitude reduces gradually as the electric motor coasts down, the problem is probably unbalance.

However if the amplitude of vibration were to disappear the instant power is turned off, the problem is electrical and possibly due to armature eccentricity.

Note: Sometimes it may be necessary to start-stop the electric motor several times to keep the rotor rotating at almost a constant speed, so that the vibration can be checked when the power is off.

There are several other electrical problems in electric motors and generators which cause vibration. For example, shorted windings, broken rotor bars, or an armature rotor which is not properly centered in the stator will cause excessive vibration.

An eccentric pulley acts like a cam and provides "reaction forces" similar to those of the eccentric gears. See illustration #63. The largest vibration will occur in the direction of belt tension at a frequency equal to 1 x RPM of the eccentric pulley. The vibration appears to be unbalance, but cannot be corrected by simple balancing techniques.

Vibration From Eccentric Forces (cont'd)

Vibration From Bent Shafts

A bent shaft acts very much like angular misalignment. This condition produces a vibration at a frequency of 1 x RPM. Bent shafts generally cause high axial vibration. A bent shaft will show the axial vibration as a rocking motion. If the shaft is severely bent, the axial rocking at one end will be 180 degrees out-of-phase with the rocking at the other end. Illustration #64 shows a bent shaft condition. The placement of the vibration transducers is important. If readings were taken radially, at horizontal and vertical positions, the bent shaft condition would appear in phase. If axial readings were taken, the bent shaft condition would appear 180 degrees out-of-phase on each side of the same bearing. When balancing is attempted, the radial vibration may be reduced, but axial vibration may remain high.

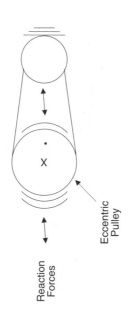

Illustration #63 - Eccentric Pulley

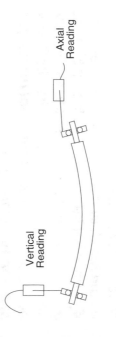

Illustration #64 - Bent Shaft Condition

Vibration From Bent Shafts (cont'd)

Note: *"Bent shaft" symptoms will often be the result of resonant whirl rather than a permanent bend. The shaft may bend at a particular resonance, such as first or second critical speed, etc. The shaft may not be bent when the unit is not running or at a non-resonant speed.*

Resonant Whirl

Resonant whirl is the condition which occurs when the rotor is resonating at a frequency equal to its own running speed. In such a situation the rotor takes the same exaggerated bends as for non-rotating part resonances. But instead of flexing back and forth, and reversing its stresses, as shown in illustration #64, the rotor simply rotates with this bent shape. There is no flexing back and forth and no reversible stresses. See illustration #65.

For example if a rotor is running resonant to its own first critical speed, its shape will be the same as for any other part resonating at its first critical. Bend a piece of wire in this shape, then rotate the wire. This illustrates that first critical situation, as shown in illustration #65A.

If a rotor's second critical is equal to its own rotating speed, then the characteristic double bend shape will result, as shown in illustration #65B.

A   Resonant Whirl
    at First Critical Speed

B   Resonant Whirl at
    Second Critical Speed

Illustration #65 - Resonant Whirl

Vibration From Bent Shafts (cont'd)

Again, the shaft will not flex back and forth but will instead rotate as a rotor with two bends. To illustrate this, bend a piece of wire into two bends, 180 degrees opposite each other and rotate it. Note, the wire when rotated, will not show flexing back and forth. Therefore, it will not experience cracking due to fatigue.

Vibration From Faulty Anti-Friction Bearings

Anti-friction bearing defects may be analyzed with a high degree of accuracy at rotating speeds as low as 50 RPM. The actual condition of the bearing may be determined by identifying the defective components of the bearing (for example cage, race, or rollers). Typical anti-friction bearings are manufactured to high standards of accuracy and with strict metallurgical control.

Balls and rollers are held to diametrical tolerances of .0001 inch (.00254 mm) or less within the bearing. Bearings made to these specifications ensure smooth vibration free operation. Illustration #66 identifies the main parts of a standard deep-groove ball bearing.

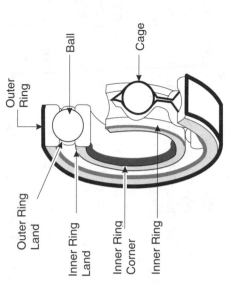

Illustration #66 - Deep Groove, Single Row Bearing

Vibration From Faulty Anti-Friction Bearings (cont'd)

The vibration spectrum is one of the most common methods for analyzing an anti-friction bearing for defects as well as many other types of defects. The vibration is measured using the amplitude - vs. - frequency plot.

A vibration spectrum graphically displays the frequencies at which vibration is occurring and the amount of vibration at each frequency.

Most bearing manufacturers have tables of bearing defect frequencies and various computer programs are available with this information.

Several important points to keep in mind when analyzing for roller bearing defects include:

- Defect frequencies are generated by discrete flaws on races and balls.
- Bearing defect frequencies are asynchronous (nonsynchronous). This is important for differentiating bearing defects from synchronous components such as gears.
- Bearing defect frequencies will change with variations in contact angle, caused by changes in thrust load, when sliding occurs.
- For equal size defects, the amplitude at the outer race defect frequency will be larger than the amplitude at the inner race defect frequency.
- In a typical failure, the race frequencies will appear first. Ball and cage defect frequencies may appear later as sidebands around the race defect frequencies.

VIBRATION CAUSES

Vibration From Faulty Anti-Friction Bearings (cont'd)

Note: Frequency indicates the defective bearing component, and amplitude indicates defect severity. By examining both the frequency and amplitude, remaining bearing life can be predicted.

Flaws on the raceways, balls, or rollers of rolling element bearings cause high frequency vibration. The frequency is not necessarily an integral multiple of the shaft RPM. For example, if the balls or rollers stick or slide in certain conditions, vibration frequencies generated are more directly related to the rubbing action and impacts rather than shaft speed.

The amplitude of vibration will depend largely on the extent of the bearing fault. It must be noted that even momentary impacts can excite natural frequency vibration. All machines have natural frequencies of vibration and are excited by impact forces, similar to striking a tuning fork.

When the rolling elements of a bearing strike a crack or pitted area in its raceway, the natural frequency of the bearing, shaft or bearing support may be excited.

These natural frequency vibrations usually appear as vibration peaks in frequency ranges many times the shaft RPM.

The vibration analysis data shown in illustration #67 is from a machine having faulty bearings. The vibration spectrums shown are for each position (axial, vertical and horizontal). Observe the vibration amplitudes crowded in the high frequencies, 15,000 to 40,000 CPM. These are usually the various natural frequencies of the bearing and its components and parts which are excited. This type of vibration signature indicates that a bad bearing is present.

Note: Defects in rolling bearing components can generate vibration peaks at frequencies related to the bearing geometry.

Vibration From Faulty Anti-Friction Bearings (cont'd)

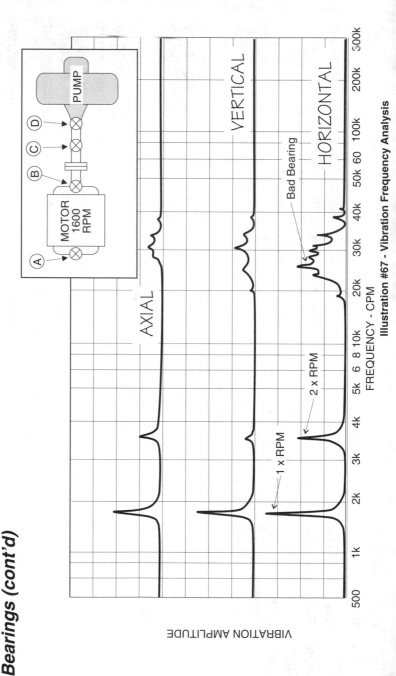

Illustration #67 - Vibration Frequency Analysis

Vibration From Faulty Anti-Friction Bearings (cont'd)

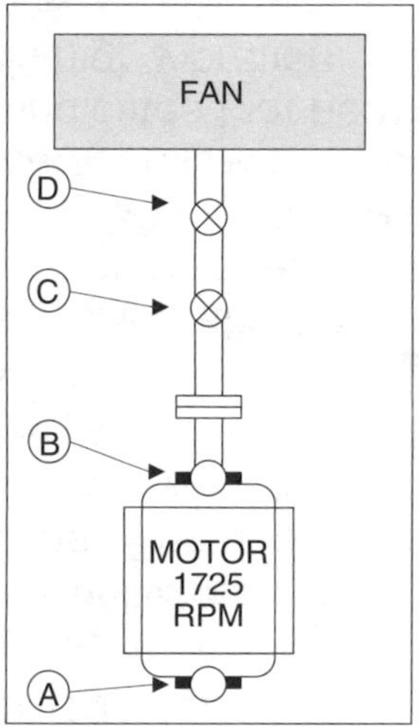

PICKUP		FILTER OUT				IN/SEC		FILTER IN
		DISPL		VELOCITY		1725	3450	37K
POINT	POS	MILS	CPM	IN/SEC	CPM	VEL	VEL	VEL
A	H	3.2	1725	.42	1725	.41	.04	.01
	V	1.6	1725	.24	1725	.20	.02	.01
	A	2.7	1725	.31	1725	.29	.02	.03
B	H	3.4	1725	.65	~	.38	.01	.36
	V	1.4	~	.38	~	.20	.01	.17
	A	2.9	1725	.36	1725	.34	.02	.09
C	H	3.9	1725	.40	1725	.36	.03	-
	V	1.9	1725	.21	1725	.18	.03	-
	A	2.7	1725	.33	1725	.29	.04	-
D	H	4.3	1725	.42	1725	.39	.05	-
	V	2.1	1725	.19	1725	.16	.02	-
	A	3.2	1725	.35	1725	.34	.03	-

Highest Frequency

Highest Vibration at High Frequency (Indicates - Bad Bearing) → .36

FAN — MOTOR 1725 RPM

Illustration #68 - High Frequency Vibration

Vibration From Faulty Anti-Friction Bearings (cont'd)

Vibration generated by the roller bearing is not normally transmitted to other parts on the machine. The bad bearing, the one which is causing the vibration, is usually the one nearest the point where the greatest vibration occurred.

Refer to illustration #68, where the amplitude of the high frequency vibration is highest at bearing "B", and at the other bearing points the vibration is well below the reading at "B". This indicates that bearing "B" is the source of this high vibration.

Anti-Friction Bearing Loads

Roller bearings are classified according to load conditions. The three loads are listed below, and see illustration #69 for examples.

1. Radial
2. Axial (Thrust)
3. Combination.

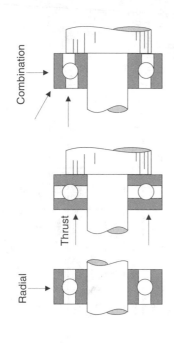

Radial   Thrust   Combination

Illustration #69 - Roller Bearing Classification by Loac

Roller bearings usually do not fail prematurely unless some type of force, other than normal wear, is responsible. Roller bearings are designed to support either a radial or axial load, or in some cases, a combination of radial and axial load.

Vibration From Faulty Anti-Friction Bearings (cont'd)

When attempting to identify what is causing the bearing to fail it is important to determine how the bearing is loaded and whether the bearing is intended to carry the load being applied.

When vibration analysis indicates symptoms of bearing problems, do not immediately eliminate the possibility that something else is causing the problem. Always make careful checks for other difficulties, such as unbalance, misalignment, and bearing mounting after replacing the bearing. This must be considered especially where premature bearing failures are frequent.

Common Causes of Anti-Friction Bearing Failure

Table #11 identifies several of the main causes of bearing failure and some general comments are provided.

A Note On "Soft Legs":

It was mentioned earlier that high frequency vibration in roller bearings may not be the direct fault of the bearing itself. The bearing may be the symptom of another critical problem within the machine.

If, for example, a high frequency vibration was detected on one of the bearings of a 1750 RPM electric motor driving a centrifugal pump through a flexible coupling, and during the vibration analysis it was noted that the vibration frequency was consistently steady at approximately 19,000 CPM, or about 11 x RPM. Furthermore, the maximum amplitude of vibration was in the axial direction. With the presence of high frequency vibration one would consider that a bad bearing existed, and the high amplitude of vibration indicated a need for immediate correction. Therefore, the electric motor was removed and its inboard bearing replaced.

Vibration From Faulty Anti-Friction Bearings (cont'd)

Some Common Causes of Anti-Friction Bearing Failure	
Causes	**Comments**
Excessive Load	– Improper bearing for applied load – Excess thrust from some source – Excess radial load being applied – Poor design or inadequate application – Fractures or overheating of bearing
Misalignment	– Improper alignment procedures – Soft legs or faulty foundation – Misaligned bearing housings – Thermal growth
Defective Shaft Journals	– Worn journal area – Not made to specifications – Rough, pitted areas
Background Vibration	– Assembly damage – Faulty bearing storage – Vibration transmitted from various sources – Shock loads, cavitation, water hammer – Mechanical looseness

Table #11A - Common Causes of Anti-Friction Bearing Failure

Vibration From Faulty Anti-Friction Bearings (cont'd)

Some Common Causes of Anti-Friction Bearing Failure	
Causes	**Comments**
Faulty Mounting Practices, Improper Fits	– Dirty contaminated conditions – Improper assembly – Poor mounting procedures – Wrong bearing location on shaft – Too tight, too loose – Improper bearing preload – Improper thrust settings – Insufficient clearances
Improper or Inadequate Lubrication	– Dirty or contaminated lube supply – Overheating of lube – Too much, not enough lube – Wrong lube for conditions – Worn or dirty seals – Worn out lube – Lube supply system is faulty

Table #11B - Common Causes of Anti-Friction Bearing Failure

Vibration From Faulty Anti-Friction Bearings (cont'd)

The electric motor was reinstalled and aligned to the centrifugal pump. Upon startup, the vibration check indicated that nothing had really changed. The high amplitude of vibration at 11 x RPM, in the axial direction was still present.

While investigating the problem it was suggested that a "soft leg" check be performed. This was not done when the motor was reinstalled and aligned. The check for "soft legs" determined that the motor's base, having four mounting points, was being pulled and distorted when the mounting bolts securing the motor to the base were tightened. Corrections were made for the "soft leg" condition by shimming the necessary legs. The distortion in the motor was corrected and the unit was realigned properly.

The vibration check after the second startup revealed no high frequency bearing vibration and the overall amplitude of vibration was low and quite acceptable.

This example demonstrates how a misalignment condition, caused by a "soft leg" condition can cause high frequency vibration. The bearing felt the force of this condition and reacted accordingly.

Vibration From Journal Bearings

Journal or friction bearings have no moving parts and are normally designed to enclose the rotating shaft to provide support and stability. A journal bearing consists of two basic parts which are the journal and the bearing. Refer to illustration #70. The journal section is a portion of the shaft which transfers the radial load to the bearing, acting as the support. The journal normally rotates, such as the shaft of a centrifugal pump. The journal and bearing act together similar to an engine's connecting rod.

VIBRATION CAUSES

Vibration From Journal Bearings (cont'd)

Axial loads are transmitted parallel to the shaft's axis, and radial loads are transmitted 90 degrees to the shaft's axis.

Fluid lubrication in radial load journal bearings depends largely on the viscosity of the lube and its adhesion to the surfaces of the journal and the bearing. The radial clearance provided in the journal bearing allows a wedge-shaped film to form between the journal and bearing. The lubricant is dragged into the clearance space by the rotation of the journal. Refer to illustration #71.

Vibration due to faulty journal bearings is generally the result of the following conditions:

- excessive bearing clearances
- oil whirl
- hysteresis whirl
- lubrication problems

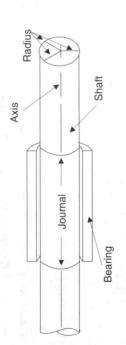

Illustration #70 - Journal Bearing Parts

Journal bearings are classified by the type of axial or radial load they carry. The axial and radial direction (load) relates to the axis and radius of the shaft. See illustration #70.

Vibration From Journal Bearings (cont'd)

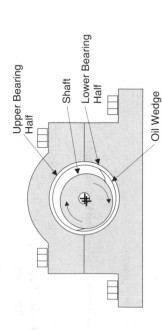

Upper Bearing Half
Shaft
Lower Bearing Half
Oil Wedge

Illustration #71 - Oil Wedge Lubrication

Excessive Bearing Clearance

A journal bearing with excessive clearance may cause some misalignment or other sources of vibration force resulting in conditions such as mechanical looseness or bearing pounding. Correct journal bearing clearances would make for less amplitude of vibration.

Journal Bearings

Excessive bearing clearances will also result in poor load distribution within the bearing, decreased bearing life, and excessive shaft deflection.

Insufficient bearing clearances may produce excessive bearing and lube temperatures, increased journal and bearing wear, constricted flow of lubricant and eventual bearing failure and finally, bearing seizure.

When referring to journal bearing clearance remember there are two types of clearance:

a. initial clearance
b. running clearance

Initial Clearance: This may come from the manufacturer and can be altered by shimming the split bearing housing, which changes the journal diameter.

Running Clearance: This is the clearance remaining in the journal bearing during normal operation.

VIBRATION CAUSES

Vibration From Journal Bearings (cont'd)

Running clearance requirements may vary depending on load, speed, temperature, application and type of bearing material.

Note: Generally, bearings for high speed application, over 3600 RPM, have greater running clearances allowing for thermal differences. Slow speed equipment, under 3600 RPM, may have reduced running clearances to provide maximum load distribution and increased fatigue life.

Journal Bearing Clearances Checks

Several methods for checking journal bearing clearances include:

a. Feeler Gage Method
b. Dial Indicator Method (Bump Test)
c. Plasti - Gage Method
d. Lead Wire Method

Note: Whatever method is selected for checking journal bearing clearance ensure the following is done:

a. Completely clean the journal and bearing area if possible.
b. Use recommended torque values for all bolts or nuts used to secure the bearing caps.
c. Attempt to determine if the bearing and journal is smooth and free of burrs, ridges or grooves.
d. Determine whether the bearing support structure is solid, free of deflections and is not distorted in any way.

Detecting A "Wiped" Journal Bearing

One may be able to detect a "wiped" journal bearing by comparing horizontal and vertical amplitudes of vibration. It should be noted that machines securely mounted to rigid supports or foundations will probably demonstrate a slightly higher amplitude of vibration in the horizontal direction. If a "wiped" journal bearing exists then there usually will be an abnormally higher amplitude of vibration in the vertical direction as well.

Vibration From Journal Bearings (cont'd)

There is good reason to suspect that the journal bearing is causing this problem. Proper inspection procedures would be required to check the bearing clearances.

Oil Whirl

Oil whirl is another common problem with journal bearings used on machines equipped with pressure lubrication systems operating at relatively high speeds.

Illustration #72 shows how the oil film is formed in a journal bearing at rest, to startup, through to normal operational speed. At rest most of the oil has been squeezed out from the load area. When shaft rotation begins, the clearance space fills with oil and there is a tendency for the journal to roll or climb up the bearing due to friction between the journal and the bearing. Further rotation of the shaft journal helps the oil to be drawn under the shaft from the clearance space, lifting the journal off the bearing.

Journal Bearings

Pressurized lube systems assist in getting pressurized fluid into the spaces, thus ensuring the journal remains free from contacting the bearing.

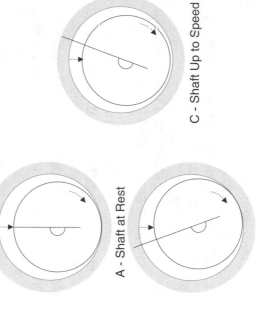

A - Shaft at Rest

B - Start Up

C - Shaft Up to Speed

Illustration #72 - Forming an Oil Film

Vibration From Journal Bearings (cont'd)

The amount of rise of the shaft depends on the machine's RPM, rotor weight, oil pressure and viscosity of the oil. As shown in illustration #71, the shaft operates in an eccentric position relative to the bearing centers, drawing oil into a wedge to produce a pressurized load-carrying film.

Note: If the eccentricity is momentarily increased from its equilibrium position, due to a sudden external shock loads, surge or speed fluctuation, additional oil is supplied to fill the clearances created by the changed position of the shaft journal. This will increase the pressure of the load-carrying film. The additional force developed by the oil film drives the shaft into a "whirling path" around the bearing. If the damping within the machine and the bearing is good, the shaft returns to its normal position in the bearing, otherwise, the shaft continues in a whirling path.

Oil whirl, sometimes referred to as "oil whip", is one of the easiest vibrations to recognize by its unusually low vibration frequency. Oil whirl frequency is normally reported to be 45% to 50% of RPM. The slight variation in percentage of frequency may be the result of instrumentation rather than in actual variations in frequency.

For example, a machine rotating at 3600 RPM may display an oil whirl frequency of 1700 CPM. This vibration analysis is shown in illustration #73 where symptoms of oil whirl begin at 800 CPM steadily climb to a peak at 1700 CPM and reduce significantly until at 1 x RPM, 3600 CPM, the next highest vibration amplitude is shown. Since the vibration frequency of the oil whirl is slightly less than 1/2 x RPM, the shaft will not appear to be still when viewed with a stroboscopic light; rather it will appear to rotate (this depends on the strobe flash rate).

Vibration From Journal Bearings (cont'd)

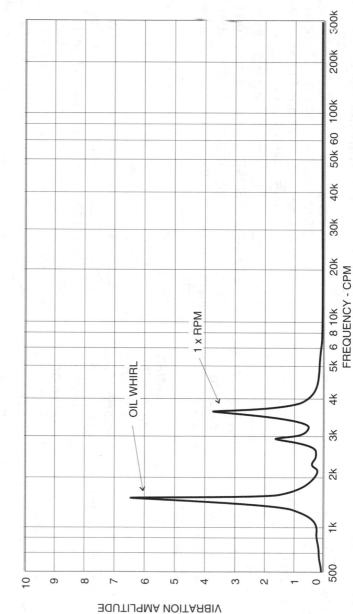

Illustration #73 - Frequency Analysis of Oil Whirl

VIBRATION CAUSES

Vibration From Journal Bearings (cont'd)

The highest vibration amplitude, at 1700 CPM, indicates that oil whirl is the cause of the vibration. The problem is normally attributed to bearing design, excess bearing or journal wear, an increase in oil pressure or a change in oil viscosity.

"Oil whirl" causes high amplitudes of vibration at slightly less than 1/2 x RPM. This vibration can be reduced by:

a. Changing the temperature of the lube oil.

b. Changing the viscosity of the oil.

c. Increasing the loading on the bearing.

d. Ensuring the bearing clearances meet the required specification.

e. Scraping the bearing to ensure that maximum contact is achieved.

f. Replacing the bearing with one designed to meet the specific operating conditions of the machine, or with one that reduces the possibility of oil whirl.

Illustration #74 shows various journal bearing configurations that help to reduce oil whirl.

Illustration #74A identifies an axial groove journal bearing where the grooves increase whirl resistance at three equally spaced points. This type of bearing design would be used in light duty/high speed applications such as gas turbines and turbochargers.

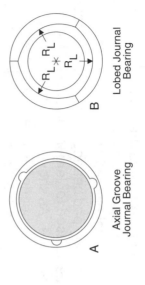

A   Axial Groove
     Journal Bearing

B   Lobed Journal
     Bearing

Illustration #74A, B - Journal Bearing Types

The centers of curvature of each of the three lobes lie well outside the clearance circle. Three axial oil feed grooves are used.

The tilting pad bearing, or pivoted shoe bearings, is used for larger, high speed industrial machines. As shown in illustration #74C, the tilting pad bearing is one of the most stable bearings as the bearing surface is divided into three or more segments, each of which is pivoted at the center. In operation, each segment (shoe) tilts to form a wedge shaped oil film, thus creating a force tending to push the shaft toward the center of the bearing. The tilting feature allows each segment to follow the shaft, therefore, increasing damping and providing overall stability.

The circumferential groove bearing, as shown in illustration #74D, has an oil groove extending circumferentially around the bearing. The oil is maintained under pressure in the groove.

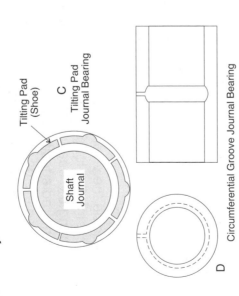

Illustration #74C,D - Journal Bearing Types

The lobed journal bearing shown in illustration #74B, is designed to provide stability against oil whirl by allowing three points of pressurized oil to center the shaft. This design is one of the most effective "anti-oil-whip" bearings.

VIBRATION CAUSES

Vibration From Journal Bearings (cont'd)

The stability provided by this bearing design is not as great as the stability provided by the tilting pad bearing. This circumferential groove design is commonly used in reciprocating loads, such as main and connecting rod bearings because of the uniformity of oil distribution.

Note: A machine that is normally stable may exhibit signs of oil whirl vibration, and this condition may only occur intermittently. This may have little to do with the condition of the journal bearing, but rather to external vibratory forces that happen to have similar frequency characteristics as the oil whirl frequency of the journal bearing.

There are two common sources of vibrations that can excite oil whirl in a journal bearing:

1. External sources of vibration from other machinery in the immediate vicinity.

2. Internal sources, such as vibration from other parts of the machine.

In either case, the oil whirl condition is excited by something having similar frequency as the bearing's oil whirl frequency.

Note: Vibration from other machinery (external sources) can be transmitted to the journal bearing through rigid structures such as piping, steel work and foundations. This condition may be referred to as "externally excited whirl."

Also, resonant vibrations such as those caused by pulsations or flow turbulence transmitted to the journal bearings, and having the same frequency as the bearing's oil-whirl, produces a whirl condition referred to as "resonant whirl."

It is recommended that whenever vibration characteristics of oil whirl are detected, a complete vibration analysis should be conducted.

Vibration From Journal Bearings (cont'd)

This analysis should include; surveying installation methods, background sources, foundation structures and piping connections. An external cause of oil whirl may exist.

Oil Whirl

Oil whirl occurs when the sub synchronous instability excites a critical speed. Oil whip and oil whirl are easily differentiated. Oil whip will remain at a constant frequency regardless of speed changes. Oil whirl will maintain a fixed percentage of a varying shaft rotating frequency.

When a rotor is operating above its first critical speed, but below the second critical, oil whip occurs at a frequency equal to the first critical speed of the rotor.

For example, if a rotor operating at 3600 RPM has a first critical speed of 2100 CPM, oil whip will occur at 2100 CPM.

There is very little chance that the frequency of oil whip will be the same as the frequency due to oil whirl, which is slightly less than 1/2 the rotor's RPM.

Oil whip can be kept to a minimum by the damping effect provided by the journal bearing itself. If the machine's stationary damping is low compared to the internal damping of the machine's rotor, vibration problems will occur. One common solution is to increase the stationary damping of the bearings and machine structure. Installing tilting pad bearings may help as well.

Note: Sub synchronous instability refers to a condition of unstable, self-excited vibration and may be caused by a rotating lubricating oil wedge (oil whirl) and/or excitation of the first critical speed (oil whip).

Improper Lubrication

Improper lubrication, lack of lubrication, or the wrong type of lubrication, can cause vibration problems in a journal bearing.

Vibration From Journal Bearings (cont'd)

Improper lubrication usually promotes excessive friction between the bearing surface and the shaft's journal area and the friction excites vibrations in the bearing and other parts of the machine.

Vibration, due to improper lubrication, where excessive friction occurs, is called "dry whip," and as some experts say, "is caused in a manner similar to wiping a moistened finger over a dry pane of glass." Damage to the bearing and journal will occur almost immediately.

The frequency of vibration due to dry whip is usually high, often producing high pitched squealing sounds normally associated with insufficiently lubricated bearings. It is not associated with any multiples of shaft RPM. If dry whip is suspected as the cause of vibration, inspect the lubricant for quantity, quality and type, check the journal bearing clearance and compare to specifications.

Vibration From Mechanical Looseness

The vibration characteristic of mechanical looseness is caused by a force such as unbalance or misalignment. However, mechanical looseness serves to aggravate the situation, transforming relatively small amounts of unbalance or misalignment into excessive amounts of vibration amplitude. Mechanical looseness, a common cause of machinery vibration, helps promote more vibration than would otherwise occur from problems such as unbalance or misalignment.

Mechanical looseness is similar to a pounding action which typically produces a vibration at a frequency of 2 x RPM and higher multiples of the machine's rotating speed.

This pounding action may result from conditions such as loose parts, loose mounting bolts, nuts, etc., excessive bearing clearances, or cracks or breaks in structural supports such as bearing housings.

Vibration From Mechanical Looseness (cont'd)

Electric motors, generators, and alternators having loose rotor bars, loose rotor windings or stator windings may also produce vibration frequencies 2 x RPM.

It is highly recommended that all rotating equipment be balanced and aligned to the tolerances set out by the equipment manufacturer. If this is done and all the machine's supports and integral components are installed and fitted properly, mechanical looseness shouldn't be a problem. A looseness problem should be identified and fixed before rebalancing and realigning. Mechanical looseness will be kept under control if balance and alignment are maintained.

In order to explain why mechanical looseness can produce vibration at a frequency of 2 x RPM refer to illustration #75. An unbalance situation is shown. Therefore, assume that unbalance is the primary cause of vibration.

Mechanical Looseness

When the heavy spot is in the 6:00 o'clock position as shown in illustration #75A, the unbalance force is directed downward, forcing the bearing down against the pedestal. In illustration #75B the heavy spot rotates to the 12:00 o'clock position, therefore the resultant unbalance force is directed upward and the bearing is lifted from the pedestal. As the heavy spot reaches 3:00 o'clock (illustration #75C), the unbalance force is directed to the side and the bearing falls down to the pedestal. Due to the weight of the rotor, the second downward impulse comes when the heavy spot is at 6 o'clock.

As the action continues, where the heavy spot shifts in position during rotation, the bearing housing lifts and falls putting strain on the bolts and pedestal. This continued action produces two applied forces for each revolution of the machine's shaft. One force is applied by the "lifting" force of the rotating unbalance and the other by gravity as the bearing housing drops to the pedestal.

VIBRATION CAUSES

Vibration From Mechanical Looseness (cont'd)

The frequency of vibration is 2 x RPM of the shaft. The effects of mechanical looseness can clearly be seen at 2 x RPM if an oscilloscope is connected to the vibration analyzer while vibration measurement is being done. See illustration #76.

Usually some mechanical clearances are inherent in all rotating equipment, so it is quite usual to find some vibration at 2 x RPM where any unbalance or misalignment is present. Excessive mechanical looseness is usually the primary cause of the problem when the amplitude of vibration at 2 x RPM is more than one half of the amplitude at the rotating speed, 1 x RPM. Refer to illustration #76.

Mechanical looseness which allows the machine to rock and bounce, as demonstrated in illustration #77, can produce vibration at frequencies of 2 X RPM, 3 x RPM, 4 x RPM, or at much higher frequencies. Corrective action is immediately required in cases where higher frequencies are predominant.

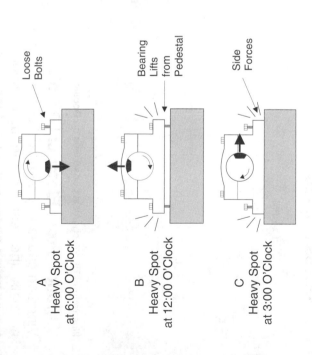

A
Heavy Spot
at 6:00 O'Clock — Loose Bolts

B
Heavy Spot
at 12:00 O'Clock — Bearing Lifts from Pedestal

C
Heavy Spot
at 3:00 O'Clock — Side Forces

Illustration #75 - Vibration From Mechanical Looseness

Vibration From Mechanical Looseness (cont'd)

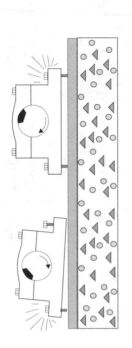

Illustration #76 - Mechanical Looseness on Oscilloscope

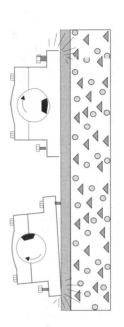

Illustration #77 - Demonstration of Mechanical Looseness

Vibration From Electrical Problems

Vibration caused by electrical problems are normally the result of unequal magnetic forces acting on the rotor or stator of electric motors, generators and alternators. These unequal forces may be due to any one or combination of electromagnetic faults.

VIBRATION CAUSES

Vibration From Electrical Problems (cont'd)

Note: Vibration of electrical machinery such as electric motors, generators and alternators can be caused by mechanical problems including unbalance, misalignment, and mechanical looseness.

Common causes of vibration due to electromagnetic problems include:

- Rotor not round
- Eccentric armature journals
- Rotor and stator misaligned; unequal air gap
- Elliptical stator bore
- Open or shorted windings
- Shorted rotor iron

The frequency of vibration resulting from electrical problems is 1 x RPM, thus appearing similar to unbalance. A common method to check for the presence of electrical vibration is to observe the change in vibration amplitude the instant electric power is disconnected from the machine.

Perform this check in the filter out mode. If the vibration disappears the instant the power is shut off, the vibration is likely due to electrical problems. Use appropriate electrical testing procedures to determine the exact cause of the vibration.

Note: If the vibration amplitude decreases only gradually after the electrical power is disconnected, the vibration trouble is probably caused by some mechanical fault such as unbalance, misalignment or mechanical looseness.

Vibration due to electromagnetic faults are generally associated to the amount of load placed on the unit (motor, generator, alternator). As the load changes, the amplitude and/or phase readings can show significant change.

Note: This may help explain why electric motors that have been tested and balanced under no-load conditions show a drastic change in amplitude of vibration when returned to service.

Vibration From Electrical Problems (cont'd)

Slip Frequency

Electrical problems with induction type electric motors can cause a vibration meter to display pulsating amplitude readings. This type of erratic vibration is related to an inherent characteristic of induction motors called "slip frequency." The slip frequency is the difference between the RPM of the rotor, and the electrical or synchronous frequency of the rotating magnetic field. Synchronous frequency is equal to the alternating current (AC) line frequency, or a sub-multiple of the line frequency that is powering the machine.

A slip frequency is always present in the vibration signature of an induction motor. If there is mechanical cause of vibration, such as unbalance, the signals from both the slip frequency and the unbalance alternately aid and oppose one another at a rate equal to the difference between the two frequencies.

Because the slip frequency is only slightly less than the 1 x RPM vibration caused by unbalance, the resulting "beat" frequency causes a noticeable, steady swing in overall amplitude readings. The beat becomes more rapid as the load is increased. If the beat vibration is excessive, correction should be made to reduce the mechanical problem, which probably would be unbalance or misalignment. In many cases the beats are not going to be harmful, but can create an annoying and distracting noise.

Torque Pulsations

Electric motors also have an inherent vibration due to torque pulses. Torque pulses are generated as the motor's magnetic field energizes the poles of the stator. The frequency of vibration is twice the AC line frequency. If the line frequency is 60 Hz, or 3600 CPM, the torque pulse frequency is 120 Hz, or 7200 CPM.

VIBRATION CAUSES

Vibration From Electrical Problems (cont'd)

Torque pulsations do not cause many vibration problems. This condition is inherent to electric motors.

Armature Related Electrical Problems

Some problems with the rotor or armature of an induction motor which cause electrical vibration include: broken rotor bars; open or shorted rotor windings; a bowed rotor; and an eccentric or out-of-round rotor.

The pulsating vibration amplitude characteristic of these problems all produce a single vibration frequency whose amplitude is modulated with time. Therefore, armature related electrical problems will generate a vibration similar to the time wave-form displayed on the oscilloscope as shown in illustration #78. For further explanation of how this vibration is generated, consider a motor armature having one broken rotor base, as demonstrated in illustrations #79A,B,C.

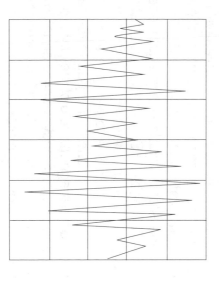

Illustration #78 - Motor Armature Problems on Oscilloscope

A two-pole motor is shown in illustration #79A,B,C for simplification. The stator windings are energized by AC current. The broken rotor bar is aligned with the lower pole at the exact instant the motor pole is energized at peak current (illustration #79A).

Vibration From Electrical Problems (cont'd)

The upper motor pole is also being energized with a polarity opposite that of the lower pole. If it is assumed that the motor poles are identical, the magnetic fields acting on the armature will be equal but opposite in polarity. However, since the lower rotor bar of the armature is broken, the magnetic forces between the armature and motor poles will not be equal and a reaction force between the armature and stator will be generated.

When the stator windings are again energized with peak AC current (illustration #79B), the broken rotor bar will not be perfectly aligned with the lower pole as it was previously. This condition is due to the fact that while the magnetic field of the stator pole is rotating at a frequency which is equal to or an exact sub-multiple of the AC current powering the motor, the motor armature itself is rotating at a frequency slightly less than this electrical frequency.

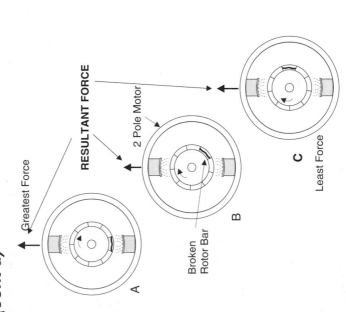

Illustration #79 - Broken Rotor Bar

Vibration From Electrical Problems (cont'd)

This lag in RPM of the armature is referred to as "slip" and while the magnetic field may be rotating at 3600 RPM, the armature may only be rotating at 3550 RPM. There is then a 50 RPM slip.

The next time the lower pole is energized at peak AC current, as shown in illustration #79B, the broken rotor bar will not be perfectly aligned as it was previously. Instead, the broken rotor bar will lag by 1/50 of a revolution. As a result, the unbalanced magnetic attraction between the motor poles and armature will not have as great a reaction force in illustration #79B as it did in illustration #79A.

The third time the motor pole is energized at peak AC current, the broken rotor bar will lag further behind, as shown in illustration #79C. Since the broken rotor bar is now further from the energized motor pole the unbalanced

magnetic forces acting on the rotor will have lower amplitude.

The effect of this rotating armature with the broken rotor bar will be to produce a single frequency of vibration whose amplitude is modulated at a rate equal to the difference between rotating speed of the magnetic field and the rotating speed of the armature. The vibration frequency generated in this case is the rotating speed of the magnetic field and not the rotating speed of the armature.

Stator Related Problems

Electrical problems in the stator of an induction motor can also result in vibration with a pulsating amplitude. In this case, the pulsation is the result of a "beat" between two separate frequencies of vibration which are very close together. See illustration #80.

Common stator related problems include: open or shorted stator windings; unequal air gap; and unbalanced phases.

There are two ways to observe whether pulsating vibration exists.

Electrical

Vibration From Electrical Problems (cont'd)

Remember, the pulsating vibrations are relatively close in frequency and their amplitudes will alternately add together and subtract at a rate equal to the difference between their frequencies. The result will be a noticeable steady pulsation or "beat" which can be observed in time wave-form on an oscilloscope.

Another method is to plot the vibration signature. See illustration #80. This indicates whether the vibration is a single frequency whose amplitude is modulated, or two frequencies that are in "beat."

The vibration signature reveals that the vibration at approximately 1800 CPM actually consisted of two frequencies very close together. The difference between the two will be pulsating at approximately a beat of 60 CPM (1800 - 1740).

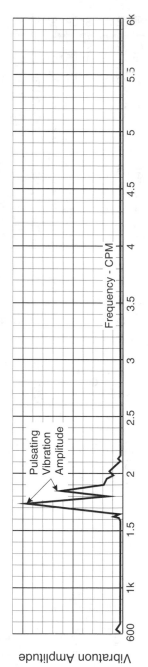

Illustration #80 - Vibration Analysis Showing Pulsating Amplitude at 1740 and 1800 CPM

Vibration From Electrical Problems (cont'd)

At 1740 CPM the vibration amplitude is noticeably higher than the amplitude of the second peak at 1800 CPM. It is clear to see that a "beat" between the two separate frequencies of vibration which are very close together.

Vibration From Belt Drive Problems

Belt drives for power transmission are classed as frictional drives. The belt transmits power by friction contact between the belt and the driving and driven sheaves.

Power transmission belts are available in several types and each has specific characteristics for optimum load, speed and friction performance. To obtain the best service from any particular belt application, such as flat belts, V-belts, synchronous belts, and multi-ribbed belts, key considerations are:

a. Select the correct belt for the job.

b. Ensure that the belt is installed correctly and used properly.

Belt drives are popular for power transmission because they have a high capacity for absorbing shock and vibration. V-belts are the most commonly used power transmission belt. They offer relatively quiet operation compared to chain or gear drives. However, V-belts can be sources of unwanted vibration, especially on machines where low levels of vibration must be maintained. For example, machines such as grinders, drills, lathes, fans, and agitators.

Vibration problems associated with V-belts are generally classified as:

a. Belt reaction to other disturbing forces in the equipment.

b. Vibration due to actual belt problems.

V-belts are often taken as the source of vibration because belts whipping and bouncing between the sheaves are more visible than the vibration of other parts of a machine, and are usually easy to change. Belt replacement is one of the first activities for trying to correct vibration problems.

Vibration From Belt Drive Problems (cont'd)

V-belts often are reacting to other disturbing forces in the machine. Several of these forces include: unbalance, eccentric sheaves/pulleys, misalignment, buildup on sheaves, and mechanical looseness. All of these examples can produce highly visible belt vibration. It is often just too easy to blame the belt. In these cases, the belt is the indicator of a vibration problem, but is not the actual problem. A complete vibration analysis of the machine should be done before replacing the drive belts.

The frequency of belt vibration is the main factor in determining the nature of the vibration problem. If the belt is reacting to other forces, such as unbalance or eccentricity coming from one of the sheaves, the frequency of belt vibration should be near the frequency coming from one of the disturbing forces (unbalance, eccentricity, etc.).

The belts often amplify or exaggerate the effects resulting from these disturbing forces. One way to check if this is happening is to use the strobe light of a vibration analyzer. The part of the machine actually causing the trouble will appear stationary under the tuned strobe light. See illustration #81.

Vibration due to actual belt defects can be identified by using frequency of vibration. In the case of belt defects, the vibration frequency is an integral multiple of 1, 2, 3, or 4 x belt RPM.

The amount of belt vibration can be measured by applying the vibration pickup on the bearing housing, perpendicular to the direction of belt tension, then parallel to the direction of belt tension. Refer to illustration #82. Belt defects usually show a higher amplitude of vibration in the direction that is parallel to the belt tension.

VIBRATION CAUSES

Vibration From Belt Drive Problems (cont'd)

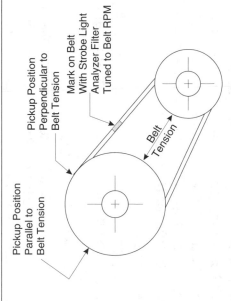

Illustration #81 - Strobe Light & Vibration Analyzer

Drive Pulley

Driven Pulley

V-Belts

Strobe Light

Vibration Analyzer

Transducer (Pickup)

Determining The RPM of A Belt (Belt Frequency)

To determine the RPM of a belt obtain the following information and use the Belt RPM formula identified.

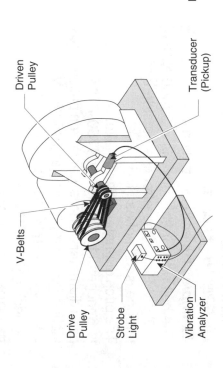

Pickup Position Parallel to Belt Tension

Pickup Position Perpendicular to Belt Tension

Mark on Belt With Strobe Light Analyzer Filter Tuned to Belt RPM

Belt Tension

Illustration #82 - Vibration Pickup Position

Need To Know:

1. Length of belt (outside circumference). Length can be measured or obtained from the belt identification code.

2. Pitch diameter of either the driver or driven pulley.

3. RPM of the drive or driven pulley.

Vibration From Belt Drive Problems (cont'd)

Note: In the calculation use the RPM of the pulley from which the pitch diameter was taken.

Belt RPM = (3.14 x Pulley Diameter) X Pulley RPM / Belt Length

Example: Refer to illustration #82.

The belt used in this drive is a 3V400 NARROW V-Belt. The effective outside circumference is 40 inches (101.6 cm).

The pitch diameter of the smaller drive pulley is 6 inches (15.24 cm) at 1750 RPM. The pitch diameter of the larger driven pulley is 10 inches (25.4 cm) turning at 1050 RPM.

#1 - Belt   RPM   =   (3.14 x 6 inches) x 1750 RPM / 40 inches

Belt RPM = 824 RPM

#2 - Belt RPM = (3.14 x 10 inches) x 1050 RPM / 40 inches

Belt RPM = 824 RPM

Belt Drives

Note #1: Belt RPM is required for tuning the strobe light to correct frequency when using it to identify belt defects (this also refers to "belt frequency"). Adjust the strobe flash until it freezes the belt.

Note #2: The RPM of either the driver or driven pulley can be determined by tuning the strobe light to a frequency of 1 x RPM, at which point the pulley would appear frozen. If the frequency of the strobe light was 1100 CPM, this will correspond to 1100 RPM at that pulley.

Belt Tension

The driver powers the driven pulley by "pull", which results in increased tension and stretch on the tight side of the unit as it overcomes the load resistance.

The slack side has no tension increase, it simply returns to the driven pulley. As shown in illustration #83, belts should operate with a distinct tight and slack side.

VIBRATION CAUSES

Vibration From Belt Drive Problems (cont'd)

tension, the slack belt can undergo excessive vibration, even from very minor disturbing forces. This condition, if continued, causes belt slippage and brings on excessive belt and pulley wear. Refer to illustration #84.

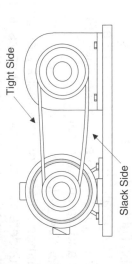

Illustration #83 - Proper Belt Tension

With multi-belt drives, it is important that all belts have the same tension. If one or more belts are slack while others are under proper

Belt Slippage

Belt slippage is commonly caused by improper tension, pulley misalignment, worn pulleys, belt mismatch, excessive loads and dirty or wet operating areas.

Belt slippage produces high frequency vibration and noise, identified as a "chirp" or "squeal." Vibration due to slippage often results in unsteady amplitude readings. On multiple V-belt installations belts may slip by varying amounts, which if continued, may either contribute to vibration effect, or in some cases reduce the vibration effect. However the net result is a vibration amplitude that increases in a cyclic, or periodic manner.

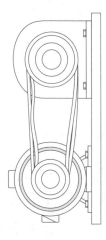

Too Loose - Slippage

Illustration #84 - Belt Tension too Loose

Vibration From Belt Drive Problems (cont'd)

The extent of belt slippage can be determined on multiple V-belt drives by using a strobe light. Safely shut down the machine, and after the belts are stopped draw a straight line across all the belts with chalk or other visible marker. Run the machine back up to normal operating speed, set the vibration analyzer to 1 x belt RPM and closely observe the lined marks on the belts under the strobe light. If the belts are slipping in relation to one another, the marks will also appear to move relative to one another. (Freeze one and watch the other).

Defective Belts

Common defects for belts include cracks on the underside, hard spots, soft spots, lumps on the belt faces, and broken away or torn pieces on the belt faces and cover.

Often longer belts are stored wrapped up in coils or bent over.

The belt will take on this set shape during packing and storing and upon installation may cause high vibration amplitude in the machine until the belt breaks in and becomes more flexible.

Misaligned pulleys can also cause the belt to wear sooner, as well as cause wear in the pulleys. Use only proper belt alignment methods, such as a straight edge, or the 4-point string/cord method. See illustration #85A,B.

Belt defect problems, as noted, will show distinct vibration frequencies that are integral multiples of belt RPM. The belt(s) will appear stationary under a strobe light. Do not attempt to touch the belts; remember, one can easily become mesmerized by what appears to be a stationary belt, but it is powered and turning at high speed under load. *Be careful when using the strobe light around belt drives.*

VIBRATION CAUSES

Vibration From Belt Drive Problems (cont'd)

A Using a Straight Edge for Alignment

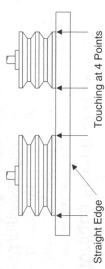

Straight Edge

Touching at 4 Points

B Using a Cord for Alignment

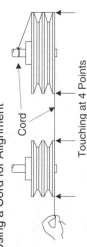

Cord

Touching at 4 Points

Illustration #85 - V-Belt Sheave Alignment

Balancing Belt Drive Pulleys

Most conventional V-belt and flat belt pulleys are statically balanced and are satisfactory for rim speeds of up to 6000 FPM (1828 metres/minute).

Dynamic balancing is necessary for belt drives where the rim speed of the pulleys exceed these speeds. In any application where vibration is a concern it is recommended that the sheaves be dynamically balanced to meet specifications.

In summary, smooth, trouble free operation of belt drives may be achieved by taking several of the following precautions:

a. Ensure that the belts are a matched set.

b. Check the belts for defects, replace all belts in a set, not just one or two.

c. Be sure the number and size of belts used will meet the horsepower and load requirements of the machine.

d. Be sure belts are properly installed aligned and tensioned to meet the machine's requirements.

e. Install proper guards and protective pieces to keep people out of the belt drive, as well, protect the drive from excessive dirt and moisture.

Vibration From Belt Drive Problems (cont'd)

f.   Make sure that the pulleys are round, with no broken sections, and are not worn excessively in the groove areas.

g.   If taper locks are used to hold the pulley to the shaft, ensure that they are properly installed and tightened.

h.   Attempt to keep other disturbing forces at the machine controlled. Take periodic checks for vibration at the bearings of the driver and driven pulleys.

Vibration From Bad Gears

Gears are used to transmit power positively, with no slippage, from one shaft to another by successively engaging teeth. Gears are used in place of belt drives or other forms of friction drive when exact speed and smooth vibration free load transfers are required.

Vibration from gear problems can be identified with a vibration analyzer. It normally occurs at the gear meshing frequency which is the number of gear teeth multiplied by the

Belt Drives/Bad Gears

RPM of the faulty gear.

Illustration #86 shows how vibration frequency is equal to the number of gear teeth multiplied by the RPM of the high speed pinion gear driven by the motor. This gear is turning at 4200 RPM and has 32 teeth. Therefore, the vibration frequency of this gear, as recorded on the vibration signatures, is 134,400 CPM. This can be seen on the horizontal readings, taken at point "C".

In complex gear arrangements, when multiple gear reductions are used, a different gear meshing frequency exists for each reduction. The gearbox drawings should be examined to identify the number of teeth per gear, calculate the gear mesh frequency of each gear reduction and identify which gear or gears are most likely at fault.

Note: If it is suspected that high vibration in the machine is caused by faulty gears, it is recommended that the gear box be dismantled and inspected.

Vibration From Bad Gears (cont'd)

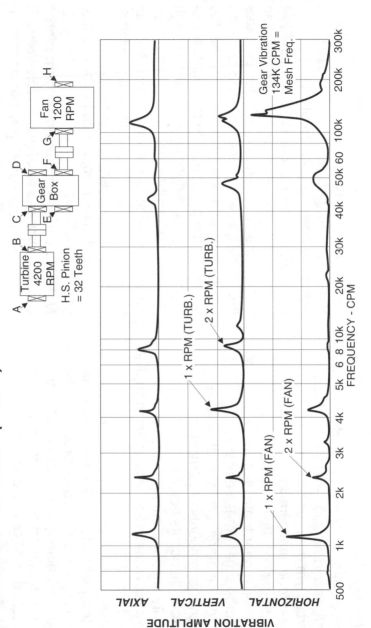

Illustration #86 - Vibration Signature for Part "C"

Vibration From Bad Gears (cont'd)

Common gear problems which result in high vibrations and vibration frequencies include:

- excessive gear tooth wear
- gear tooth inaccuracies
- improper backlash settings
- improper gear tooth clearances
- improper gear mesh patterns
- foreign material contaminating lube
- incorrect amounts of lubrication
- wrong lubricants being used
- faulty support bearings
- excessive loads and thrusts being applied to the gears
  - wrong gear choice for load and speed
  - poor gear materials for load and speed

In addition to the listed gear problems, the vibration characteristic recorded at the gears may be due to an outside force such as a misaligned shaft or bad bearings.

Bad Gears

For example, referring to the vibration analysis in illustration #86, a high frequency vibration may be present in the gearbox, indicating possible gear problems.

If the axial vibration occurring at turbine RPM frequency on the gearbox (point "C") is also high on the turbine (point "B") this indicates that misalignment of the coupling between the turbine and the gearbox may be the source of the problem. Correcting this misalignment may reduce or eliminate the high frequency gear vibration.

Where a turbine is the main drive, thermal growth could cause misalignment problems. It would be necessary to align this drive accurately and make adjustments for thermal growth conditions.

Note: Misalignment must be considered as a primary cause of many vibrations. It is important that rotating equipment technicians and millwrights perform up-to-date and accurate alignments on all rotating equipment.

VIBRATION CAUSES
Vibration From Bad Gears (cont'd)

The vibration amplitude and frequency from gear drives may be quite erratic in some cases. Randomly shifting load conditions on the gears may cause shifts in vibration frequencies and amplitude. If it is possible, try to maintain a steady load during the period the vibration readings are taken. Always remember to record any special load conditions. There may be little that can be done to resolve this problem, other than trying to steady loads, reducing any shock loads, or changing to a type of lubrication more recommended for erratic loads.

Note: Uncharacteristic noise and usually high frequency is associated with gear vibration. Correcting gear faults and other associated forces may reduce excessive gear vibration and substantially reduce the high noise levels.

Note: Gear mesh frequency vibration may excite the natural frequency of the gear. This often shows up as an additional spike, as in illustration #86, where the hump is displayed at 48,000 CPM.

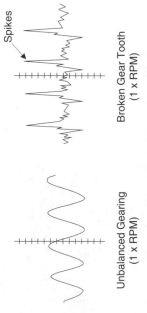

Unbalanced Gearing
(1 x RPM)

Broken Gear Tooth
(1 x RPM)

Illustration #87 - Oscilloscope Showing Unbalanced Gears and a Broken Tooth

Another problem associated with gear drives are damaged gear teeth. The vibration frequency is 1 x RPM if one tooth is broken. An oscilloscope connected to the vibration analyzer may help to distinguish this problem from unbalance because a spike-like signal is displayed and caused by the single damaged gear tooth. See illustration #87.

If more than one gear tooth is damaged, a vibration frequency equal to the number of broken teeth multiplied by the RPM may be displayed.

Resonance

Vibration From Resonance

Every part of a machine has a "natural frequency." This is the frequency at which the part "naturally likes" to vibrate. This natural frequency is the same as saying "resonant frequency."

If a machine part is struck, it will vibrate at its natural frequency until the internal damping characteristics diminish the amplitude of vibration to zero. Refer to illustration #88.

Note: Never apply direct hammer blows to a ball or roller bearing.

A recommended method for determining whether a part is vibrating at its natural frequency or responding to a vibration coming from a driving force is to perform a "bump" test. Turn off the machine and bump the structure with a force sufficient to cause vibration. The bumping causes the structure to vibrate at its natural resonant frequency. This vibration should appear on a vibration analyzer's frequency meter and the natural resonant frequency can be recorded.

Note: If the bump vibration diminishes too quickly to record the vibration frequency on the frequency meter, simply bump the structure several times in succession and rapidly enough to sustain a frequency reading.

A condition of resonance exists when the bump frequency (natural frequency) matches a vibration frequency while the machine is running.

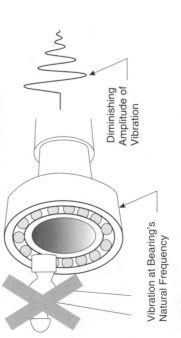

Diminishing Amplitude of Vibration

Vibration at Bearing's Natural Frequency

Illustration #88 - Vibration at Natural Frequency

VIBRATION CAUSES

Vibration From Resonance (cont'd)

For example, if the natural frequency of the rotor is 1100 CPM and the machine operates at a speed of 1100 RPM then a match condition exits. If this condition continues, the resulting amplitude of vibration may be enough to cause problems or failure of the machine and its components.

There are several methods for correcting resonance vibration. If the frequency of the exciting force could be altered so that it no longer coincided with the natural frequency of the machine or structure then there would no longer be resonance.

Exciting forces (forces which coincide with the machine's natural frequency) can be altered by changing the RPM of the machine. If it is impractical or impossible to change the RPM of the exciting force, alter the natural frequency by changing the damping characteristics of the machine or structure by modifying the stiffness and/or the mass.

The natural frequency can therefore be changed by increasing or decreasing the stiffness or mass of the system.

It is also possible to greatly reduce the exciting force. Performing accurate and reliable alignments, and closely balancing rotating parts will possibly reduce the effects of vibration at resonance. All attempts should be made to separate the natural and exciting frequencies in order to reduce the effects of vibration due to resonance.

Vibration From Aerodynamic and Hydraulic Forces

During the design of systems for fluid and air/gas flows several forces must be considered in order to reduce the affects of vibration to the system caused by these forces. Machines which handle gases, such as air, natural gas and boiler exhaust gases, may have vibrations and noise coming from the reaction of the blading or vanes on the impeller or fan which contacts the gas.

Vibration From Aerodynamic and Hydraulic Forces (cont'd)

This reaction is also the same for impellers in contact with fluids such as water, oil, or a brine solution. This type of vibration is quite common for pumps, fans and blowers; and is readily identified by the fact that the frequency of vibration is equal to the number of blades or vanes on the impeller or fan multiplied by the RPM of the machine.

If a fan with eight blades, used for moving large volumes of air, is rotated at 1100 RPM, some vibration amplitude may be recorded through vibration analysis at 8800 CPM. This type of vibration, displayed at 8800 CPM, is caused by the aerodynamic forces associated with the air volumes and flows from suction through to discharge and onwards down the piping system.

Hydraulic forces causing excessive vibration at frequencies equal to shaft RPM multiplied by the number of blades or vanes on the impeller are caused by fluid flow problems.

These are usually caused by things such as poor suction and improperly designed piping. Therefore, if aerodynamic or hydraulic forces cause excessive vibrations to the machine, it could be concluded that improper design of the machinery, piping, or duct work causes either or both of these forces.

In order to reduce the effects of aerodynamic and hydraulic forces in pumping and air/gas flow systems, more serious planning should be incorporated in the system design. Occasionally neglected during system planning is the important concept of design economies which originate with the project and continue through its useful life. For example, careful study of head conditions and pump location may produce worthwhile savings over a long period without a major increase in the initial cost of building the system.

Vibration From Aerodynamic and Hyraulic Forces (cont'd)

A wise choice of pipe sizes, based on planned or estimated future loads, is an example of how careful planning can reduce a variety of problems associated with aerodynamic and hydraulic forces causing excessive vibration, which in turn causes many mechanical problems and part failures.

Three common troubles associated with aerodynamic and hydraulic forces causing vibration are:

a. cavitation
b. recirculation
c. flow turbulence

Cavitation

Cavitation is commonly associated with aerodynamic and hydraulic forces causing excessive vibration to the machine. Cavitation normally occurs when a pump is operating with abnormally high suction lift or insufficient "net positive suction head available" (NPSHA).

Pump experts insist that more pump troubles result from incorrect determination of "net positive suction head available" (NPSHA) than from any other cause. NPSHA difficulties can greatly reduce pump capacity and efficiency, leading to cavitation damage. Liquids at any temperature above their freezing point have a corresponding vapor pressure which must be taken into account for designing efficient pumping systems. Reducing the pressure in a pump's suction line below the vapor pressure of the liquid can cause flashing (i.e., formation of vapor from the liquid). If the suction pressure were to remain above the vapor pressure of the liquid a positive suction pressure condition would exist and eliminate flashing.

Note: Few non-positive displacement pumps of typical design can effectively pump vapor. Liquid flow to the pump falls off and the unit is said to be "vapor-bound." Many positive displacement pumps handle vapor, although they will also be damaged by excessive cavitation.

182   VIBRATION CAUSES

Vibration From Aerodynamic and Hydraulic Forces (cont'd)

Note (cont'd): The most common method used to avoid this condition is to provide enough head on the pump suction so that the pressure in the suction pipe and impeller is always greater than the vapor pressure of the liquid handled. The NPSHA can be altered to suit that required by the pump for efficient operation if changes can be made in the piping size and length, level of the liquid supply, etc. The vapor pressure of a liquid can be changed by increasing or decreasing the liquid temperature at suction, although this is not always possible.

With insufficient NPSHA, cavitation may occur in the pumping system and this could possibly lead to vibration problems. The following illustrations demonstrate the process occurring during cavitation in a centrifugal pump.

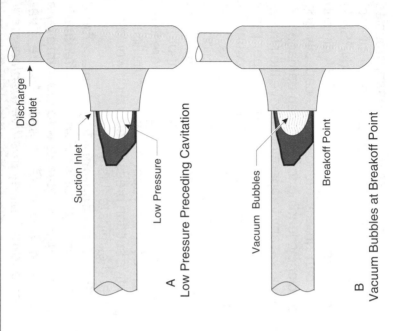

Discharge
Outlet

Suction Inlet

Low Pressure

A
Low Pressure Preceding Cavitation

Vacuum Bubbles

Breakoff Point

B
Vacuum Bubbles at Breakoff Point

Illustration #89A, B - Insufficient NPSHA

VIBRATION CAUSES

Vibration From Aerodynamic and Hydraulic Forces (cont'd)

The pressure decreases until a vacuum is created and the liquid flashes to vapor if the pressure in the pipe is lower than the liquid's vapor pressure. Liquid flow into the pump is reduced and the capacity limit of the pump at this inlet pressure has been reached. This condition is known as the "break-off point." Refer to illustration #89B. The pump is approaching an operating condition which can cause serious damage.

When the inlet pressure has almost reached the flash point, vapor pockets form bubbles on the underside of the impeller's vanes, near its base. Refer to illustration #89C. As the bubbles move from the low pressure area at the inlet to the high pressure area near the tip of the vane, the bubbles violently collapse.

This causes the bubbles to break so quickly that the liquid hits the vane with extreme force, often hard enough to gouge out small pieces of the impeller and even into the pump housing.

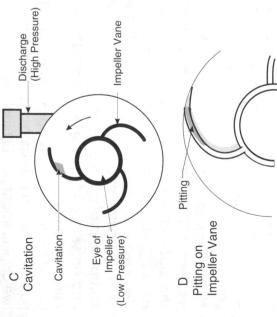

C
Cavitation

Discharge
(High Pressure)

Impeller Vane

Cavitation

Eye of
Impeller
(Low Pressure)

D
Pitting

Pitting on
Impeller Vane

Illustration #89C, D - Insufficient NPSHA

When the pump operates with insufficient NPSHA, a low suction pressure is developed at the pump's inlet. See illustration #89A.

Vibration From Aerodynamic and Hydraulic Forces (cont'd)

The damage is generally termed "pitting" and the noise heard outside the pump during cavitation is caused by the violent collapse or implosion of the vapor bubbles. See illustration #89D.

Note: The impact from the vapor bubbles as they collapse under pressure, excites the natural frequencies of the pump housing, impeller and other related parts. Because the impact might occur at random intervals and locations within the pump or piping, the resulting vibration and noise are also random in amplitude and frequency.

Cavitation does not only apply to centrifugal pumps. A similar condition can occur in positive displacement pumps such as rotary and reciprocating types.

Excessive suction lift, insufficient NPSHA, or operation at too high a speed are common causes of cavitation.

Pitting, vibration, and noise are common troubles stemming from cavitation. While severe cavitation is usually accompanied by excessive noise and damage to the pump, mild cavitation may produce nothing more than a small reduction in pump efficiency, moderate wear of pump parts, and less-than-serious amplitudes of vibration at random frequencies.

The following list identifies several conditions to avoid in order to reduce cavitation and any accompanying vibration. This list is specific to centrifugal pumps using mixed flow impellers, either of the closed or open design. Avoid whenever possible:

- Heads much lower than head at peak efficiency of the pump.
- Capacities much higher than capacity at peak efficiency of the pump.
- Net positive suction head lower than recommended by the manufacturer.
- Liquid temperatures higher than that for which the system was originally designed.

Vibration From Aerodynamic and Hydraulic Forces (cont'd)

- Net positive suction head less than net positive suction head required.
- Speeds higher than the manufacturer's recommendations.

Note: One method used to determine whether the loud noise heard coming from the pump is indeed cavitation is to partially close off the pump's discharge valve.

If there is a noise reduction, it may be concluded that cavitation exists. Partially closing of the discharge valve causes a back pressure in the pump housing (volute chamber). The flow is reduced, the NPSHA drops and the pressure in the suction increases.

The noise commonly associated with cavitation sounds like marbles or rocks rattling inside a can.

Illustrations #90A,B,C, refer to the "head terms" common to pumping systems.

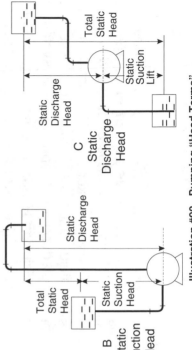

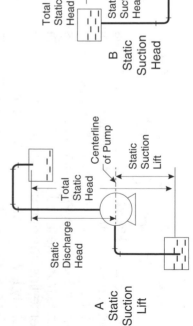

Illustration #90 - Pumping "Head Terms"

Vibration From Aerodynamic and Hydraulic Forces (cont'd)

Total Static Head: This is the vertical distance between the liquid supply level and the discharge level of the liquid being pumped.

Static Suction Lift: This is the vertical distance from the liquid supply level to the pump centerline, the pump being located above the supply level (illustrations #90A and #90C).

Static Suction Head: Where the pump is located below the liquid supply level a static suction head exists. This type of suction design provides for positive suction at the pump's inlet. Refer to illustration #90B. Numerically, this is the vertical distance between the liquid supply level and the pump centerline.

Static Discharge Head: This is the vertical distance from the pump centerline to the point of free delivery of the liquid. Be careful when trying to determine the point of free delivery when measuring static discharge head.

Note: *The horizontal piping runs are not considered as part of the static suction lift, so far as lift is concerned.*

Priming, or keeping the suction line full of fluid, reduces any "starving" problems upon startup for this type of suction system.

Friction Head: This is the equivalent head needed to overcome the resistance of the piping, valves, and fittings in the pumping system. Friction head occurs in both suction and discharge piping and varies with the liquid flow rate, pipe size, interior condition of the pipe, type of pipe, number of bends, and nature of the liquid being handled. Any reputable piping or pump supplier can provide comprehensive friction-loss tables

Velocity Head: Liquid moving through a pipe at any velocity possesses kinetic energy due to its movement.

Vibration From Aerodynamic and Hydraulic Forces (cont'd)

Velocity Head is the distance through which the liquid must fall to acquire a given velocity. Depending on the nature of the pumping installation, velocity head may or may not be an important factor in the total head on the pump.

Total Head is the sum of the total or dynamic suction lift and the total or dynamic discharge head.

Where there is a suction head, the total head on the pump is the difference between the discharge and suction heads. Illustration #91 identifies both friction and velocity head as factors in determining total head on a pump.

Recirculation

Recirculation in centrifugal pumps is a flow reversal at the inlet or at the discharge tips of the impeller. All impellers exhibit a point of discharge recirculation and a point of suction recirculation at some specific capacity and depending on the size and speed of the pump, the effects of recirculation can be very damaging to the impeller and pump housing. Recirculation in the pump produces random fluctuations of vibration and frequency; similar to those displayed under cavitation conditions caused by insufficient NPSHA.

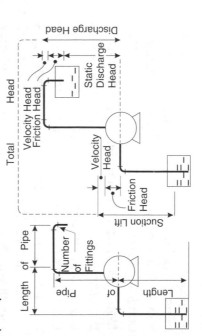

Illustration #91 - Factors Associated with "Total Head"
Both friction head and velocity head are usually discussed in reference to factors in the total head on a pump.

Vibration From Aerodynamic and Hydraulic Forces (cont'd)

In order to further identify some of the symptoms associated with recirculation and vibration it is important to make the distinction between suction and discharge recirculation.

Note: Just as in cavitation, recirculation problems in the pump produce noise and vibration and the effects of the reversing fluids promote progressive damage to the pressure surface of the impeller's vanes, and to the casing area surrounding the impeller. Illustration #92 shows the damage to the pressure side of the discharge vane from recirculation.

Suction vs. Discharge Recirculation

The capacity at which suction recirculation occurs is dependent on the design of impeller inlet; the capacity at which discharge recirculation occurs is dependent on the design of the impeller outlet.

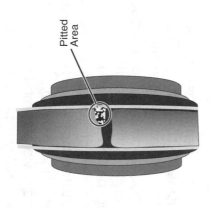

Pitted Area

Illustration #92 - Damaged Impeller Discharge Vane

There are many explanations to the cause or causes of recirculation. What conditions must prevail to trigger the flow reversal? The magnitude of the forces involved produce random vibration, damage metal surfaces, promote pressure pulsations, and the axial and radial forces impose extra load on the pump impeller, shaft, and bearings.

Vibration From Aerodynamic and Hydraulic Forces (cont'd)

Listed below are the physical failures and symptoms associated with recirculation:

Discharge Recirculation Symptoms:

- Cavitation damage to the pressure side of the impeller's vane at the discharge.
- Axial movement of the shaft with or without damage to the thrust bearing.
- Cracking or failure of the impeller shrouds at the discharge of the impeller.
- Shaft failures on the outboard end for double suction and multi-stage pumps.
- Damage to the tongue or diffuser vanes of the pump's casing.

Suction Recirculation Symptoms:

- Cavitation damage to the pressure side of the vanes at the inlet.
- Cavitation damage to the stationary vanes in the suction.

- Random cracking/rattling noise in the suction as contrasted to the steady crackling/rattling noise associated with inadequate NPSHA.
- Surging flows of the suction.

Discharge Recirculation

Illustration #93A demonstrates the flow reversal occurring at the impeller discharge. Why this happens is difficult to explain. The outward and inward flow in the same vane passage produces a shearing action and a high velocity vortex is produced. This vortex will cavitate provided the pressure at the base is reduced to the vapor pressure of the fluid. The result of this action is noise, vibration, and pitting damage to the metal surface of the vanes and shrouds. See illustration #92 for an example of the damage.

Aerodynamic & Hydraulic

Vibration From Aerodynamic and Hydraulic Forces (cont'd)
Suction Recirculation

The reversal of the flow has fluid being directed into the eye of the impeller near the hub, and ejected at the impeller eye diameter. A fixed vortex, like a swirling action, is produced that travels around with the rotation of the vane system. This cavitates and attacks the metal surface of the pressure side of the vane in the area approximately midway between the impeller's vane and shroud.

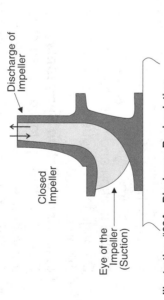

Illustration #93A - Discharge Recirculation

Illustration #93B shows the flow reversal occurring at the impeller's inlet during recirculation.

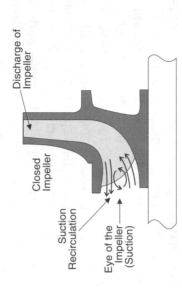

Illustration #93B- Impeller Recirculation

Note: **The similarity between patterns of cavitation damage from recirculation and from inadequate NPSHA may often lead to an incorrect conclusion as to the cause of the damage. With recirculation, the damage proceeds from the pressure side of the inlet edge of the vane through the metal to the low pressure side.**

Vibration From Aerodynamic and Hydraulic Forces (cont'd)

Note (cont'd): With cavitation, resulting from inadequate NPSHA, the damage starts at the low pressure side of the vane and proceeds through the metal to the high pressure side. Illustration #94 identifies the points on the impeller vanes where damage occurs from both recirculation cavitation and cavitation from poor NPSHA.

Suction Recirculation
Cavitation Damage
(High Pressure Side)

Cavitation Damage
from Low NPSHA
(Low Pressure Side)

Discharge Recirculation
Cavitation Damage
(High Pressure Side)

Illustration #94 - Damage to Impeller Vanes

Flow Turbulence

Flow turbulence is also associated with aerodynamic and hydraulic forces causing vibration. Flow turbulence is caused by resistance to the normal flow of liquids or gases in piping systems. The resistance is usually caused by friction between the fluid or gas and the internal walls of the piping, too many sharp bends, too many fittings, and/or any other form of obstruction in the piping system.

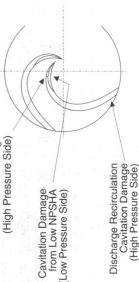

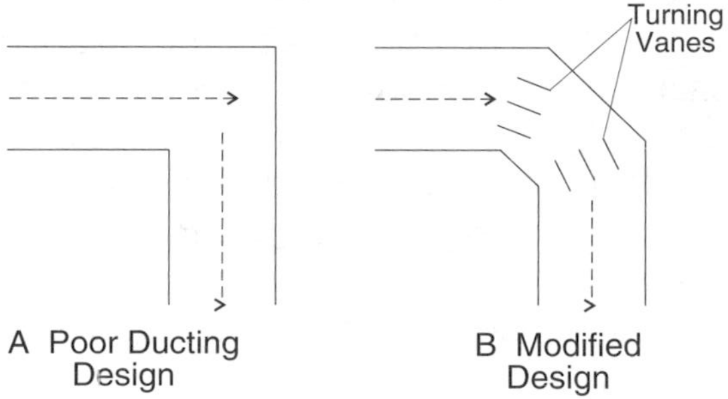

Turning
Vanes

A Poor Ducting
Design

B Modified
Design

Illustration #95 - Correcting Flow Turbulence

Vibration From Aerodynamic and Hydraulic Forces (cont'd)

Illustration #95A shows a common cause of flow turbulence in ducting systems. It is a poorly designed system as the flow of air or gas has to make a sharp right angle turn. This design creates turbulence and causes excessive vibration throughout the duct and into the rotating equipment connected to the duct system. Redesigning the duct work, by using two 45 degree sections, and if possible, by also installing fixed turning vanes into the duct causes the air or gas flow to turn more gradually. This will significantly reduce the flow resistance, therefore, reducing the turbulence and vibration. See illustration #95B.

Several methods for reducing flow turbulence and accompanying vibration in piping systems for handling liquids are recommended.

Aerodynamic & Hydraulic

As a general rule, the suction piping of a pumping system should never be smaller than the pump inlet connection.

If at all possible, the suction pipe should be two or more pipe sizes larger than the pump inlet connection. This ensures lower friction head losses in the suction line.

Flow turbulence can also be caused by the mixing of high velocity and low velocity fluids or gases. Illustration #96 demonstrates various interconnected piping systems, each line having flows with varying velocity mixing together. This illustration also shows a variety of obstructions such as valves, bends, gages and piping connections which all cause some amount of flow turbulence and subsequent vibration throughout the system.

VIBRATION CAUSES

Vibration From Aerodynamic and Hydraulic Forces (cont'd)

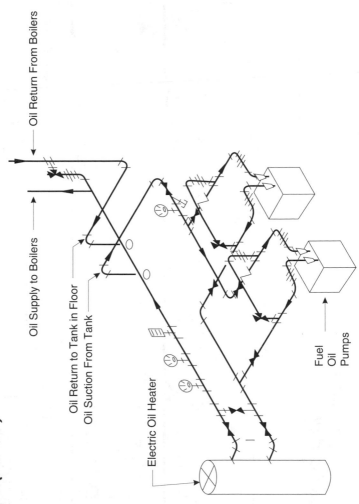

Oil Return From Boilers

Oil Supply to Boilers

Oil Return to Tank in Floor
Oil Suction From Tank

Electric Oil Heater

Fuel
Oil
Pumps

Illustration #96 - Interconnected Piping System

Vibration From Aerodynamic and Hydraulic Forces (cont'd)

Aerodynamic & Hydraulic

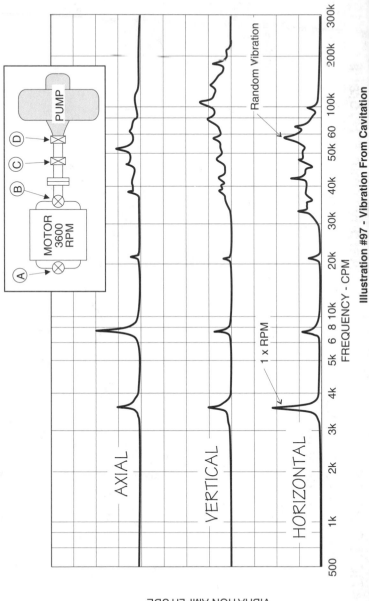

Illustration #97 - Vibration From Cavitation

Vibration From Aerodynamic and Hydraulic Forces (cont'd)

Random Vibration

Noise and vibration associated with cavitation, recirculation, and flow turbulence have very similar characteristics. This type of vibration is normally random in nature, quite different to the steady vibration caused by unbalance and misalignment. Any vibration from random sources, such as aerodynamic and hydraulic forces, display unstable amplitude and frequency characteristics. The vibration analysis recorded in illustration #97 is common vibration due to cavitation. There is a steady rate of vibration at 3600 CPM, or 1 X RPM, which may indicate an unbalance or misalignment condition. Considerable random vibration, noted by many sharp spikes, sit at 30,000 CPM to 100,000 CPM. This type of spectrum is usually associated with aerodynamics and hydraulic flow problems.

Vibration From Reciprocating Forces

Vibration and noise analysis of reciprocating machinery is usually quite complex and relatively new to industry. The complexity is normally due to having many frequencies of vibration involved. Normal frequencies are 1 or 2 x RPM; however, higher orders of frequencies are also commonly encountered, depending on the number and configuration of pistons.

Machines common to industry, classed as reciprocating, include: reciprocating compressors; piston pumps; spark ignition engines such as gasoline, propane and natural gas, and diesel engines, where ignition is from heat of compression. Each one of these reciprocating machines have vibration resulting from the reciprocating motion inherent in the design.

Vibration From Reciprocating Forces (cont'd)

The inherent vibration found in these types of machines results from the inertia forces of the reciprocating parts, such as the piston through the piston rod or connecting rod, to the crankshaft where torque and torsionforces occur. Varying internal pressures onthe piston heads and varying loads effect the vibration amplitude and frequency.

The problems with reciprocating machines which cause excessive vibration and noise-can either be mechanical or operational problems.

Mechanical problems causing vibration in reciprocating machinery include:

- Unbalanced parts, such as flywheels, gears, pulleys, pistons, connecting rods.
- Misalignment, between the reciprocating machine, a driver and driven unit (a reciprocating compressor and electric motor, or diesel engine driving a generator).

Reciprocating Forces

- Bent shafts, including the crankshaft.
- Crankshaft deflection; caused by mis-alignment of main bearings or weakened frame and poor foundation supports.
- Faulty bearings, worn connecting rod and crankshaft bearings.
- Mechanical looseness, where something on the machine is loose causing vibration and noise to be transmitted.
- Bad gears (such as timing gears) where damaged teeth cause excessive vibra-tion at high frequencies.

Operational problems causing vibration on reciprocating machines include:

- Blow-by, where gases leak by the piston rings.
- Faulty suction and discharge valves on a compressor causing unequal loading and vibration.
- Injector problems on engines, causing excess or insufficient fuel delivery to the cylinders, causing misfire or pre-ignition

VIBRATION CAUSES

Vibration From Reciprocating Forces (cont'd)

- Ignition problems on spark ignition engines.
- Improper clearances and settings for heads, and valves.
- Fuel and air ratio mixture problems on engines.

Note #1: In many cases, whether the vibration is caused by mechanical or operational problems, the vibration characteristics are nearly the same making it difficult to determine the exact causes without further analysis.

Note #2: When taking vibration readings from reciprocating machinery it is important to maintain a steady RPM at an even load setting for all readings, as this makes comparing vibration readings taken from various points more reliable.

There are several methods for distinguishing between mechanical and operational problems in reciprocating machinery.

An operational problem such as too lean a fuel mixture on a gasoline engine will decrease the engine's power, and probably increase the amplitude of vibration. Faulty ignition, inconsistent spark on a gasoline engine or a faulty fuel injector on a diesel engine will cause misfiring and reduces the engine's efficiency and increase the vibration. Usually operational problems cause unequal reciprocating forces, and this may display a much greater increase in vibration in a direction parallel to the reciprocating motion and only a small increase in vibration in the direction perpendicular to this motion.

Mechanical problems, such as imbalance, may display little or no change in overall efficiency. Vibration caused by mechanical problems, such as unbalance, misalignment, mechanical looseness and faulty bearings, may show a substantial increase in vibration in two or more directions.

Vibration From Reciprocating Forces (cont'd)

It is recommended that a history of vibration readings for each reciprocating machine be developed. Until there is solid analysis data and some history, it will be difficult to obtain, or even set valid bench marks for vibration amplitude. As earlier outlined, measuring vibration on reciprocating machinery is relatively new. Begin taking readings, and establish reliable information. This will eventually help control or reduce vibration of reciprocating machinery, vibration that in the past has often caused a great deal of mechanical and operational problems. Broken parts were replaced, the machinery was started up again, but was the cause of the vibration really corrected?

There is also specialized equipment and diagnostic techniques developed for more in-depth analysis of reciprocating equipment.

Reciprocating/Rubbing

In addition to time wave forms phase marked vibration signatures are very valuable, as this method plots vibration amplitude against crankshaft position. This method permits the analyst to determine at what point during rotation the vibration is occurring.

Vibration From Rubbing

The condition known as "rubbing" refers to unwanted friction, through contact, between stationary and rotating parts of a machine.

Rubbing generates vibration at 1 x RPM, 2 x RPM, and at higher frequencies. If the rubbing condition is continuous, it is unlikely any particular vibration characteristic will be noticed. However, continuous friction due to rubbing can excite high frequency resonance in other parts of the machine.

Rubbing, when it exists, is usually the result of a bent shaft, highly flexible shaft, broken or damaged parts, or distortion of internal and external components.

VIBRATION CAUSES

Vibration From Rubbing (cont'd)

This bowed shaft, caused by the constant rubbing creates vibration which does not stabilize when the rotor reaches full operating speed. The vibration amplitude grows with time. The time necessary for a noticeable increase in vibration, after operating speed is reached, may vary from less than a minute to over an hour or more.

Vibration From Rotor Flexibility

Vibration problems occur from long rotors and relatively flexible shafts, and in many machines, from high speeds.

Whenever a shaft or rotor that has been balanced on a balancing machine to the recommended tolerances continues to vibrate excessively in operation, it should be examined to see whether its flexibility is causing the vibration. For example, excessive vibration of long rotors such as those in multi-stage centrifugal pumps may be caused by excessive flexibility caused by one or more unbalanced impellers.

When unbalanced impellers are the problem, the vibration may be reduced by balancing the rotor to a smaller tolerance than normal for the pump's speed.

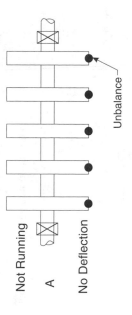

Not Running

A

No Deflection

Unbalance

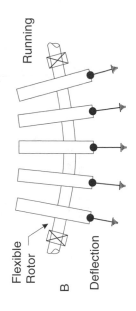

Running

Flexible Rotor

B

Deflection

Illustration #98 - Rotor Deflection

Vibration From Rotor Flexibility (cont'd)

Several impellers are installed on the long rotor shaft, as shown in illustration #98. Although it may be assumed that all the impellers have been balanced within the prescribed tolerance, some will obviously be balanced closer than others. *One recommendation to correct this is to install the most unbalanced impellers toward the rotor ends and the better balanced impellers near the center of the rotor.*

A pump impeller, such as the one shown in illustration #99, is mounted at the end of the shaft in an "over-hung" position. In this position, an unbalanced impeller can cause excessive vibration because of high deflection at running speed. Even small amounts of unbalance would deflect the shaft at operating speed, throwing the mass of the impeller off-center in the direction of the original unbalance, thereby adding to it.

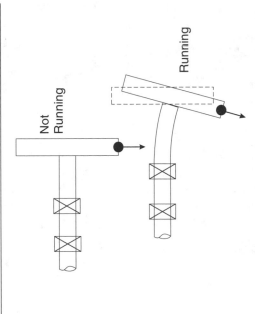

Illustration #99 - Overhung Impeller

This new unbalance causes further deflection, which in turn results in additional unbalance, and causes even further deflection. This escalation continues until equilibrium is reached, at this point the vibration is usually excessive.

Vibration From Rotor Flexibility (cont'd)

Slight deflections caused by an unbalance may be enough to make the rotor touch a stationary part, such as a labyrinth seal in a turbine. The rotor shaft at that point will heat up because of the increased friction. The heat causes the shaft to expand, leading to possible seal failure and maybe slight bowing the shaft. This would deflect the rotor even further off-center, causing a harder rub. All of these problems accumulate to cause excessive vibration.

Rotor bending can also be caused by improperly aligned bearings. This can lead to bowed shafts and vibrations caused by unbalance. Usually the vibration frequency is 2 x RPM, but it may occur at 1 x RPM as well.

A flexible rotor, with a bow or a rub condition can often be detected by its predominant characteristic: *a vibration that does not stabilize when it reaches operating speed*.

This type of vibration grows with time. The time necessary for a noticeable increase in vibration, after operational speed is reached, may vary from several minutes to many hours.

Vibration From Beats or Pulsations

"Beat" vibration takes the form of noticeable beats or pulsations occurring at regular intervals. This beat vibration can result from a single exciting force which is continually changing in amplitude and frequency. Two machines rotating at constant speed for example, often create a vibration that is not constant in amplitude. Vibration increases then declines, at times the vibration is almost zero, then it increase again to a maximum then decreases. It is usually found that the high and low amplitudes of vibration continuously repeat in cyclical beats. If one of the machines is stopped, the vibration from the one still running will continue steady and without intermittent pulsations.

Vibration From Beats or Pulsations (cont'd)

Two electric motors mounted on the same structure may each have an acceptable level of vibration, but if both are operating at approximately the same speed, beat vibration may be recorded. Beat vibration occurs where two or more machines are operating in the same vicinity, but at slightly different or approximate speeds to each other.

In many plants it is common to find two or more pumps connected to the same header or piping system. The rotating speed of each pump is not exactly the same as the other, probably due to the different slip speed of their drive motors. The beat vibration is most often determined by finding the arithmetic difference between the two frequencies of the motors driving the pumps. For example, one pump may be running at 1750 RPM and the other at 1740 RPM. The beat vibration is therefore 10 CPM, or the difference between the frequencies of the two.

If the difference in speeds were greater, then the beat vibration would be higher.

In order to reduce the intensity of the beat vibration, consider the following:

a. Setting the machines on separate foundations.

b. Placing vibration mounts or dampers under the frames of both.

c. Change the rotational speeds of the motors so they differ by more than 20%.

Another method for reducing the intensity of beat vibration is to precisely balance the rotating equipment to the lowest tolerance that is practical. This may not eliminate the problem totally, but the beat vibration will be less intensive.

Vibration From Beats or Pulsations (cont'd)

The effect of a beat on vibration amplitude usually causes the vibration reading to increase and decrease in a synchronous rhythm. The amplitude of vibration isn't the only factor related to beat; the other factor is phase. One method commonly used to spot this is to put a strobe light on a reference mark. If beat vibration exists, the reference mark will appear to be oscillating back and forth. If the beat vibration is relatively small, then the phase oscillation will be slight, usually only a few degrees. The larger the beat vibration, coming from other machines, the wider the angle of oscillating phase.

Vibration and Noise From Hydraulic Systems

There are specific vibration and noise characteristics associated with hydraulic systems.

The following discussion identifies several of the more common vibration and noise characteristics transmitted from various parts of the hydraulic system.

Hydraulic Pumps

Mechanical energy is transformed into hydraulic energy at the pump. Most hydraulic pumps are of the positive displacement type, where the pump suction is sealed from the pump discharge positively, by the close tolerances of the rotating or reciprocating internal pumping parts. There is no slippage of the fluid between the suction side of the pump to the discharge side. Under normal operating conditions, a steady, narrow-band noise is generated.

The maximum rate of energy change, as required by the system, determines the noise level coming from the hydraulic pump. If the pump is under an increased pressure build-up during the pumping cycle, the noise level increases.

Vibration and Noise From Hydraulics (cont'd)

If the load in the system fluctuates, there is a relationship to the system pressure, and this causes the noise levels to fluctuate.

Different types of positive displacement pumps have different noise levels. Screw type pumps usually have the lowest noise level, gear pumps are usually the noisiest, while vane pumps and piston pumps have intermediate noise levels.

Noise levels coming from hydraulic pumps are affected by shaft speed, pump size and operating pressure. Problems such as poor suction and cavitation, high or low hydraulic oil viscosity, and problems like loose or worn pump parts can also cause excessive noise and vibration.

Accurate pump and motor alignment, and proper assembly are important in minimizing noise and vibration on hydraulic pumps.

Further improvements can be achieved by using vibration isolators or dampers, and by isolating the hydraulic pump and motor assembly from any supporting structure in the room. Acoustical isolation may also be required.

This isolation requires that the pump be located either remote from the area where low load noise levels are desired, or in some type of a sound-dampening enclosure.

Hydraulic Fluid

During the pumping process the fluid is energized and a narrow band of noise and vibration is produced. Other fluid noises, more in the broad-band range, are caused by turbulence, cavitation rattle, abrupt changes in the fluid flow, high pressure or severe resistance to fluid flow.

VIBRATION CAUSES

Vibration and Noise From Hydraulics (cont'd)

Lines and Fittings

Many problems of excessive noise and vibration in hydraulic systems result from poorly designed piping systems. The lines and fittings can greatly effect system noise and vibration. Some common problems include:

- Obstructions formed by diameter changes in connectors, reducers, elbows, etc.
- Sudden changes in flow direction, such as 90 degree elbows and tees, which cause turbulent flow.
- Lines may vibrate in resonance with the noise and vibration generated from the pump.
- Inadequate hangers or supports for the lines.
- Constant expansion and contraction problems in the lines due to sudden temperature changes in the vicinity, or of the hydraulic fluid.

Some methods for correcting problems with hydraulic lines and fittings include:

- Keep lines and their connectors near to a constant diameter throughout the system.
- Keep the flow direction fairly constant, and avoid sharp, sudden bends.
- Use flexible hose instead of rigid pipe or tubing if there is a lot of movement, or surging/pulsations.
- Use proper hangers and supports.
- If hose cannot be used, some isolation in the connectors can be achieved by using O-ring type fittings.
- Provide proper bends of large radius in the lines.

Hydraulic Valves

Noise and vibration often results from the various flow control, pressure control and directional control valves used throughout the system.

Vibration and Noise From Hydraulics (cont'd)

There are many types and designs of each of these valves. Pilot operated valves are generally less jerky, and therefore, are quieter and have less vibration. Special valves in a hydraulic system, such as cushion valves, counter-balance valves, and check-valves, can also reduce some of the noise and vibration in the system.

Hydraulic Actuators

Pressurized hydraulic fluid is sent to the hydraulic actuator where it overcomes the resistance load placed on the actuator.

The actuator can be rotary or linear in design, such as gear or vane motors or hydraulic cylinders. The actuator must overcome the load resistance placed upon it.

If the resistance is great, increased noise and vibration will result in many areas of the system. The actuator may also produce noise and vibration.

Linear actuators, if improperly mounted or assembled incorrectly, can produce noisy, jerky, and chattering operation. Rotary actuators must be mounted solidly to a base or frame, and the lines and fittings attached to it must be secure. Often, a rotary actuator, such as a hydraulic motor, is under extremely high torque loads, therefore it is important that the motor is mounted solid, with no flexing. Under extreme loads, the actuator will produce more noise, and shudder and strain, causing increased vibration. On a properly designed system, actuators should be able to be stalled without too much sign of stress.

SECTION THREE QUESTIONS
Vibration Causes

1. Finding the part of a rotating machine causing vibration is accomplished by analyzing the frequency and amplitude.

   □ true   □ false

2. The _____ of vibration is normally some multiple of the RPM of the part in trouble.

   □ severity
   □ amplitude
   □ frequency
   □ velocity

3. Many vibration and balancing specialists suggest that _____ is the most common cause of vibration in rotating equipment.

   □ mechanical looseness
   □ machinery unbalance
   □ faulty bearings
   □ misalignment

4. List seven primary causes of unbalance in rotors of rotating machinery and equipment.

   Answer: _____

5. Eccentricity exists when the true or geometric centerline of a part does not coincide with its rotating centerline.

   □ true   □ false

6. A mistake is often made when technicians mount a coupling halve to the electric motor shaft. They cut the key flush with the end of the coupling halve hub. Explain why this is a problem.

   Answer: _____

7. What are two forces which commonly cause distortion of rotating parts?

   Answer: _____

8. Blow holes and sand traps are commonly referred to as _____ when discussing unbalance of rotating parts.

    ☐ casting imperfections
    ☐ internal faults
    ☐ embedment properties
    ☐ shock zones

9. Dynamic balancing of rotating equipment parts is imperative when operating at high speeds, above 3600 RPM.

    ☐ true   ☐ false

10. In most cases, the vibration and frequency data collected from an unbalance condition indicates that the predominant vibration frequency is _____ of the unbalanced part.

    ☐ 1 x RPM   ☐ 2 x RPM
    ☐ 3 x RPM   ☐ many times RPM

11. In most cases, the vibration and frequency data collected from an unbalance condition indicates that the amplitude of vibration is usually less in the radial directions of measurement than in the axial direction of measurement.

    ☐ true   ☐ false

12. In unbalance conditions, phase analysis normally shows unstable phase readings.

    ☐ true   ☐ false

13. Generally, _____ is considered to be the second main cause of vibration in rotating equipment today.

    ☐ machinery unbalance
    ☐ coupling misalignment
    ☐ mechanical looseness
    ☐ faulty bearings

14. Alignment tolerances for aligning driver and driven sections of rotating equipment together with couplings depend on such factors as:

    Answer: _____

    _____

15. Identify the three types of misalignment encountered when two machines are coupled together.

    Answer: _____

    _____

16. There is a general misconception that the shaft alignment for _____ couplings is not critical.

    ☐ flexible   ☐ rigid

17. List six conditions which should be checked before aligning two coupled shafts.
    Answer: _____

18. _____ vibration is usually the best indicator of misalignment.
    ☐ radial   ☐ axial

19. _____ misalignment will primarily subject‡ the shafts of the driver and driven machines to high amounts of axial vibration.
    ☐ parallel offset   ☐ angular

20. The condition where the rotating shafts centerline is not in the same position as the rotor's geometric centerline is called:
    ☐ out-of-round   ☐ eccentricity
    ☐ parallelism   ☐ phase angle

21. An eccentric gear is one example of eccentricity which can be corrected by performing routine balancing procedures.
    ☐ true   ☐ false

22. An eccentric pulley acts like a cam and provides reaction forces similar to those of eccentric gears.
    ☐ true   ☐ false

23. The largest vibration on an eccentric pulley will occur _____ the belt tension.
    ☐ in the direction of
    ☐ at right angles to

24. A bent shaft produces the highest vibration at:
    ☐ 1 x RPM   ☐ 2 x RPM
    ☐ 3 x RPM   ☐ many times RPM

25. Bent shaft symptoms can be the result of resonant whirl rather than a permanent bend.
    ☐ true   ☐ false

26. Resonant whirl is the condition which occurs when the rotor is resonating at a frequency _____ its own running speed.
    ☐ opposite to   ☐ half of
    ☐ equal to   ☐ two times

27. The diametrical tolerances of an anti-friction bearing are held to _____ or less.

☐ 0.01 inch   ☐ 0.001 inch
☐ 0.0001 inch   ☐ none of the above

28. The vibration spectrum is one of the most common methods for analyzing an anti-friction bearing for defects.

☐ true   ☐ false

29. Defect frequencies in anti-friction bearings are generated by:

☐ the lubrication
☐ unbalanced bearing parts
☐ discrete flaws on raceways and rollers
☐ shock loads

30. When the rolling element of an anti-friction bearing strikes a crack or pitted area what may be excited?

☐ the bearing's natural frequency
☐ the shaft's natural frequency
☐ the bearing support's natural frequency
☐ all of the above

31. List three loads common to anti-friction bearings.
Answer: _____

32. When attempting to identify what is causing the bearing to fail it is important to determine how the bearing is loaded.

☐ true   ☐ false

33. Can background vibrations be a cause of failure for an anti-friction bearing?

☐ yes   ☐ no

34. Generally, the practice for correcting a soft foot condition on an electric motor is to:

☐ balance the rotor
☐ insulate the armature
☐ align the coupling to the driven unit
☐ shim the appropriate motor foot or feet

35. Journal bearings are classified by the type of axial or radial load they carry.

☐ true   ☐ false

36. List two key factors which good fluid lubrication for radial loaded journal bearings depend on.
Answer: _____

37. Excessive bearing clearances can result in poor load distribution within the bearing.
☐ true   ☐ false

38. When referring to journal bearing clearance there are two types of clearances. What are these and provide a brief explanation of each.
Answer: _____

39. Oil whirl is one of the easier causes of vibration to recognize by its unusually high vibration frequency.
☐ true   ☐ false

40. Can vibration due to oil whirl be reduced by increasing the loading area on the journal bearing?
☐ yes   ☐ no

41. Vibration, due to improper lubrication, where excessive friction occurs, is called:
☐ oil whirl   ☐ oil whip
☐ dry whip   ☐ friction loss

42. Mechanical looseness typically produces a vibration at a frequency of:
☐ 1 x RPM   ☐ 2 x RPM
☐ 3 x RPM   ☐ ¹/₂ x RPM

43. It is highly recommended that all rotating equipment be balanced and aligned to the tolerances set out by the equipment manufacturer. By doing this, there should be less chance of having _____ problems.
☐ lubrication
☐ mechanical looseness
☐ hydraulic imbalance
☐ oil whirl

44. List six common causes of vibration due to electrical problems in electric motors, generators or alternators.
Answer: _____

45. The frequency of vibration resulting from electrical problems is typically:
☐ 1 x RPM   ☐ 2 x RPM
☐ 3 x RPM   ☐ many times RPM

46. As the load changes on an electric motor, the amplitude and/or phase readings usually show:

❑ no change   ❑ significant change

47. Explain the term 'slip frequency' as it is applied to induction type electric motors.
Answer: _____

48. Belt drives are popular for power transmission because of their capacity to _____.

❑ slip under heavy loads and start up conditions
❑ absorb shock loads
❑ absorb vibrations.
❑ all of the above

49. The frequency of belt vibration is the main factor in determining the nature of the vibration problem.

❑ true   ❑ false

50. Belt defects usually show a higher amplitude of vibration in the direction that is _____ to the belt tension.

❑ right angles   ❑ parallel

51. The RPM of either the driver or driven pulley can be determined by tuning a strobe light to flash at a frequency of 1 x RPM, at which point the pulley would appear frozen.

❑ true   ❑ false

52. Belt slippage produces _____ frequency vibration and noise.

❑ low   ❑ high

53. Why is caution necessary when using a strobe light around belt drives?
Answer: _____

54. Vibration resulting from gear problems normally occurs at _____.

❑ 1 x RPM
❑ a frequency equal to the gear meshing frequency
❑ ¹/₂ x RPM
❑ 2 x RPM

55. List five distinctive gear tooth problems which can result in high vibrations and vibration frequencies.
Answer: _____

56. Randomly shifting load conditions on the gears may cause shifts in vibration frequencies and amplitude.

☐ true ☐ false

57. Every part of a machine has a natural frequency. Explain what this statement means.

Answer: _____

58. A bump test can be performed in order to determine what the machine parts natural frequency is.

☐ true ☐ false

59. The natural frequency of a machine part can be changed by:

☐ modifying the stiffness and/or mass of the part
☐ changing the rpm of the machine
☐ all of the above

60. Identify two things which can be done to help reduce the effects of vibration at resonance.

Answer: _____

61. Machines, such as fans, which handle large volumes of gases or air, may have vibrations and noise coming from the reaction of the blading or vanes which are in contact with the gases or air they are handling.

☐ true ☐ false

62. If a fan with six blades used for moving large volumes of air is rotating at 700 RPM, some amount of vibration should be recorded at 4200 CPM.

☐ true ☐ false

63. Improper design of piping and ducting systems for pumps or fans can be a cause for vibration. Two forces are referred to in these situations. They are:

Answer: _____

64. Cavitation normally occurs when a pump is operating with:

☐ low suction lift
☐ insufficient net positive suction head available
☐ excessive start and stoppage of the fluid flow
☐ an unbalanced pump impeller

65. Reducing the pressure in a pump's suction line below the vapor pressure of the liquid:

☐ causes the liquid to freeze
☐ causes the liquid to flash
☐ has no effect on the liquid
☐ increases the pump suction capacity

66. Most non-positive displacement pumps of typical design can effectively pump vapor.

☐ true   ☐ false

67. The impact from the vapor bubbles during cavitation, as they collapse under pressure, excite the _____ of the pump housing, impeller, and other related parts.

☐ synchronous frequencies
☐ non-synchronous frequencies
☐ natural frequencies
☐ vibration velocity

68. List six conditions to avoid in order to reduce the effects of cavitation for centrifugal pumps using mixed flow, or either open or closed impellers.
Answer: _____

69. Recirculation in a centrifugal pump can produce random fluctuations of vibration and frequency.

☐ true   ☐ false

70. Flow turbulence is caused by resistance to the normal flow of liquids or gases in piping or ducting systems.

☐ true   ☐ false

71. List four causes of flow turbulence.
Answer: _____

72. As a general rule, the suction piping of a pump's piping system should be smaller in diameter than the pump's inlet piping connection.

☐ true   ☐ false

73. Any vibration from random sources, such as aerodynamic and hydraulic forces display:

☐ stable amplitude and frequency characteristics
☐ unstable amplitude and frequency characteristics

74. The problems with reciprocating machines which cause excessive vibration and noise come from two primary sources. These are:
Answer: _____

75. When taking vibration readings on reciprocating machinery it is not necessary to maintain a steady RPM at an even load setting.

☐ true ☐ false

76. It is recommended that a history of vibration readings for each reciprocating machine and its parts be developed. Explain why this is necessary.

Answer: _____

77. The condition known as _____ refers to unwanted friction, through contact between stationary and rotating parts of a machine.

☐ dry whirl
☐ resonance
☐ rubbing
☐ critical speed

78. Usually the vibration is caused by bowed or bent shafts at 2 x RPM, but may also be displayed at 1 x RPM.

☐ true ☐ false

79. A flexible rotor, with a bow or rub condition, can often be detected by its predominant characteristic:

☐ a vibration which stabilizes when operating speeds are reached
☐ a vibration that does not stabilize when it reaches operating speed

80. Which type of vibration takes the form of noticeable beats or pulsations occurring at regular intervals?

☐ rubbing
☐ resonant
☐ synchronous
☐ beat

81. In order to help reduce the intensity of the beat vibration, consider placing vibration mounts or dampers under the frames of machines.

☐ true ☐ false

82. Would it be accurate to say that there are specific vibration and noise characteristics associated with hydraulic systems?

☐ yes ☐ no

83. At the hydraulic pump:

☐ fluid (hydraulic) energy is transformed into mechanical energy

☐ mechanical energy is transformed into fluid (hydraulic) energy

84. If the hydraulic pump is under an increased pressure build-up during the pumping cycle, the noise level normally _____.

☐ decreases   ☐ increases

85. Which type of hydraulic pump listed below generally is considered to have the lowest noise level?

☐ screw pump
☐ vane pump
☐ piston pump
☐ gear pump

86. Many problems of excessive noise and vibration in hydraulic systems result from poorly designed piping systems.

☐ true   ☐ false

87. Common types of valves for hydraulic systems used for reducing jerkiness and vibration symptoms include:
Answer: _____

88. Hydraulic actuators receive pressurized hydraulic fluid for overcoming the resistance load placed on them.

☐ true   ☐ false

89. Linear type hydraulic actuators can be quite jerky and chatter during their operation if:

☐ the hydraulic fluid is too pressurized
☐ improperly mounted or assembled incorrectly
☐ the load is too much for the actuator
☐ the electric motor driving the actuator has electrical problems

90. If a hydraulic actuator is stalled out, there will be considerable internal damage done to it.

☐ true   ☐ false

SECTION FOUR

EQUIPMENT BALANCING

Introduction

As described in the Section Three, unbalance is one of the primary causes of vibration. When a machine has vibration problems, it is easy to conclude that the solution is to add or remove weights to balance the rotating parts.

However, many vibration problems can be solved by studying the history of the machine, with special regard to any operational or maintenance changes that may have occurred. Talk to the operators and maintenance people, and review the maintenance records. Make a list of all the points that may be associated with the vibration increase. Some of the items on the list may include:

1. Have there been any changes in operating procedures that may have caused the vibration change, such as:

- change in rotating speed
- change in product type or density

- change in operating pressure
- change in temperature
- start up or shut down of other machines that are close by, or connected to the same process via piping, etc.

2. Has there been any recent maintenance work on the machine? For example:

- coupling alignment
- hubs sheaves or gears mounted on shafts
- bearings or other parts replaced
- parts installed or removed
- work on rotors or shafts, such as straightening, building up and machining, new blades fitted, etc.
- changes made to associated equipment such as piping, hangers, supports, ducting, etc.

Introduction (cont'd)

3. Has the vibration increase been gradual or sudden?

If the vibration has suddenly increased and no maintenance or operating changes have been made, then possibly something has come loose on the rotor, a blade has been thrown, or debris could have broken free from a rotating part. Knowledge of the machine and its internal components will be of value in this diagnosis.

If this analysis does not point towards a possible cause, then detailed vibration analysis will probably have to be carried out, keeping in mind the machine's history, to find the reason for the increase in vibration.

If the cause of the vibration is unbalance, and balancing has to be performed, then a decision has to be made on whether to use a *balancing machine*, or perform *in-place balancing*.

In-Place Balancing

Balancing can be performed "in place" or by using a balancing machine. "In-place" balancing is preferable wherever possible. This involves running the machine, either on site or in the shop, taking the necessary readings and making the proper corrections. The instrumentation used may be a simple hand held vibration meter or a complex vibration analyzer that is pre-programmed to do all the calculations.

The latter will give more accurate results in a shorter time, and will also perform the more complicated balancing procedures. Excellent results can also be achieved with the basic instruments that are only used to measure vibration. ***A thorough understanding of vibration and balancing is preferred, and sometimes essential, no matter what methods are used.***

210   EQUIPMENT BALANCING

Balancing Machine

In-place balancing is not always feasible with machines that are fully enclosed and require considerable disassembly to reach the rotating parts. In-place balancing can also introduce certain problems. Starting and stopping some machines to obtain the necessary data for balancing may take considerable time, effort and expense. In these cases the rotor may have to be removed from the machine and balanced separately on a balancing machine.

Rotating parts that have been removed from a machine for repair may require balancing before being re-installed. Rotating parts manufactured for high speed machinery are normally balanced on some type of balancing machine before being assembled.

Balancing machines are available in a large variety of types and sizes

Balancing Machine

Production balancing machines are designed to efficiently balance large numbers of identical parts.

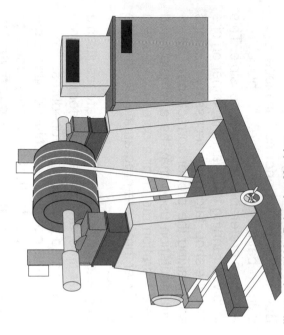

Illustration #100 - Balancing Machine

EQUIPMENT BALANCING

Balancing Machine (cont'd)

A typical balancing machine required for a maintenance shop would be designed to accommodate rotating parts of many shapes and sizes.

A typical maintenance balancing machine is shown in illustration #100. The rotor is supported by the balancing machine while being rotated so that dynamic balancing can be performed.

The instrumentation used with the balancing machine may be a vibration analyzer/balancer used for field analysis, or permanent instrumentation may be built in.

Illustration #101 will help to determine whether to use in-place balancing or a balancing machine.

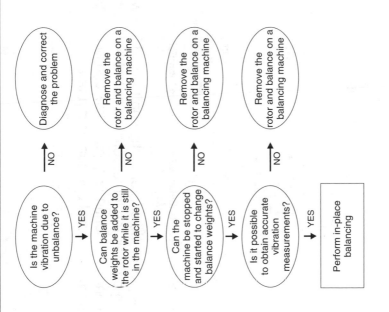

Illustration #101 - In-Place vs. Balancing Machine

Unbalance

Unbalance of a rotating part of a machine occurs when there is an unequal distribution of weight around the axis of rotation. In other words, the axis of weight distribution does not coincide with the axis of rotation. The International Standards Organization (ISO) defines it as "that condition which exists in a rotor when vibratory force or motion is imparted to its bearings as a result of centrifugal forces".

The net result of unbalance is the generation of centrifugal forces when the part is rotated. The amount of force generated is dependent on the speed of rotation and the amount of unbalance. It is this rotating force that causes vibrations which generally are detrimental to the life of the machine.

Illustration #102 shows how an out of balance rotor causes vibration. This not only occurs horizontally, but also in all other directions.

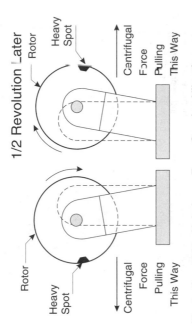

Illustration #102 - Unbalance Force Causing Vibration

A plot of the center of the shaft would follow an orbit as the force from the out-of-balance condition continually pulls the center away from its normal position as it rotates.

EQUIPMENT BALANCING

Unbalance (cont'd)

The amount of centrifugal force created by an out of balance weight can be calculated as follows:

Using Imperial Units:

$$F = 1.77 \times R \times W \times (RPM / 1000)^2$$

Where:

F = The force generated in pounds

R = Radius of the out of balance weight in inches

W = Weight of the out of balance weight in ounces

Using Metric Units:

$$F = 0.011 \times M \times R \times RPM^2$$

Where:

F = The force generated in Newton's

R = Radius of the out of balance weight in metres

M = Mass of the out of balance in kilograms

Using Gram-Inch Units:

$$F = 0.0625 \times R \times W \times (RPM / 1000)^2$$

Where:

F = The force generated in pounds

R = Radius of the out of balance weight in inches

W = Weight of the out of balance in grams

These equations indicate that the force generated is proportional to the square of the RPM. This means that if the RPM is doubled, the force will be quadrupled. It is this force generated by the unbalance that causes vibration.

For examples of using these formulae, see pages 225 and 226 on Trial Weights.

The amount of unbalance is usually stated as the product of the unbalance weight and its distance from the rotational axis.

If imperial units (ounces and inches) are used, the unbalance will be stated in ounce-inches. For example, if a 2 ounce weight is placed at a radius of 8 inches on a rotor, the amount of unbalance would be:

2 x 8 = 16 ounce-inches.

Unbalance (cont'd)

If metric units (grams and millimetres) are used, then the unbalance will be stated in gram-millimetres or gram-metres.

A combination of these two units (metric and imperial) can also be used, and in this example, the unbalance will be stated in gram-inches.

If the RPM is known, then the actual force generated can be calculated using one of the above equations.

Note: Any combination of weight and radius can be used to achieve the same amount of unbalance. For example if an unbalance of 16 ounce-inches is required and the weight is to be placed at a radius of 6 inches, then the weight required is 16/6 = 2.66 ounces.

Types of Unbalance

As defined previously, unbalance is the unequal distribution of weight around the center of rotation.

Unbalance/Types of Unbalance

Actually there are two axes to consider, the one about which the part rotates (rotational axis), and the one about which the weight is equally distributed (weight distribution axis). For a part to be in balance both of these axes have to be coincidental.

When balancing is performed, usually by adding or removing weight, the position of the weight distribution axis is changed so that it coincides with (or becomes closer to) the rotational axis.

Static Unbalance

Static unbalance occurs when the weight distribution axis is offset but parallel to the rotational axis. See illustration #103.

Static unbalance will cause a rotor that is supported between bearings and is free to rotate, to turn so that the heavy spot moves to the bottom when it comes to rest.

Types of Unbalance - Static (cont'd)

Any frictional resistance in bearings and seals will cause the rotor to stop before the heavy spot reaches the bottom.

Note: Quasi-static and dynamic unbalance will also react similarly when checked for static unbalance.

To balance this part, weight equal to the unbalance has to be added exactly opposite the heavy spot, or enough material has to be removed from the heavy spot to eliminate the unbalance weight.

The rotor shown in illustration #103 has a static unbalance. Notice that the heavy spot is in the center of the rotor. If it was not in the center but concentrated toward one end, then the weight distribution axis would not be parallel to the rotating axis and the unbalance would be quasi-static.

In all three examples in illustration #104 the rotor will appear balanced when supported on bearings. The condition shown in illustration #104B is not acceptable at high speed because the out of balance force and the two balance weights will deflect the rotor.

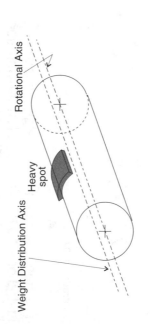

Weight Distribution Axis

Heavy spot

Rotational Axis

Illustration #103 - Static Unbalance

Types of Unbalance - Static (cont'd)

Types of Unbalance

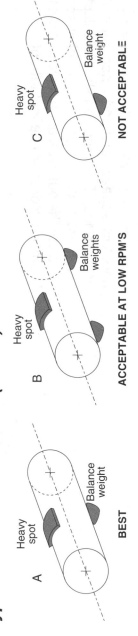

A	B	C
Heavy spot	Heavy spot	Heavy spot
Balance weight	Balance weights	Balance weight
BEST	ACCEPTABLE AT LOW RPM'S	NOT ACCEPTABLE

Illustration #104 - Correcting Static Unbalance

The heavy spot and two weights shown in illustration #104B will cause further vibrations due to the weight shift. The RPM where this will occur at will depend on the stiffness of the rotor.

Although the rotor in illustration #104C will appear to be statically balanced, it is not acceptable because the combination of the heavy spot and the balance weight will now cause the rotor to have a quasi-static unbalance, which will become apparent when the rotor is rotated.

To check if a rotor's unbalance is static, the rotor has to be rotated and the phase angles and amplitudes of the vibration checked at both ends of the rotor. If the phase readings and amplitudes are the same then the unbalance is static.

Note: Overhung rotors will not act in this manner. For balancing overhung rotors see page 249.

Types of Unbalance - Static (cont'd)

Static unbalance can be balanced in one plane only. The plane being the one on which the rotor center-of-gravity is situated. If this plane is not suitable for making corrections then two other planes will have to be used. See illustrations #104A and #104B.

If the unbalance is not static then corrections will have to be made in at least two balancing planes.

Couple Unbalance

Illustration #105 shows a couple unbalance which occurs when the weight distribution axis intersects the rotational axis in the center of the rotor. This type of unbalance would have to be balanced in two planes.

If a rotor with this condition were supported between bearings and free to rotate, it would be statically in balance. This means that it would not come to rest at the same place each time it was rotated and allowed to stop.

If the rotor is rotated and phase readings taken at each end of the rotor, they will occur 180 degrees apart, and the amplitude of the vibration will be the same at both ends.

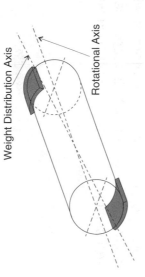

Weight Distribution Axis

Rotational Axis

Illustration #105 - Rotor With Couple Unbalance

Quasi-Static Unbalance

This type of unbalance is very similar to the couple unbalance and is a combination of static and couple unbalance. For an example see illustration #106

Types of Unbalance

Types of Unbalance - Quasi-Static (cont'd)

The weight distribution coincides with the rotational axis at some point other than the center of the rotor. Quasi-Static unbalance would have to be balanced in at least two planes. The phase readings would be 180 degrees apart but the vibration readings would be greater on one side than the other.

Dynamic Unbalance

In a true Dynamic unbalance the weight distribution axis and the rotational axis do not coincide at all. See illustration #107. The phase readings from each end would be neither the same or 180 degrees apart, but somewhere in between. This is the most common type of unbalance in rotors. It will also show up as being unbalanced when checked statically. Dynamic unbalance will have to be corrected in at least two planes.

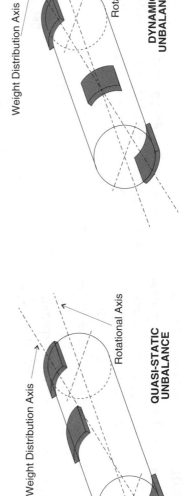

Illustration #106 - Quasi-Static Unbalance

Illustration #107 - Dynamic Unbalance

Natural Frequency

All machine parts including shafts, rotors, frames, bearing supports etc. have a fundamental natural frequency at which they will vibrate if something (such as the force from a rotating unbalance) causes them to start vibrating. An example of this is shown in illustration #108 where a shaft is supported between two bearings.

If the shaft is excited by striking it with a block of wood it will vibrate at its natural frequency. No matter how hard the part is struck, the frequency will stay the same and only the displacement will change. The time it takes for the vibrations to stop will depend on the internal damping characteristics of the part. In illustration #108 the time for one complete cycle is the same at (a) and (b).

The fundamental natural frequency of some rotors can be checked by performing the same test as described above, that is by performing a bump test.

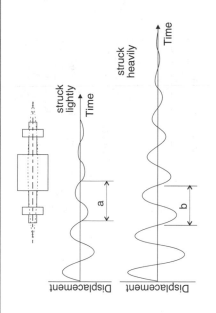

Illustration #108 - Natural Frequency of a Shaft

If the vibration diminishes too quickly to get a reading, the machine may have to be struck a number of times in quick succession. ***Obviously care has to be taken not to damage the rotor.***

Natural Frequency

Natural Frequency (cont'd)

The above test will only produce one natural frequency. In actual fact a rotor will have a number of natural frequencies.

The natural frequency of a machine part will not change unless the mass or stiffness of that part is changed.

If the mass of a rotor is increased while the stiffness stays the same then the natural frequency will be lower. On the other hand, if stiffness is increased then the natural frequency will be increased. This is shown in illustration #109.

Musical instruments are among some common items where the natural frequency of vibration is used. A guitar string under tension will vibrate at its natural frequency when plucked to produce the required sound. If the stiffness is changed by changing the tension of the string then the natural frequency and therefore the tone is changed.

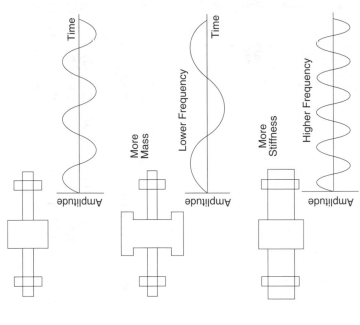

Illustration #109 - Effect of Mass and Stiffness

Critical Speeds

When a child on a swing is given a single push it will swing backwards and forwards at its natural frequency. When the swing is given another push to help it on its way each time it changes direction, the amount of displacement increases and it goes higher and higher.

This produces a condition known as resonance. A similar condition can occur on a rotating machine's shaft or rotor, the push on the rotor coming from the force generated by unbalance.

When a rotor rotates at a speed which equals its natural frequency, then any unbalanced forces will excite the rotor in the same way as the person pushing the child on the swing. The result is also similar, in that the displacement will increase far more than when the shaft rotates at any other speed.

The speed at which this increased vibration or resonance occurs is known as the *critical speed*.

Illustration #110 shows a plot of vibration amplitude versus the rotating speed. When the speed goes past the critical speed, the vibration level drops.

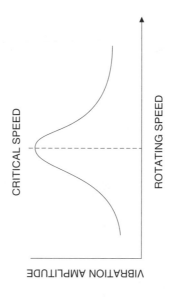

Illustration #110 - Graph of Vibration Amplitude vs. Speed

Critical Speeds (cont'd)

If the speed is increased further, the rotating speed may coincide with the second natural frequency of the shaft and the rotor will experience a second critical speed.

A further complication to the number of criticals is that a machine may have arises from the fact that machines are made up of many parts, some of which will have a natural frequency that may significantly affect the levels of vibration at various speeds.

Resonance of bearing supports may also show up as a critical speed.

Illustration #111 shows a plot of machine vibration vs. RPM as the machine is run up to operating speed.

Critical Speeds

The two critical speeds occur when the rotating speed coincides with the natural frequency of the bearing supports and the rotor.

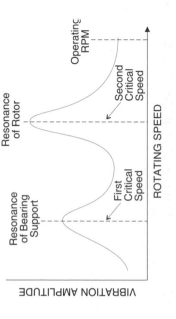

Illustration #111 - Vibration vs. RPM

EQUIPMENT BALANCING

Critical Speeds (cont'd)

The rotor of a machine may have more than one critical speed depending on how fast it is rotated. As it reaches its first critical speed it will flex due to the centrifugal forces from the out of balance. This bending or flexing causes a new out of balance condition.

If the speed is increased the rotor may go through more critical speeds, each one causing the rotor to flex in a different manner. Illustration #112 shows a rotor having three criticals.

When possible, rotating machines are designed so that their operating speeds do not coincide with one of the critical speeds. This is relatively easy with constant speed machines such as turbo-generators, but is more difficult with variable speed machines. Although it is possible to operate a well damped rotor at its critical speed, it is inadvisable.

Rigid or Flexible Rotors

A rotor is considered to be rigid if it operates below 70% of its first critical speed. If a rotor operates above its first critical speed then it would be considered a flexible rotor.

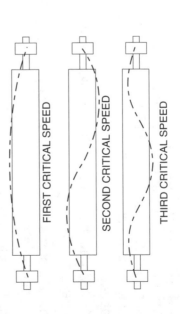

FIRST CRITICAL SPEED

SECOND CRITICAL SPEED

THIRD CRITICAL SPEED

Illustration #112 - Rotor with 3 Critical Speeds

Balancing Tools

The following list indicates some of the tools and instruments required for in-place balancing. The type of machine and method of balancing may change the requirements somewhat. It is assumed that the normal millwright or mechanics' hand tools are available.

1. A vibration analyzer with the following features:

a. measures amplitude in velocity or displacement

b. has a tunable filter

c. has phase measuring capability

2. An accurate weigh scale suitable for measuring trial and balance weights.

3. A calculator.

4. Polar graph paper.

5. Compass, ruler or straight edge and protractor.

6. Trial weight material such as modeling clay or beeswax, adhesive weights, sheet lead, fiberglass tape, hose clamps, weight material (steel, copper or brass), bolts and washers if there are tapped holes in the rotor.

Trial Weights

When a rotating part has to be balanced, the location and amount of unbalance is unknown. Trial weights are added to a known location to produce a change from the original unbalance readings.

The changes in the unbalance readings provide the information for calculating the location and size of balance weights. The calculation may be performed manually or by use of a programmed vibration analyzer or computer.

Trial Weights (cont'd)

How Much Trial Weight

For the density of some common materials used for trial and balance weights see table #12, page 253.

When adding a trial weight to a rotor, the amount of weight and the radius at which it rotates is very important.

The amount of force generated by an out of balance weight can be calculated by the following equations.

Imperial:

$$F = 1.77 \times R \times W \times (RPM / 1000)^2$$

where:

F = The force generated (lbs)

R = Radius of the out of balance weight (ins)

W = Weight of the out of balance (ounces)

Metric SI:

$$F = 0.011 \times R \times M \times RPM^2$$

where:

F = The force generated Newton's (N)

R = Radius of the out of balance weight in metres (m)

M = Mass of the out of balance (kg)

If the combination of weight and radius is too small then there may not be a great enough change in the unbalance readings for them to be useful. If the product of the weight and radius is too great, then some damage may result, especially if the machine is operating above its critical speed.

To obtain the correct trial weight, use one of the above formulae to calculate the mass, radius and RPM that will produce an unbalance force of approximately 10% of the rotor weight supported by the bearing.

Trial Weights (cont'd)

Imperial Example: If a rotor weighs 1600 pounds and is supported by two bearings, the required trial weight for each plane would have to produce 80 pounds of force (10% of 800 pounds).

Using Imperial units:

$F = 1.77 \times W \times Rx \ (RPM/1000)^2$

From this: $W = F/(1.77 \times Rx \ (RPM/1000)^2$

This is assuming the location radius of the trial weight has been determined.

Where:

W = Weight of trial weight in ounces

R = Assumed radius is 10 inches

F = 80 pounds

If the above unit rotates at 1725 RPM

Trial Weight = $80/(1.77 \times 10 \times (1725/1000)^2)$

= 1.52 ounces

Metric Example: If a rotor weighs 730 kg and is supported by two bearings, the downward force is 730×9.8 Newton's.

The force on each bearing is then: $730 \times 9.8 / 2 = 3577N$

10% of 3577 is 358N, which is the force the trial weight has to generate.

$F = 0.011 \times m \times R \times RPM^2$

From this $m = F / (0.011 \times R \times RPM^2)$

m = mass of the trial weight in kg

R = Assume the radius is 0.254 meters

$F = 358N$

If the above unit rotates at 1725 RPM

Trial weight = $358/(0.011 \times 0.254 \times 1725^2)$

= 0.043 kg = 43 grams

Trial Weights (cont'd)

As stated previously, the information required to determine the size of the Trial Weight is:

1. Rotor weight supported at the bearings.
2. RPM of the rotor.
3. The radius at which the trial weight is to be placed.

Attaching Trial Weights

When attaching trial weights, care has to be taken that they are attached securely enough that they will not be thrown off as the rotor is rotated, but yet be easily removable when the amount and location of the final balance weight has been calculated.

If the rotor has some type of flange, such as in illustration #113, modeling clay or synthetic beeswax is ideal. If the rotor is large and heavy the clay or beeswax may be used in conjunction with lead or steel to increase the weight.

Some machines provide a place for bolting on trial weights and balance weights. Other methods are clamps (including hose clamps), tack welding, soldering, brazing, glue or cement, self adhesive weights such as vehicle wheel weights etc. On smooth shafts and rollers, fiber-glass tape is sometimes used.

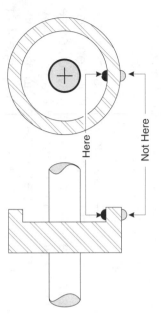

Here

Not Here

Illustration #113 — Trial Weight Located Inside Flange

Phase Angle Measurement

As mentioned in previous chapters, a strobo-scopic light can be used for a number of different purposes. Its primary purpose in balancing is to check phase angle. The strobe light can be set up to synchronize its flash with the noise or vibration being measured. If the vibration is due to unbalance then the strobe will flash once each revolution of the shaft or rotor, and the heavy spot will always be at the same position when it flashes.

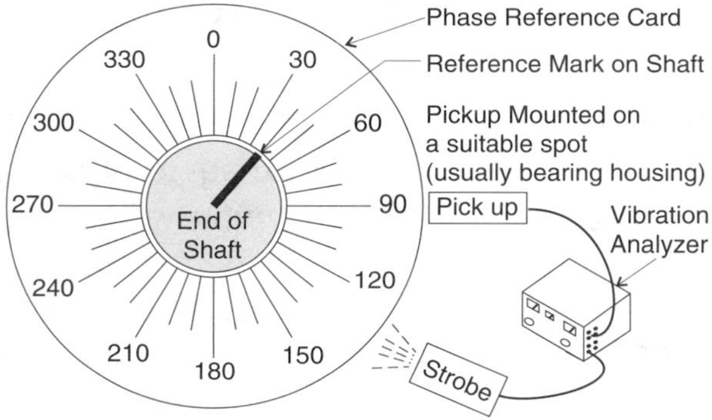

To accurately locate the shaft position when the flash occurs, a reference mark on the end of the shaft and a phase reference card can be used. See illustration #114.

Illustration #114 also shows the strobe light and pick-up connected to a vibration analyzer. The strobe flash is set to synchronize with the vibration. Unfiltered readings may be used if there are no other predominant vibrations. If there are vibrations present at frequencies other than the rotating speed, then filtered readings should be used. With the filter tuned to the rotor RPM it will give the maximum amplitude at that frequency.

Note: If the rotor is well balanced there will not be enough vibration for the strobe to flash consistently every revolution, there will not be a clear reference mark on the end of the shaft and the flash will be erratic. See illustration #115.

Phase Reference Card
Reference Mark on Shaft
Pickup Mounted on
a suitable spot
(usually bearing housing)

Pick up

Vibration
Analyzer

Strobe

End of
Shaft

0
30
60
90
120
150
180
210
240
270
300
330

Illustration #114 - Degree Card on End of Shaft

Phase Angle Measurement (cont'd)

Well Balanced Rotor

Erratic Strobe Flash
will not "Freeze" the
End of the Shaft

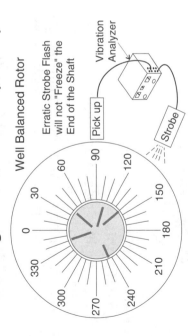

Illustration #115 - Erratic Strobe Flash

To illustrate phase angle measurement:

- The test rotor in illustration #116 has been unbalanced by adding a weight.
- The pick-up is located at 90°.
- The strobe flashes every revolution because of the unbalance, and the reference mark is frozen at a particular point (300° in this example).
- The strobe flashes sometime after the heavy spot passes the pick-up.

- The distance that the heavy spot moves past the pick-up before the flash occurs is known as the flash angle or phase lag.
- In illustration #116 the flash angle is 55°, and the heavy spot is located at 145° because the pick-up is at 90° (90° + 55° = 145°).

This initial phase angle of 300° is dependent on the flash angle and the location of the reference mark. It provides an initial reference when performing the balancing calculation. The flash angle depends on a number of variables such as rotating speed, size and type of rotor, support stiffness, type of bearings, measurement parameter (velocity or displacement), pick-up location and direction and type of pick-up. When the flash angle is known for a particular machine or rotor, the information can be used to simplify balancing if the same, or a similar machine has to be balanced. See pages 241 to 243 on Balancing in One Run.

Phase Angle Measurement (cont'd)

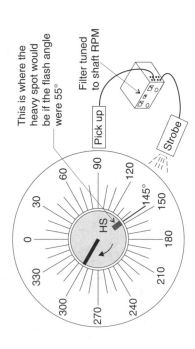

This is where the heavy spot would be if the flash angle were 55°

Filter tuned to shaft RPM

Pick up

Strobe

Illustration #116 - Unbalanced Rotor

Trial Weights

A trial weight is placed on a rotor as part of the balancing procedure to see what effect it will have on the phase angle and the amplitude of vibration. The relative position between the trial weight and the original heavy spot will be unknown when balancing, because the location of the original heavy spot is unknown.

If by chance the trial weight is placed directly on the original heavy spot, the phase angle will not be affected, but the amplitude of vibration will increase. If the trial weight is located exactly 180° from the original heavy spot, the result will be either:

1. a reduction in the vibration amplitude (if the force from the trial weight is less than the force from the original heavy spot), or

2. a 180° shift in the phase angle (if the force from the trial weight is greater than the force from the original heavy spot).

In most cases the trial weight will not be placed in either of these two positions, but will be somewhere in between. This will have the effect of creating a new heavy spot. The new heavy spot will be somewhere between the original heavy spot and the trial weight.

If the magnitude of the trial weight is exactly the same as the original heavy spot, then the new heavy spot will be mid-way between the two.

Phase Angle Measurement (cont'd)

If the magnitude of the trial weight is greater than the original heavy spot, then the new heavy spot will be closer to the trial weight. If the original heavy spot is greater than the trial weight, then the new heavy spot will closer to the original heavy spot.

Effect of a Trial Weight

To show the effect placing a trial weight, consider the rotor shown in illustration #116:

• Another weight is placed 120° in an anti-clockwise direction from the original heavy spot to represent a trial weight.

• To simplify the example, the trial weight is the same magnitude as the original heavy spot.

• This will cause a new heavy spot to be created, which in this case will be exactly in between the original heavy spot and the trial weight (60° from each). See illustration #117.

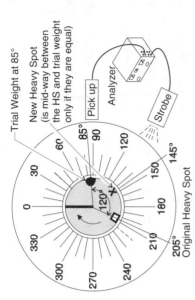

Illustration #117 - Trial Weight Placed

Note: Before the trial weight was placed, the original heavy spot caused the strobe to flash. After the trial weight was placed the new heavy spot caused the strobe to flash.

• Because the flash angle in this particular set-up is 55°, the strobe flashes when the new heavy spot is 55° past the pick-up.

Phase Angle Measurement (cont'd)

- The original heavy spot has moved 60° in a clockwise direction, as well as the reference mark which now shows a phase angle of 360° instead of 300°.

- The new heavy spot, which is a combination of the original heavy spot and the trial weight, is located 60° in an anti-clockwise direction from the original heavy spot.

- This caused the phase angle (reference mark) to move 60° in a clockwise direction because the shaft now rotates further (60°) before the new heavy spot causes the strobe to flash.

- This example was simplified by using a trial weight and an unbalance weight that were equal, which caused the new heavy spot to be exactly in between the two.

- If the trial weight had been heavier than the original heavy spot, then the new heavy spot would have been closer to the trial weight

Phase Angle Measurement

- It can be seen that the reference mark, or phase angle moved in a clockwise direction.

- If the trial weight was moved further anti-clockwise then the phase angle (reference mark) would move further clockwise.

- If the trial weight was moved clockwise, the phase angle (reference mark) would move opposite in the anti-clockwise direction.

Note: The phase angle moves opposite to the direction the unbalance is moved, and by the same amount.

The original unbalance weight shown in illustration #116 was 10 grams and the vibration displacement was 7 mils at 300°. If the original unbalance weight is increased to 20 grams and placed in the same position, the amplitude will be 14 mils at 300°.

Note: The amplitude of vibration is proportional to the amount of unbalance.

EQUIPMENT BALANCING

Before Balancing

The machine must be in sound condition. Check for obvious damage such as cracks in the rotor or shaft. The bearings should have the correct amount of clearance. Ensure there is no buildup of material on the rotor, if there is, balancing to correct an uneven deposit build up will only be a temporary solution, as the deposit is likely to break off later.

From the previous data taken, check to see which location gives the highest amplitude readings (horizontal or vertical). Use this location for taking readings while balancing. Also use the same orientation for both bearing locations (both horizontal or both vertical).

When using filtered readings, make sure that the analyzer is properly tuned to the rotating speed of the rotor for all runs, to ensure that it is measuring the maximum amplitude and correct phase angles.

If the machine is started from a cold condition, allow it to reach full operating temperatures before completing the balancing operation.

Where there is a large amount of background vibration and the frequency of the background vibration is close to the balancing speed it will make the balancing more difficult and limit the accuracy of the final balance.

Depending on the capability of the analyzer, check for any large changes in vibration and phase as the machine either runs-up to speed or coasts down. Illustration #118 shows plots of phase and amplitude versus speed. If the analyzer does not have this capability, observe the amplitude (with the analyzer measuring the overall vibration) as the machine coasts down. If there is just a steady decline with no peaks, then the machine is running below the first critical. See page 223 on Rigid or Flexible Rotors.

Before Balancing (cont'd)

If the machine is operating above the first critical, it is important that the trial balance weights are carefully selected so that no damage occurs to the machine as it runs through the critical speed. See pages 224 to 226 on Trial Weights for calculating the correct amounts.

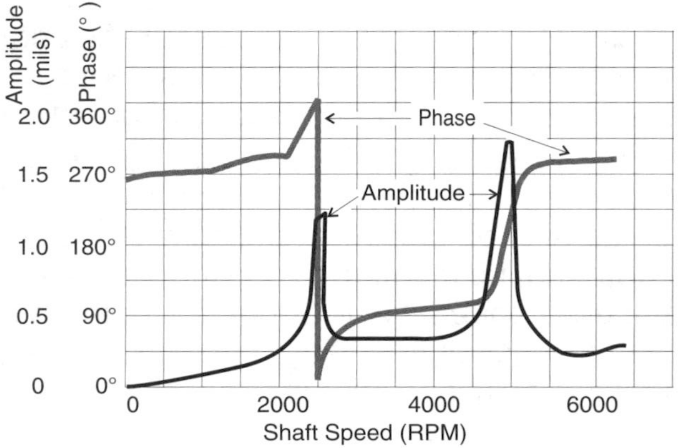

It is also important to note from illustration #118 that each time the machine passes through a critical speed, there is a 180° shift in the phase angle.

Because of the phase angle shift, balancing should not be attempted with the rotor running close to a critical speed, as any minor change in speed can make a major change in the phase angles measured.

Balancing Methods

Although it was stated previously that only a static unbalance can be balanced using a single plane, two plane balancing can also be achieved using single plane techniques. See Two Plane Balancing on page 247. The RPM and the length of the rotor compared to the diameter will also effect whether or not the balance will be single, two plane or multi-plane. See illustration #119.

Illustration #118 - Shaft Speed vs. Ampl. and Phase (rundown)

Single Plane Balancing

Static Balancing: Static balancing is only effective if the unbalance is a true static un-balance or if the rotor is thin compared to the diameter and running at fairly low speeds. See illustration #119.

The rotor has to be free to rotate so that the heavy spot will rotate to the bottom when it comes to rest. Turn the rotor a number of times to make sure that the same spot is at the bottom each time. This will be the heavy spot.

Selecting Single Plane, Two Plane or Multi-plane Balancing

L/D ratio excluding shaft	Balance Correction		
	Single Plane	Two Plane	Multi-plane
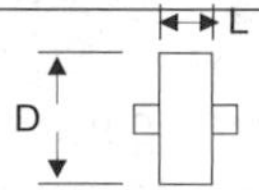 Less than 0.5	0 - 1000 RPM	Above 1000 RPM	Not applicable
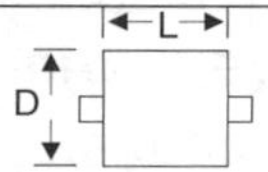 More than 0.5 but less than 2	0 - 150 RPM	150 - 2000 RPM or >70% of first Critical	Above 2000 RPM or >70% of first Critical
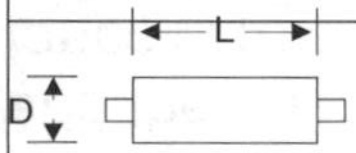 More than 2	0 - 100 RPM	Above 100 RPM to 70% of first Critical	Above 70% of first Critical
	Note: RPM = machine operating speed		

Illustration #119 - Single, Two or Multi-Plane Balancing

Single Plane - Static (cont'd)

Place weights opposite this until the rotor stops in a different place each time it is turned and then allowed to come to rest. Any resistance to rotation will reduce the effectiveness of this method.

Vector Method: The vector method allows a balance to be completed by making two runs (a third run will be performed to check the results). Run one is to measure the original amount of vibration and phase reading. After a trial weight is added the machine is run a second time and vibration and phase readings are taken again. From this information, a plot is made (on polar graph paper) to determine the amount and location of the final balance weight. The trial weight is removed and the balance weight installed.

A third run will probably be made to check the balance.

If vibration is still too high, the procedure may be carried out again to adjust the magnitude and/or position of the balance weight to bring

Balancing Methods

vibration within the required tolerance.

The step by step procedure is:

Step 1: Set up a reference mark on the shaft and install a phase reference card. If a phase reference card is not available, it may be necessary to make one. See illustration #120. Alternatively, the shaft or coupling hub may be marked in degrees around the circumference.

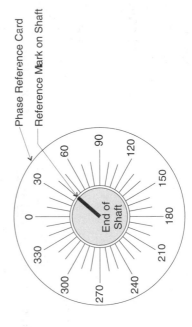

Illustration #120 - Shaft with Reference Mark and Card

Single Plane - Vector (cont'd)

Step 2: Run the machine and record the amount of unbalance (displacement or velocity) and measure the phase angle. This is the original unbalance. As an example, the displacement was 5 mils and the phase angle was 120 degrees. This will be referred to as run "O".

Step 3: Attach a trial weight to the rotor in any suitable position (see pages 224 and 227 on How Much Trial Weight and Attaching Trial Weights).

Note: The relative position of the trial weight to the reference line is not important, provided the trial weight is securely attached but can be removed when the final balance weight has been calculated. Assume a trial weight of 10 grams.

Step 4: Take run number two. Measure the amount of vibration and the phase angle. In this example it was 6.4 mils at 40 degrees. This is referred to as run "O + T".

Step 5: Plot a vector to represent the original run (run "O", 5 mils at 120 degrees) on the polar graph paper. Choose a suitable scale so that the largest unbalance reading will fit on the paper. See illustrations #121 and #122.

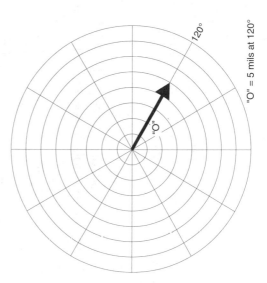

"O" = 5 mils at 120°

Illustration #121 - Plot Run "O"

Single Plane - Vector (cont'd)

Step 6: Plot a vector to represent run number two (run "O+T", 6.4 mils at 40 degrees) on the polar graph paper.

Step 7: Draw in vector "T" by connecting vectors "O" and "O + T". See illustration #123.

Measure and record the length of "T" using the same scale that was used for the vectors drawn previously. It was found to be 7.3 mils.

Also measure the angle (θ) between "T" and "O". This was 58°.

Check the direction of the phase shift from "O". In this example it was anticlockwise.

Step 8: Calculate the required balance weight by using the following formula.

Balance Weight = Trial Weight x "O"/"T"

Balance Weight = 10 grams x 5/7.3

= 6.8 grams.

This is the weight required to balance the rotor.

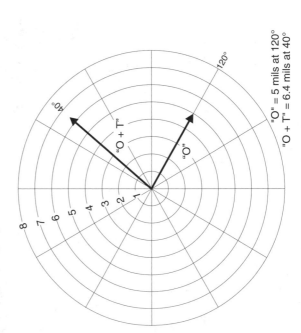

"O" = 5 mils at 120°
"O + T" = 6.4 mils at 40°

Illustration #122 - Run "O+T"

EQUIPMENT BALANCING

Single Plane - Vector (cont'd)

The angle (θ) is the angular distance that the balance weight has to be placed from the trial weight but in the opposite direction to the phase shift.

Remove the trial weight and place the balance weight of 6.8 grams, 58° from the trial weight position measured in a clockwise direction.

The balance weight must be placed at the same radius as the trial weight.

The rotor should now be balanced. Run the rotor to see if the balancing was successful. If the vibration needs be reduced further, the procedure can be repeated.

Step 10: To repeat the procedure, use the same polar graph paper on which the original calculations were made, and also the original run "O". Consider the 6.8 gram balance weight to be the new trial weight.

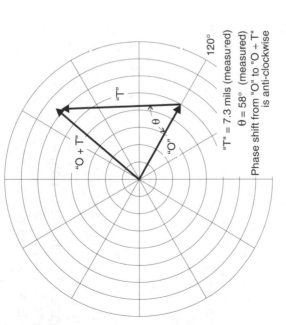

"T" = 7.3 mils (measured)
θ = 58° (measured)
Phase shift from "O" to "O + T"
is anti-clockwise

Illustration #123 - Plot Vector "T"

Step 9: Illustration #123 shows that the shift in phase from "O" to "O + T" was in an anti-clockwise direction.

240   EQUIPMENT BALANCING

Single Plane - Vector (cont'd)

Assume that the new "O + T" (after balancing) was found to be 1 mil at 260°. Draw this on the graph paper as shown in illustration #124.

From the graph (illustration #124) measure the "T_{new}" and θ_{new}. They are found to be 5.8 mils and 7° respectively. As before, the new balance weight and its location can be determined.

New balance wt. = Trial weight x "O"/"T_{new}"

$\qquad = 6.8 \times 5/5.8 = 5.9$ grams

Because the phase shift from "O" to "O + T_{new}" was clockwise and the new angle (θ) was 7°, then the new balance weight is placed 7° from the old balance weight measured in an anti-clockwise direction. The old balance weight of 6.8 grams is removed.

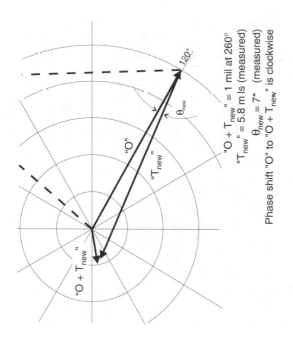

"O + T_{new} " = 1 mil at 260°
"T_{new} " = 5.8 m ls (measured)
$\theta_{new} = 7°$ (measured)

Phase shift "O" to "O + T_{new}" is clockwise

Illustration #124 - Repeat Balance

Single Plane (cont'd)

Balancing in One Run

After a machine or rotor has been balanced, it is possible (and may be beneficial) to balance it, or a similar machine, in one run.

To be able to balance on one run, two pieces of information are required.

1. Flash angle

2. The rotors sensitivity to unbalance

1. Flash Angle: The flash angle consists of mechanical lag, electrical lag and strobe lag. Using the previous example, the phase of the original reading "O" was 120°.

Rotate the rotor so that the phase marker on the end of the shaft is at 120° and note the location of the balance weight. See illustration #125. The heavy spot that caused the vibration is 180° from the balance weight.

The angle from the pickup to the heavy spot, measured in the direction of rotation, is the flash angle.

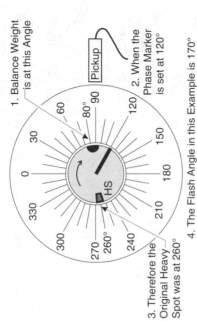

1. Balance Weight is at this Angle

2. When the Phase Marker is set at 120°

3. Therefore the Original Heavy Spot was at 260°

4. The Flash Angle in this Example is 170°

Illustration #125 - Determining the Flash Angle

In this example, with the reference mark positioned at 120°, the balance weight is at 80°. The original heavy spot will be exactly 180° away from the balance weight location, placing it at 260°.

Single Plane - One Run (cont'd)

The pickup was positioned at 90°, therefore the flash angle is 260 - 90 = 170°. On this rotor the heavy spot will always be 170° past the pickup in the direction of rotation.

Note: The reference mark has nothing to do with the flash angle, as it is just an arbitrary mark placed anywhere on the rotor.

2. Rotor Sensitivity: The rotor's sensitivity to unbalance is also obtained from the information taken during balancing.

In the previous example, the original amplitude from the unbalance "O" was 5 mils and to correct this unbalance required 5.9 grams. The sensitivity of this particular rotor to weight changes is therefore 5.9 grams / 5 mils = 1.18 grams/mil at the same radius that was used for the previous balance.

If this rotor later requires rebalancing, then using the same vibration instruments and knowing the flash angle and the sensitivity to weight changes, balancing can be accomplished using only one run.

The following steps are a procedure for balancing in one run. The set up of the instruments must be the same as when the flash angle and sensitivity were calculated.

1. Install a degree card and mark a reference line on the rotor or shaft. Run the machine and record the amplitude and phase of the vibration. For this example assume a displacement of 3.5 mils at 340°.

2. Stop the machine and turn the shaft to position the reference mark at 340°. See illustration #126. With the shaft in this position we know that the flash angle is 170° and that the heavy spot will be 170° away from the pickup location, measured in the direction of rotation. This locates the heavy spot at 260°.

EQUIPMENT BALANCING

Single Plane - One Run (cont'd)

The balance weight has to be placed exactly 180° away from the heavy spot, which will put it at 80°, which is 100° away from the reference mark in a clockwise direction.

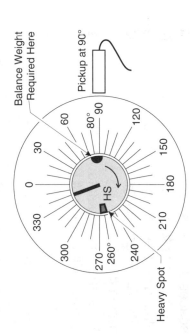

Illustration #126 - Locate the Heavy Spot

3. The amount of weight for balance is calculated, the unbalance displacement is 3.5 mils and the sensitivity is 1.18 grams per mil. The balance weight required is 3.5 x 1.18 = 4.13 grams

Four Run Method

The four run method is a way of single plane balancing without using phase readings. It is often used on cooling tower fans, flywheels and other low speed devices that can be balanced in the single plane, with a minimal amount of equipment.

As this method does not use phase angles, and the vibration measuring instrument does not require a strobe attachment, a simple hand held vibration meter will be adequate. A compass is needed for drawing circles .

Cooling Fan Balance Example:

If the machine is running, take a vibration reading in displacement or velocity mode. Record this reading as run 0 (zero). It is assumed there is a suitable safe place to position the pickup, and that the vibration of the fan is high enough to consider balancing. Shut off the machine and check the rotor for a suitable place to attach weights in three places, as close to 120° apart as possible. Note the angles.

Single Plane - Four Run (cont'd)

Note: The angles between the three points need not be exactly 120 degrees, but the exact angle must be determined.

The fan in this example has six blades which spaces the blades 60 degrees apart (360°/6 = 60°). It is found that trial weights can be placed on the end of the fan blades. Therefore "A" "B" and "C" will be as shown in illustration #127.

Mark the three points "A" "B" and "C" as shown in illustration #127.

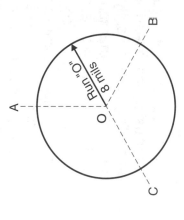

Illustration #127 - Fan Showing Weight Attachment Points

Balancing Methods

If necessary, make any changes (such as cleaning dirt build-up from the blades) then take run 0 again.

If for example, run "0" is 8 mils, draw a circle with a radius to represent the 8 mils.
Mark the three points "A" "B" and "C" on this circle, with "A" at 0 degrees and "B" and "C" at angles that were determined when inspecting the rotor. See illustration #128.

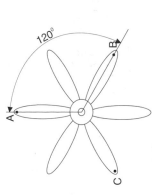

Illustration #128 - Run 0 Showing Points A B & C

EQUIPMENT BALANCING

Single Plane - Four Run (cont'd)

Attach a suitable trial weight to point "A" on the fan. See page 225 on How Much Trial Weight. For this example, it is calculated as 4 ounces. Run the fan back up to speed and take another vibration reading, which will be called run "A". In this example run "A" was 14 mils.

On the graph paper at point "A" draw a circle with a radius that represents 14 mils using the same scale as when run "O" was plotted. See illustration #129.

Stop the fan and move the trial weight from position "A" to position "B". Run the fan and take a vibration reading. This will be run "B". In this example run "B" = 3.6 mils.

Stop the fan again, move the trial weight to position "C", run the fan and take reading "C". In this example run "C" = 17 mils.

Runs "B" and "C" can now be plotted similarly to run "A". See illustration #130. Remember the scale has to be the same for all 4 runs when plotting this graph.

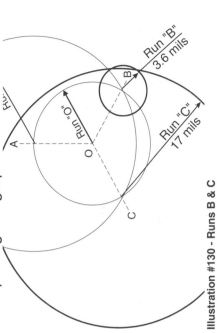

Illustration #130 - Runs B & C

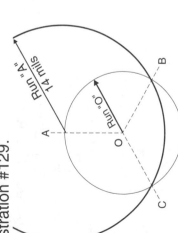

Illustration #129 - Run A

Single Plane - Four Run (cont'd)

The amount of balance weight and location, is found from this graph (illustration #131). Notice that at some point the three circles "A", "B" and "C" intersect at a common point, referred to as "D". Draw a line from the center of the original circle to point "D". This line indicates the position of the balance weight that is required. If O-A is at zero degrees then measure the angle A-O-D to find the required angle of the balance weight. In this example it is 101 degrees.

To find the required amount of balance weight, multiply the trial weight with a balance factor. The balance factor equals run "O" divided by length O - D. This balance weight, to be placed at the same radius as the trial weight is positioned at 101 degrees from O - A.

To calculate the Balance Weight (BW) required to balance the fan:

BW = Trial Weight x (run"O" / length O - D)

In this example the trial weight was 4 ounces, run "O" was 8 mils and length O - D measures 10.2 mils.

BW = 4 x (8/10.2) = 3.12 ounces

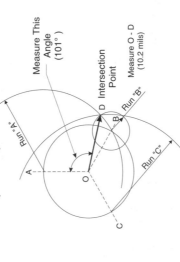

Illustration #131 - Determining the Angle

As there is no fan blade at 101 degrees from "A" the calculated correction weight will have to be divided up between two fan blades that are adjacent to 101 degrees. For more information on this, see Dividing a Calculated Balance Weight on page 254.

EQUIPMENT BALANCING

Two Plane - Cross Effect

Balancing in two planes to solve dynamic un-balance problems is somewhat more complex than single plane balancing. The main reason for this is the effect of the unbalance on one side or plane of the rotor effecting the amplitude and phase at the other side or plane. This is usually referred to as the "cross effect" or "correction plane interference".

Illustration #132 shows a well balanced rotor.

Any weight changes that are made to plane "A" will produce a significant change in the amplitude of vibration at bearing "A" and a much smaller change in amplitude at bearing "B". The phase angle of the vibration produced at bearing "B" will not be the same as that at bearing "A".

Similarly any weight changes made at plane "B" will also produce vibration changes at both ends, bearing "B" being effected more than bearing "A".

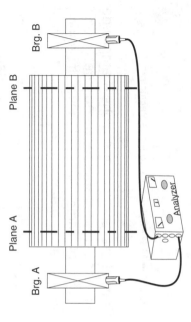

Illustration #132 - Balanced Rotor

Any amplitude and phase readings taken at bearing "A" are not only due to the unbalance at that end, but also due to the cross effect of any unbalance at the opposite end. Similarly any unbalance readings at bearing "B" are due to the unbalance close to "B" plus the cross effect from the other end.

When starting to balance it is impossible to know what the cross effect will do to the phase and amplitude readings at each end.

Balancing Methods

Two Plane - Cross Effect (cont'd)

The amount of cross effect will vary with different rotors. The rotor shown in illustration #132 will probably have much less cross effect than the rotor shown in illustration #133.

Illustration #133 - Rotor with Large Cross Effect

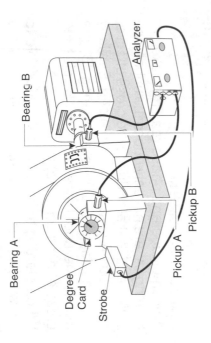

Brg. A   Plane   Plane   Brg. B
            A   B

Separate Single Plane Solutions

This method is probably the simplest, and will work for most cases. Each plane is individually treated as a single plane problem.

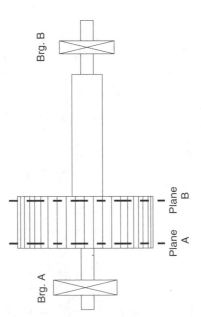

Illustration #134 - Setup for Two Plane Balancing

Start at the end with the highest amplitude readings and balance using the vector method of single plane balancing. If bearing "A" is being balanced first, then the trial weight and resulting balance weight is placed in a suitable location as close to bearing "A" as possible. This will be Plane "A".

EQUIPMENT BALANCING

Two Plane - Single Plane Solutions (cont'd)

Then balance the other end (using bearing "B" and plane "B") again using single plane methods. Plane "B" will be as close as possible to bearing "B".

Recheck the amplitude at bearing "A" as the cross effect of the balance weights applied to the plane "B" will have affected these readings. The amplitude readings should be much lower than they were originally and this end can be balanced again if the amplitude is not low enough.

Each time any changes are made at one end the other end has to be checked to see if the cross effect was enough to require it to be balanced.

Note: Depending on how much cross effect there is on a particular machine the balance procedure will have to be performed several times on each end to achieve a satisfactory balance.

Two Plane Vector Calculations

This method completes a two plane balance in only three balancing runs. Run one, original unbalance and phase readings are taken for both ends. Run two, a trial weight is placed at one end and unbalance and phase readings are again taken for both ends. Run three, the first trial weight is taken off and another one placed on the other end. Phase and vibration readings are again taken for both ends.

This information can be used to calculate or draw vectors to find out what balance weights are required and the relative angle to place them.

Note: The procedure for this is quite involved and is usually dealt with on balancing courses offered by technical colleges and various vibration equipment manufacturers. Computer programs are available and many vibration analyzers are programmed to perform this type of balancing.

Balancing Methods

Two Plane - Overhung Rotors

Many pumps, blowers and fans have rotors that are mounted outboard of the two support bearings, as shown in illustration #135.

If the length to diameter ratio of the rotor is considerably less than 0.5 (see illustration #119 on page 235), then it may only be necessary to correct for a static unbalance in one plane only.

If the length to diameter ratio is substantially greater than 0.5, then balancing will probably have to be carried out in two planes (planes "A" and "B" in illustration #135). One simple procedure is described as follows:

Step 1: Using the single plane vector method, balance the rotor in plane "A" using the vibration readings at bearing "A".

Step 2: Check the vibration at bearing "B". If it is not acceptable, balance for the vibration in plane "B" using the single plane vector method.

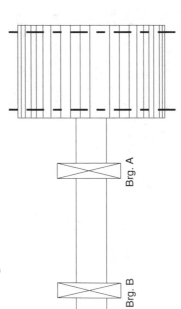

Illustration #135 - Overhung Rotor

This type of rotor can cause difficulty when balancing in two planes using the separate single plane solutions, because of the large cross effect of any changes to the weight distribution of the rotor.

EQUIPMENT BALANCING

Two Plane - Overhung Rotors (cont'd)

Note: Any weight added to plane "B" will alter the balance achieved in plane "A". To counteract this, a weight equal to any trial weight or balance weight that is added to plane "B" has to be also added to plane "A", located 180° from it. See Illustration #136.

When placing the trial weight in plane "B" during the balancing in this plane, place an equal weight 180° away from this in plane "A" as shown in illustration #136.

Draw the vectors and calculate the amount of weight and the phase of the required balance weight at plane "B".   Remove both trial weights and place the balance weight in plane "B", and also place an equal weight in plane "A" 180° from the balance weight in plane "B".

Step 3: Recheck the vibration at bearing "A" to ensure that it is still acceptable. If it is not, then rebalance in plane "A" using the same single plane method as before. After this is done, recheck at bearing "B" and if necessary rebalance plane "B".

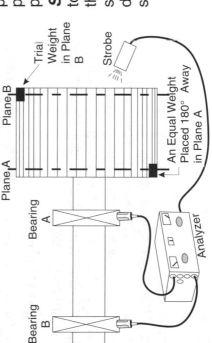

Illustration #136 - Trial Weights 180° apart

Multi-Plane Balancing

Some complex flexible rotors may require balancing in more than two planes. It is beyond the scope of this chapter to adequately cover this type of balancing. Multi-plane balancing is usually accomplished using computer software supplied with the many vibration analysis and balancing instruments that are available.

Weight Changes

Some discussion was already made on adding weights under the section on Attaching Trial Weights. When the amount of weight for completing the balancing operation has been calculated, then one of two procedures is performed. Either weight is added to the rotor in the position calculated, or weight is removed 180° from the position the balance weight was to be added, and at the same radius. See table #12 for the density of some common materials.

Multi-Plane Balancing/Weight Changes

When attaching the balance weights a semi-permanent method will be used. Some of the more common methods are as follows:

Bolting: This may involve drilling and tapping into the rotor if a suitable position is available. Note that if a hole is drilled and not completely filled by the bolt then that amount of metal should be taken into account and added to the calculated balance weight. The weight of the bolt head and any washers used should be part of the calculated balance weight.

Welding-Soldering-Brazing: Steel or lead weights may be attached by one of these methods.

Epoxy Resins: Pieces of lead or steel may be glued to the rotor with epoxy, or leaded epoxy may be used.

Removing Weight

On some rotors the easiest method of changing the weight distribution is not by adding weight, but by removing it.

Weight Changes (cont'd)

Weight removal is accomplished either by drilling holes, or by milling, grinding or shaping. Metal is removed 180° from where the weight addition was calculated and at the same radius.

The density of the material will determine how much material has to be removed to accomplish a given weight change.

With the milling, grinding or shaping method it can be quite difficult to calculate the actual volume of material removed. Although it may be possible to weigh the material removed periodically to achieve the desired amount. Drilling is probably the most accurate method as the exact diameter of the hole is known and the depth is easily monitored.

Care must be taken not to weaken, or destroy any flow characteristics of the part being worked on. Metal removal may also cause premature corrosion or erosion or be a source of buildup. It is advisable to consult the manufacturer on this.

Common Metal Densities		
	oz/in^3	g/cm^3
Lead	6.53	11.30
Copper	5.14	8.89
Brass	4.88	8.45
Steel	4.53	7.84
Cast Iron	4.19	7.25
Aluminum	1.62	2.80

Table #12 - Metal Densities

Changing the Radius of Balance Weights

After using a certain location for the trial weights to balance a rotor it may be found that the radius that was used is not suitable for the permanent balance weight. A simple formula is used to recalculate the balance weight required if the radius has to be changed.

$$\text{Weight}_1 \times \text{Radius}_1 = \text{Weight}_2 \times \text{Radius}_2$$

Weight Changes (cont'd)

For example, if it was found that to balance a machine, a 35 gram weight is required at a radius of 40 cm and the best radius for the permanent balance weight is 62 cm, then using the above formula, the new balance weight is calculated as follows:

$$35 \times 40 = Weight_2 \times 62$$
$$Weight_2 = 35 \times 40 / 62$$
$$Weight_2 = 22.58 \text{ grams.}$$

This weight at a radius of 62 cm will have the same effect on the rotor as 35 grams at a radius of 40 cm.

Dividing a Calculated Balance Weight

It is quite possible that after calculating the amount and location of a balance weight, that it is impossible to place the balance weight in that position. A classic example is the fan that was shown in the Four Run Method on pages 243 to 246.

Weight Changes

As can be seen from illustration #137 there is no fan blade to attach the weight to at the required 101° location. The following will show how the weight can be split into two components and attached to the two blades closest to the required position.

Illustration #137 shows the fan in question with the required location of the 3.12 ounce correction weight.

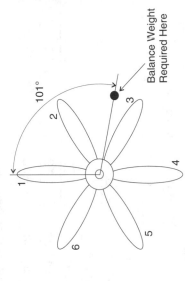

Balance Weight Required Here

Illustration #137 - Fan Requires Balance Weight at 101°

EQUIPMENT BALANCING

Dividing Weight (cont'd)

Using polar graph paper, mark out the angular location of the blades where the weight corrections can be made. See illustration #138.

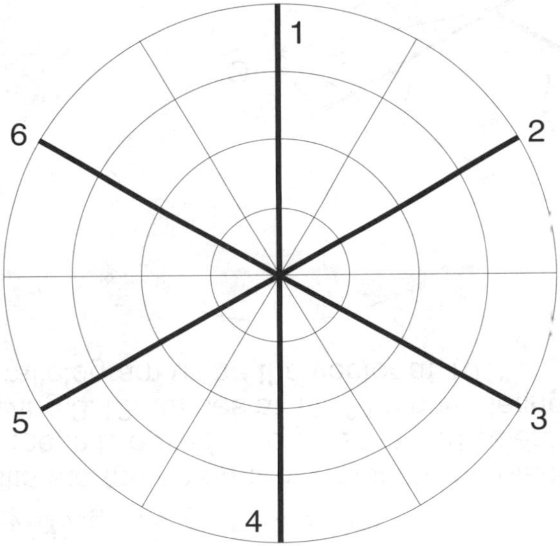

Draw in a vector representing the necessary correction weight at the required angle (illustration #139). The length of the vector will represent the 3.12 ounces required. It can also be seen that 101° falls in between blades 2 and 3.

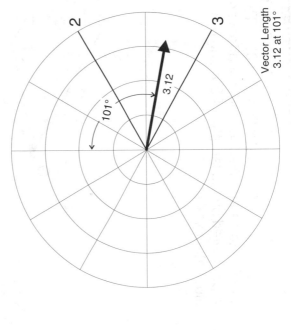

Vector Length
3.12 at 101°

Illustration #139 - Vector Representing Balance Weight

Illustration #138 - Location of Fan Blades

256 EQUIPMENT BALANCING

Dividing Weight (cont'd)

Estimate the amount of weight to be placed on these two blades to give the equivalent of having 3.12 ounces at 101° by completing a parallelogram using the vector at 101°.

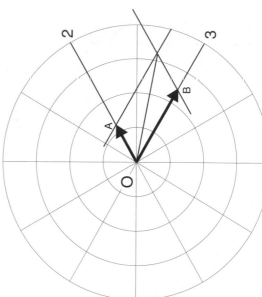

Illustration #140 - Draw Parallelogram

Weight Changes

Draw line x - x parallel to O-3 and line y - y parallel to O-2 (illustration #140). The weights to be attached to blades 2 and 3 are represented by the lengths of 0-A and 0-B in illustration #141.

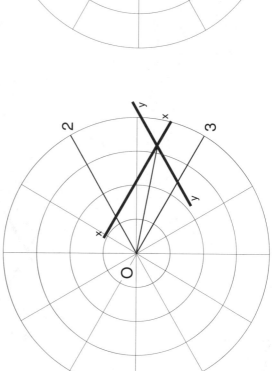

Illustration #141 - Measure Lengths 0-A and O-B

EQUIPMENT BALANCING

Dividing Weight (cont'd)

From illustration #141, 0-A equals 1.2 ounces and 0-B equals 2.4 ounces. Note that these weights have to be placed at the same radius as the original trial weight. If it is required to change the radius of a balance weight see pages 253 and 254 on Changing the Radius of Balance Weights.

Combining Balance Weights

After balancing, a number of balance weights may be attached to the rotor. This may be due to balancing in two planes using the single plane vector method, where two or three runs were done to eliminate cross effect.

Note: Any number of balance weights can be combined and represented by a single weight.

Assume three separate weights were used on the rotor shown in illustration #142.

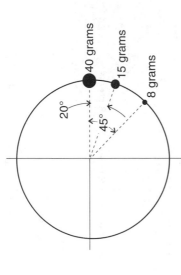

Illustration #142 - Rotor with Three Balance Weights

Draw a vector representing the largest weight as shown in illustration #143. From the end of this vector, draw another vector representing the next size of weight, at the same angle relative to the first vector shown in illustration #144.

Combining Weights (cont'd)

40 grams at 90°

Illustration #143 - Vector Representing 40 grams

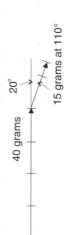

40 grams   20°

15 grams at 110°

Illustration #144 - Vector of 40 + 15 grams

Draw in the third vector from the end of the second, again with a length that represents the weight and at the correct angle relative to the first weight (illustration #145).

Complete the vector diagram with the resultant vector length representing the required amount of the replacement weight and it's angle relative to the largest of the three balance weights (illustration #146).

Weight Changes

The three original balance weights can be removed and replaced with this single replacement balance weight.

Note: It must be placed in the correct angular position relative to the first weight used in the vector diagrams and be at the same radius as the weights it is replacing.

45°

8 grams at 135°

Illustration #145 - Vectors 40 + 15 + 8 grams

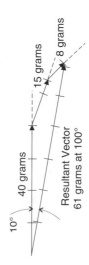

10°

40 grams

15 grams

8 grams

Resultant Vector
61 grams at 100°

Illustration #146 - Vector Combination

EQUIPMENT BALANCING

Balancing Tolerances

Attempting to obtain perfect balance every time balancing is performed would often be a waste of time and money. However, with some rotors and machines it would be false economy to leave the residual balance too high. If the residual unbalance or operating vibration level has not been specified then consultation with manufacturers, experience and application of recognized standards will help in deciding whether or not the level of vibration, or the residual unbalance for a particular machine or rotor is acceptable.

When in-place balancing has been performed, or a newly assembled machine is test run, the level of vibration that is acceptable when it is at operating speeds will normally be specified. The amplitude of vibration (either displacement or velocity measurement) is usually the criteria used to determine whether or not the machine is "balanced".

The level of vibration that is acceptable may be obtained from standards published by various engineering organizations (API, ISO, Hydraulics Institute, etc.), equipment manufacturers, or from past balancing experience at the plant. If guidelines are not available, then vibration severity charts may be of use. See Section Two of this book for examples.

When severity charts or tolerance formulae are used, be sure to note where the vibration is to be measured. It is often at the bearing supports or housings, but may also be specified as the relative shaft vibration which would be measured using non-contact pickups. Note also if the vibration readings are to be filtered or unfiltered readings.

When parts or rotors are balanced on a balancing machine the maximum amount of residual unbalance is usually specified.

Balancing Tolerances (cont'd)

Residual unbalance may be measured in ounce-inches, gram-inches or gram-millimetres depending on the units of measurement.

If the balancing machine does not give a direct unbalance readout, an accurate determination of the residual unbalance of a rotor can be carried out by using the following procedure.

- Select a test weight (TW) that will increase the amount of vibration approximately 5 to 10 times. Record the amount of vibration and location (0°).

- Attach the same test weight every 30° (45° is sometimes used) around the rotor and record the resulting vibration readings and the corresponding angle.

- On graph paper plot the readings as shown in illustration #147

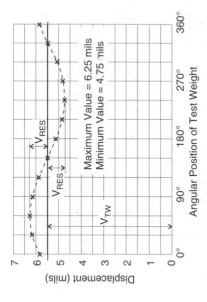

Illustration #147 - Checking Residual Unbalance

- Determine the maximum and minimum values and draw in a line through the mid point.

  V_{TW} is the vibration due to the test weight.

  V_{TW} = (max. value + min. value) / 2

  V_{RES} is the vibration due to the residual unbalance.

  V_{RES} = (max. value - min. value) / 2

EQUIPMENT BALANCING

Balancing Tolerances (cont'd)

The residual unbalance is calculated as follows:

Assume a test weight = 2 ounces
Assume the radius of test weight = 5 inches
From illustration #147:

Vibration due to Residual Unbalance (V_{RES})
V_{RES} = (max. reading - min. reading)/2
= (6.25-4.75)/2 = 0.75 mils

Vibration due to Trial Weight (V_{TW})
V_{TW} = (max. reading + min. reading)/2
= (6.25 + 4.75)/2 = 5.5 mils

Sensitivity (Effect of Test Weight)
= Test Weight unbalance (wt x radius) / V_{TW}
= 2 x 5 ounces-inches / 5.5
= 1.82 oz-in /mil

Residual Unbalance = Sensitivity x V_{RES}

= 1.82 x 0.75
= 1.365 oz-in.

If the rotor has been balanced in two planes, then the same procedure can be carried out for the other plane.

Residual Unbalance Tolerances

To show some typical examples of unbalance tolerances, three American Petroleum Institute (API) standards and one ISO standard are discussed below.

From API 616, 617 and 619 there are two formulae used to calculate maximum residual unbalance for centrifugal compressors, rotary type positive displacement compressors and gas turbines, for refinery service.

API 616 Gas Turbines for General Refinery Services.

API 617 Centrifugal Compressors for General Refinery Services.

These two standards specify a single formula for the maximum residual unbalance per plane, which is:

Residual Tolerances (cont'd)

Balancing Tolerances

Imperial Units:

Maximum residual unbalance (oz-in)

$$U_{max} = 4W/N$$

Where:

W = Journal static load in pounds
N = Maximum continuous speed in RPM

Metric SI Units:

Maximum residual unbalance (gram-mm)

$$U_{max} = 6350 W/N$$

Where:

W = Journal static load in kilograms
N = Maximum continuous speed in RPM

API 619 Rotary Type Positive Displacement Compressors for General Refinery Services

This standard specifies that the maximum residual unbalance is to be the lesser of the following two equations.

Imperial Units:

1. Max. residual unbalance (oz-in)

$$U_{max} = 56347 \ W/N^2$$

2. Max. residual unbalance (oz-in)

$$U_{max} = 4 \ W/N$$

W = Journal static load in pounds
N = Max. continuous speed in RPM

Metric SI Units:

1. Max. residual unbalance (gram-mm)

$$U_{max} = 89 \times 10^6 \ W/N^2$$

2. Max. residual unbalance (gram-mm)

$$U_{max} = 6350 \ W/N$$

W = Journal static load in kilograms
N = Max. continuous speed in RPM

The first equation, gives an unbalance force approximately equal to 10% of the journal load.

The second equation is the same as for API 616 and 617.

EQUIPMENT BALANCING

Residual Tolerances (cont'd)

An example of applying these two formulae is as follows:

A symmetrical rotor weighs 3000 lb., rotates at 3600 RPM and is supported between two bearings. The load in each bearing journal is 1500 lb.

Imperial Units:

1. Max. residual unbalance

   Umax = 56347 W/N^2

   Umax = 56347 x 1500 /3600^2

   Umax = 6.52 oz-in.

2. Max. residual unbalance

   Umax = 4 W/N

   Umax = 4 x 1500 / 3600

   Umax = 1.67 oz-in.

Metric Units:

Note: The same unit has a load of 1500/2.2 = 681.82 kg on each bearing journal.

1. Max. residual unbalance

   Umax = 89 x 10^6 W/N^2

   Umax = 89 x 10^6 x 681.82 /3600^2

   Umax = 4682 gram-mm

2. Max. residual unbalance

   Umax = 6350 W/N

   Umax = 6350 x 681.82 / 3600

   Umax = 1203 gram-mm

Note: The first equation will result in lower residual unbalance requirements than the second equation when rotating speeds become high. With the 3000 lb. rotor the point at which this occurs is around 14500 RPM.

Residual Tolerances (cont'd)

International Standards Organization ISO

ISO provides a set of guidelines for rigid rotors (a rigid rotor has its maximum operating speed at least 70% below first critical speed). This guide takes into account the operating speed and type of equipment being balanced.

The type of machine is identified from table #13 to determine the rotor classification.

The rotor classification is then applied to the chart of recommended balancing tolerances, along with the maximum operating speed (as shown in illustration #148) to give a total allowable residual unbalance range in ounce-inches per 1000 pounds of rotor weight. The upper limits of the range are for rotors installed in rigid heavy frames, the lower limit is for machines with light weight flexible frames.

Balancing Tolerances

	ISO Classification of Rotors
Rotor	Type of machine
G-40	motor car wheels, rims
G-16	rotating and oscillating motor parts, propshafts, parts of crushing machines and agricultural machines.
G-6.3	propshafts with special requirements, centrifugal drums, fans, crankshafts (engines with 4 or more cylinders), flywheels, machine and machine-tool parts, motor armatures.
G-2.5	power turbine rotors, turbo-generator rotors, machine-tool drives, medium and large motor armatures, small armatures.
G-1.0	jet turbines, tape-recorder and gramophone drives, grinder drives, small motor armatures with special requirements.
G-0.4	high precision grinder spindles, gyroscopes.

Table #13 - Classification of Rotors by Machine Type

Note: If the rotor was balanced in two planes then the allowable residual unbalance for each plane is one half of the total.

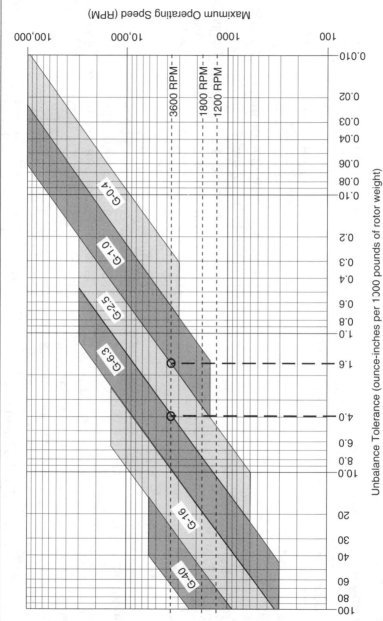

Illustration #148 - Unbalance Tolerance Guide for Rigid Rotors

Residual Tolerances (cont'd)

Using the previous example:

A symmetrical rotor weighs 3000 lb., rotates at 3600 RPM and is supported between two bearings.

Assuming that this is a gas turbine. Determine the rotor classification from table #13. In this example it will be G2.5.

From the unbalance tolerance guide, illustration #148, at 3600 RPM and G2.5 the unbalance tolerance is between 1.6 and 4.0 oz-in per 1000 lb. of rotor weight.

Total Unbalance tolerance

= rotor wt x 10^{-3} x unbalance tolerance

Upper limit = $3000 \times 10^{-3} \times 4.0$

= 12.0 oz-in.

Lower limit = $3000 \times 10^{-3} \times 1.6 = 4.8$ oz-in.

If this rotor was balanced in two planes then the maximum residual unbalance would be one half the above amounts for each plane

Upper limit = 12.0/2 = 6.0 oz-in.

Lower limit = 4.8/2 = 2.4 oz-in

Conclusion

Comparing the API standards shown, the API 619 will always have an equal or lower residual tolerance than the API 616 & 617. This is especially true on very high speed rotors. The API has separate standards for various types of machines and residual unbalance is only one of many requirements that are to be followed.

The ISO standard is unique in that it gives residual unbalance standards for machines based on their general type. Note that the ISO standard is for rigid rotors only.

Obtain and consult any specific standards for the rotor or machine being balanced to ensure that all requirements are met. If standards have not been specified, these guide lines will establish a starting point. When first establishing limits it is preferable to err towards the lower limits, although quality and type of bearings, or accuracy of the balancing machine may be the limiting factor when very low balancing tolerances are attempted.

SECTION FOUR QUESTIONS

Balancing

1. If the vibration levels of an operating machine were to suddenly increase and no operating or maintenance changes were made, the probable cause would be:

   ☐ worn bearing
   ☐ worn coupling
   ☐ a rotating part broken off
   ☐ built up debris broken free
   ☐ both a rotating part broken off and a built up debris broken free

2. Where and when is balancing usually performed?
   Answer: _____

3. If a pump is vibrating due to an unbalance after changing the impellor, would it be preferable to:

   ☐ perform "in-place" balancing
   ☐ remove the impellor and balance it on a balancing machine

4. Is it possible to perform in place balancing using a hand held vibration meter that does not measure phase?

   ☐ yes   ☐ no

5. List the three tasks that must be possible to allow balancing to be completed "in place".
   Answer: _____

6. What causes the vibration when an unbalanced rotor is rotated?
   Answer: _____

7. A weight of 3 ounces is placed at 15 inches radius on a rotor that is to rotate at 900 RPM. What centrifugal force (pounds) will be produced by the weight?
   Answer: _____

8. A weight of 80 grams is placed at 68 mm radius on a rotor that is to rotate at 1200 RPM. What centrifugal force (newtons) will be produced by the weight?
   Answer: _____

9. A weight of 80 grams is placed at 15 inches radius on a rotor that is to rotate at 1800 RPM. What centrifugal force (pounds) will be produced by the weight?

Answer: _____

10. If a hub weighing 34 pounds was mounted off center 0.013 inches, what amount of unbalance in ounce-inches would be the result?

Answer: _____

11. A welding repair to the outside of a fan blade caused a weight increase of 95 grams at a radius of 1.5 m. What would be the resulting unbalance in gram-mm?

Answer: _____

12. A 120 gram piece of a pump impellor was broken off at 23 inches radius. What would be the resulting unbalance in gram-inches?

Answer: _____

13. A 2 ounce trial weight is located at a radius of 27 inches on a rotor. To replace this trial weight with one that will have an equal effect at 11 inches radius. what magnitude will the new trial weight be?

Answer: _____

14. A 2 ounce trial weight is located at a radius of 420 mm on a rotor. To replace this trial weight with one that will have an equal effect at 142 mm radius, what magnitude will the new trial weight be?

Answer: _____

15. A 75 gram trial weight is located at a radius of 280 mm on a rotor. To replace this trial weight with one that will have an equal effect at 182 mm radius, what magnitude will the new trial weight be?

Answer: _____

16. A rotor having a static unbalance can be balanced in one plane only.

☐ true   ☐ false

17. A rotor having a couple unbalance can be balanced in one plane only.

☐ true   ☐ false

18. A rotor having a dynamic unbalance can be balanced in one plane only.

☐ true   ☐ false

19. Phase readings taken at each end of a rotor that has a couple unbalance would be 180° apart.

☐ true   ☐ false

20. Phase readings taken on each end of a rotor that has a static unbalance would be:

☐ the same   ☐ 90° apart
☐ 180° apart   ☐ 270° apart
☐ none of the above

21. Phase readings taken on each end of a rotor that has a dynamic unbalance would always be:

☐ the same   ☐ 90° apart
☐ 180° apart   ☐ 270° apart
☐ none of the above

22. The speed at which there is an increase in vibration due to the unbalance forces exciting the rotor at its natural frequency is known as the _____.

Answer: _____

23. The natural frequency of a rotor would depend on the method of exitation:

☐ true   ☐ false

24. If the stiffness of a rotor were increased, the natural frequency would be:

☐ higher   ☐ lower

25. If mass were added to a rotor without changing the stiffness, the natural frequency would be:

☐ higher   ☐ lower

26. A critical speed would be reached when the rotating speed coincided with the natural frequency of the rotor.

☐ true　　　☐ false

27. A rotating machine may have a number of critical speeds.

☐ true　　　☐ false

28. A rotor is considered "rigid" if it is operated at a speed between its first and second critical speed.

☐ true　　　☐ false

29. It is only the rotating parts on a machine that will have natural frequencies.

☐ true　　　☐ false

30. What three items of information are required to calculate the magnitude of a suitable trial weight?

Answer: _____

31. When adding a trial weight to a rotor, what amount of centrifugal force should the trial weight generate (relative to the weight supported by the bearing)?

☐ 5%　　　☐ 10%
☐ 15%　　　☐ 20%

32. A rotor weighs 2200 pounds and is equally supported on two bearings. The rotating speed is to be 1200 RPM. Calculate a suitable trial weight in ounces if the radius of the trial weight location is 18 inches:

Answer: _____

33. A rotor has a mass of 420 kg. What downward force is produced by this mass due to gravity?

☐ 2812 N　　　☐ 420 N
☐ 42000 N　　　☐ 4116 N

34. A rotor has a mass of 824 kg and is equally supported on two bearings. The rotating speed is 1725 RPM. Calculate a suitable trial weight in grams if the radius of the trial weight location is 400 mm.

Answer: _____

35. The distance that the heavy spot moves past the pick-up before the flash occurs is known as the _____.

Answer: _____

36. What would be the effect of placing a trial weight on a rotor if the trial weight is smaller in magnitude than the original heavy spot, and if it is located 180° from the original heavy spot?

☐ there would be an increase in vibration amplitude and a 180° phase shift

☐ there would be a decrease in vibration amplitude and a 180° phase shift

☐ there would be an increase in vibration amplitude and no phase shift

☐ there would be a decrease in vibration amplitude and no phase shift

37. What would be the effect of placing a trial weight on a rotor if the trial weight is larger in magnitude than the original heavy spot, and it is located 180° from the original heavy spot?

☐ there will be 180° change in phase angle

☐ there will be no phase angle change

38. The phase angle moves in the same direction that the unbalance is moved when positioning the balance weight.

☐ true   ☐ false

39. The amplitude of vibration is proportional to the amount of unbalance.

☐ true   ☐ false

40. If there is a build up of dirt or product on a rotor, it should be left in place when balancing so that the initial vibration readings are unchanged.

☐ true   ☐ false

41. The reason that the speed of rotation should not be close to a critical speed while balancing is:

☐ a minor change in speed will cause a larger change in phase angle

☐ the vibration amplitude will be at a minimum

☐ it is not possible to obtain displacement measurements at the critical speed

☐ any velocity measurements taken will be inaccurate

42. When rotating speed passes a critical speed the phase angle would make a _____ degree shift:

☐ 45   ☐ 90

☐ 180   ☐ 270

43. If a rotor had a length to diameter ratio of 0.3 and the operational speed was 900 RPM, it could be balanced using single plane balancing.

☐ true   ☐ false

44. A rotor has a length of 7 feet, a diameter of 1 foot, and a first critical speed of 2400 RPM. If its operating speed were 1400 RPM, the least number of planes to select for balancing would be:

☐ single plane balance
☐ two plane balance
☐ multiplane balance

45. The following readings were taken when doing a single plane balance on a rotor using the vector method:
   Run "O" = 4 mils at 320°
   A trial weight of 75 grams is attached
   Run "O + T" = 7 mils at 230°
   Plot these two runs on polar graph paper. Calculate the required balance weight and its position relative to the trial weight position.
   Answer: _____

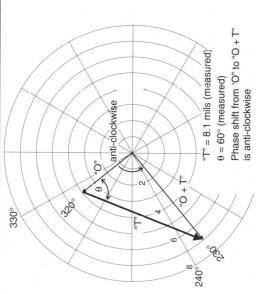

"T" = 8.1 mils (measured)
θ = 60° (measured)
Phase shift from "O" to "O + T" is anti-clockwise

46. After balancing question #45, a third run was made to check the effectiveness of the balancing. The vibration was found to be 1 mil at 10° ("O + Tnew"). Using the original run "O" of 4 mils at 320°, calculate the new balance weight and location.

Answer: _____

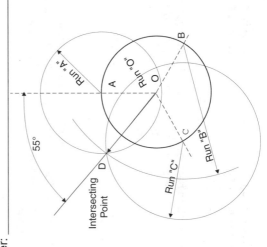

"Tnew" = 3.5 mils (measured)

θnew = 13° (measured)

Phase shift from "O" to "O + Tnew" is clockwise

47. What two items of information are required to be able to balance in one run?

Answer: _____

48. A fan is to be balanced using the 4 run method. There are 6 blades spaced 60° apart. Points A, B, and C will be 120° apart. A 100 gram trial weight is used. The following readings were taken as the trial weight was consecutively placed on A, B, and C:

Run "O" = 10 mils; Run "A" = 12 mils; Run "B" = 24 mils; Run "C" = 14 mils

Construct a diagram showing all 4 runs and calculate the amount and location of the balance weight required.

Answer: _____

49. In the illustration shown, a trial weight is placed on plane A. This would only have an effect on the amplitude and phase at bearing A. Bearing B would not be effected.

☐ true   ☐ false

50. The amount of cross effect that occurs when a balance weight is placed at one end of a rotor will be the same for all rotors.

☐ true   ☐ false

51. When two plane balancing a rotor as shown in question 49, using separate single plane solutions, the end with the largest amount of vibration would be balanced first.

☐ true   ☐ false

52. It is not possible to balance an overhung rotor using separate single plane solutions.

☐ true   ☐ false

53. If it is impractical to add weight to a certain location on a rotor, the same effect can be achieved by removing the same amount of weight _____ away from that location:

☐ 90°
☐ 180°
☐ 270°
☐ 360°

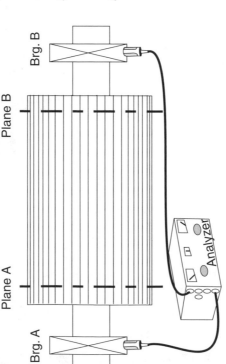

Plane A   Plane B

Brg. A   Brg. B

Analyzer

54. It is has been calculated that a balance weight of 70 grams is required at 290° at a 20 inch radius on a rotor. It is impossible to add weight at this location, but weight can be added at 270° and 300° at the same radius. What replacement weights are required at these two locations?

Answer: _____

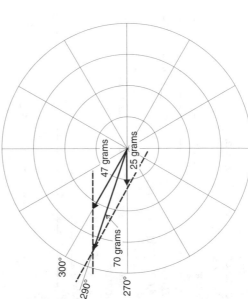

55. Three weights are added to a rotor as shown in the illustration. Using a vector diagram, estimate the single weight that can be used to replace these weights.

Answer: _____

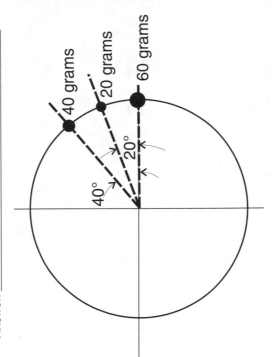

56. What will be the maximum residual unbalance of a 2400 pound rotor, that runs on two equally loaded bearings at 3600 RPM, if the maximum residual unbalance is to be the lesser of the two following equations:

1. $U_{max} = 4$ W/N   2. $U_{max} = 56347$ W/N²

Answer: _____

57. A 700 kg rotor, equally supported on two bearings, runs at 4,000 RPM. Calculate the maximum residual unbalance in gram-mm. The maximum residual unbalance is to be the lesser of the following two equations

1. $U_{max} = 6350$ W/N   2. $U_{max} = 89 \times 10^6$ W/N²

Answer: _____

58. A power turbine rotor supported by two bearings, runs at 3600 RPM, weighs 4000 pounds and is to be balanced in two planes. Using table #13 and illustration #148 what is the maximum residual unbalance per plane? Assume the machine has a heavy rigid frame (use the upper limit).

Answer: _____

SECTION FIVE

LUBRICATION PRINCIPLES AND ANALYSIS

Introduction

Lubrication is used in rotating equipment to reduce the effects of friction between mating parts, to prevent wear and corrosion, and to guard against solid and liquid contamination. The lubricant is required to form a film between the rolling and sliding surfaces of bearings and gears to prevent metal contact even under heavy loads and high speeds.

This section of the book will discuss the basic principles of lubrication and lubrication analysis, as they pertain to common rotating equipment parts and components. As friction and anti-friction bearings form the primary means for supporting the loads of most rotating machines, the main focus of this section will be on lubrication principles and analysis of bearings.

Lubrication Functions

The main function of any lubricant, whether grease or oil, is:

a. To form a film between mating components, such as bearings and gears, which move relative to one another, so that metal contact is prevented. The film must be sufficiently thick in order to prevent contact, even under conditions of heavy load, high speed, and high and low temperature extremes; and variations in machinery vibration.

b. To reduce the effects of friction and eliminate unnecessary wear.

c. To protect against the adverse effects of corrosion.

d. To seal the rotating equipment's components from contaminants, such as dirt, dust, water or other liquids.

e. To cool moving parts, by directing the heat transfer from friction and operations, through the lubricant to other parts of the system.

If a lubricant is to fulfill these primary functions, it should meet the following basic requirements:

Lubrication Functions (cont'd)

- Maintain a protective film on moving parts.
- Resist high temperatures and remain effective in extreme cold temperatures.
- Resist corrosion and rust.
- Prevent moving parts from sticking together.
- Prevent sludge formation.
- Flow easily at low temperatures.
- Prevent foaming and bubbling.
- Resist breakdown after prolonged use.

Lubricant Selection

The selection of a lubricant, whether it is a grease or an oil, depends on four basic conditions:

1. The operating temperature range.
2. The load placed on bearings, gears, etc.
3. The speed of rotation.
4. The type of environment the machine operates in.

Grease lubrication: Is usually selected for applications in which the bearing operates under normal speeds and temperature conditions. The film strengths of grease is particularly important in bearings which operate under heavy load and rotate slowly.

Oil lubrication: Is usually preferred when the speed of rotation or operating temperature makes it impossible to use grease, and when heat has to be removed from the bearing unit by the lubricant.

Friction

Whenever two mating surfaces move against each other, friction is produced. A lubricating fluid is used to separate the two surfaces, and in doing this, friction is reduced. Friction, in excess, causes heat, wear, and reduced efficiency in the machine. However, friction can be useful in rotating equipment, as it is in braking systems, clutches and belt drives. In these cases, lubrication is usually not integral to the operation of these devices.

Friction (cont'd)

Illustration #149 demonstrates how a film of lubricant serves to reduce the friction between two metal parts which are moving relative to each other. The lubricant forms a thin layer between the two moving parts. The lubricant adheres firmly to the surfaces to be separated. When the two parts move relative to one another, the film is exposed to internal shear stresses. The illustration shows how the layers of lubricant are being pulled apart, therefore, friction is required to have the film remain between the two parts. The lubricant must offer some resistance within itself to remain effective in this sliding application.

The friction between two rough mating surfaces is far greater than two polished, flat surfaces. As shown in illustration #150A the two rough metal surfaces are in metal-to-metal contact and any sliding movement would produce friction.

Friction

With the film of lubricant in place, as shown in illustration #150B the metal surfaces are separated, and the only friction is within the fluid itself.

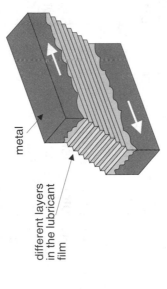

metal

different layers
in the lubricant
film

Illustration #149 - Friction Between Layers

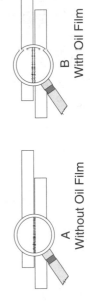

A
Without Oil Film

B
With Oil Film

Illustration #150 - Metal-to-Metal Contact

Friction (cont'd)

Friction is generally defined as being resistance to motion between two surfaces in contact. Two types of friction are common to components of rotating equipment:

1. Sliding friction
2. Rolling friction

Sliding friction exists when two parallel surfaces move relative to each other, as shown in illustrations #149 and #150. Sliding friction is found in journal bearings and gear systems using gear types which are helical, hypoid, spiral bevel, or worm design. The sliding action of the gear tooth is produced by the helix angle the gear tooth is designed to.

Rolling friction exists when parts are designed to roll together on mating surfaces with theoretically no sliding motion. This is the case in the design of anti-friction bearings using roller shapes such as ball, spherical, cylindrical, tapered, or needle.

Spur gear teeth also display some rolling friction at the tooth's pitch line. When the gear teeth are in mesh, there is rolling friction as the two teeth roll together in full mesh at each tooth pitch line. Refer to illustration #151 for types of rolling elements and illustration #152 which demonstrates rolling friction in spur gears.

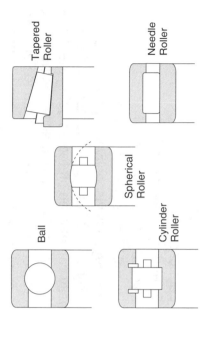

Illustration #151 - Types of Rolling Elements

Friction (cont'd)

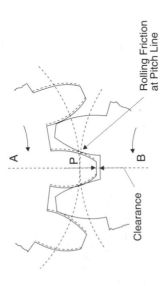

Clearance

A

P

B

Rolling Friction
at Pitch Line

Illustration #152 - Rolling Friction in Spur Gear Mesh

Basic Lubrication Principles

The main function of any lubricant is to form a film which separates the surfaces of the two mating parts in order to reduce friction and wear. There are several important basic principles which one needs to understand when discussing lubrication selection and analysis. The following principles of lubrication will be explained:

Friction/Lubrication Principles

● Viscosity
● Consistency
● Lubricant Film
● Boundary - Layer Lubrication
● Hydrodynamic Lubrication
● Partial Hydrodynamic Lubrication

Viscosity: Oil viscosity is a measure of the fluidity of an oil at a given temperature. Viscosity can also be stated as being the fluid's resistance to flow at a specific temperature. The viscosity must be adequate to separate the moving parts at the operating temperature of the machine. Often oil viscosity is expressed as being either low or high viscosity. When rotating equipment manufacturers recommend a particular viscosity oil, they would determine the normal operating temperature to arrive at the viscosity recommended. Oil becomes thinner or less viscous as it increases in temperature and gets thicker or more viscous as the temperature drops.

Basic Lubrication Principles (cont'd)

If the ambient temperature is quite low, a thinner oil, or low viscosity oil, is needed. If the ambient temperature is high, a thicker, or high viscosity oil, is needed.

For practical reasons, an oil of the lowest viscosity which will retain an unbroken oil film between the surfaces of the two mating parts is the most suitable for purposes of lubrication. This is because a higher viscosity oil than that necessary to maintain the oil film results in a waste of power due to the extra energy required to overcome the internal friction of the oil itself.

Use the following rules-of-thumb for selecting the oil viscosity required for a particular type of equipment.

a. "the lower the temperature, the lighter the oil"

b. "the higher the temperature, the heavier the oil'"

c. "the heavier the load, the heavier the oil"

d. "the lighter the load, the lighter the oil"

e. "the faster the speed, the lighter the oil'"

f. "the slower the speed, the heavier the oil'"

Consistency: Consistency is another fundamental principle of lubrication and is used to define the degree of stiffness which a grease possesses. Consistency of the grease depends on the type and quantity of thickener used, the operating temperature and the type of mechanical conditions the grease has to perform in.

At low temperatures, normal greases become quite stiff so they offer poor lubrication qualities. At high temperatures, many types of greases soften up and provide minimal film between the surfaces of the mating parts.

Basic Lubrication Principles (cont'd)

Lubricant Film: The lubricant film separates the surfaces of two mating parts. The film should be thick enough to do this completely, therefore, the film thickness depends on the smoothness of the surface, the occurrence of foreign contaminants and the required service life. As well, the film thickness depends on the oil's viscosity and on operating conditions, particularly temperature, speed of rotation and load.

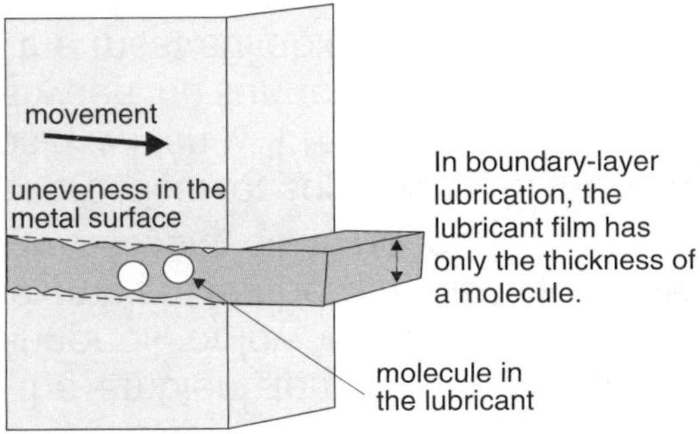

uneveness in the metal surface

movement

In boundary-layer lubrication, the lubricant film has only the thickness of a molecule.

molecule in the lubricant

Illustration #153 - Boundary-Layer Lubrication

Lubrication Principles

Boundary-Layer Lubrication: As shown in illustration #153, boundary-layer lubrication refers to the thickness of the lubricant being approximately the same thickness as individual oil molecules. This condition is present when the quantity of the lubricant is insufficient or the relative movement between the two surfaces is too low. This results in a higher coefficient of friction, therefore, the chances for metal contact are high.

When the coefficient of friction rises, friction losses also increase. There will be a corresponding increase in heat, which raises the lubricant's temperature, thereby reducing its viscosity so that the load-carrying capacity of the film is even lower. The most severe case would have the two surfaces seizing together.

Hydrodynamic (Full Film) Lubrication: Hydrodynamic lubrication, as demonstrated in illustration #154, is obtained when two mating surfaces are completely separated by a cohesive film of lubricant.

LUBRICATION

Basic Lubrication Principles (cont'd)

The thickness of the film thus exceeds the combined unevenness of the surfaces. The coefficient of friction is lower than with boundary-layer lubrication. Hydrodynamic lubrication prevents wear in moving parts, and metal-to-metal contact is prevented.

Partial Hydrodynamic Lubrication: Partial hydrodynamic lubrication or elasto-hydrodynamic lubrication occurs in heavily loaded contact surfaces, for example, surfaces which change their shape under a heavy load and return to their original shape when the load is removed. The contact surfaces have elastic characteristics or are partially loaded for short periods of time.

This occurs in ball bearings. When a ball under load rolls along the raceway of a bearing race, significantly higher pressure occurs at the point of contact. The deflected surfaces are pressed together and flattened out for a very brief moment.

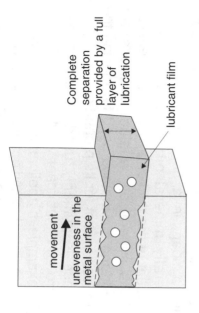

Illustration #154 - Hydrodynamic Lubrication

The condition can be referred to as "elastic deformation." When the ball rolls on, the contact surfaces return to their original shape. The lubricant is almost totally forced away from the point of high pressure contact, almost allowing the two surfaces to come into direct contact with one another.

Basic Lubrication Principles (cont'd)

Surface Finish: Whether the lubrication is boundary-layer, hydrodynamic or partial hydrodynamic, the overall surface finish of the mating parts must be carefully analyzed. In machine component applications where the lubrication operation is hydrodynamic, peak surface variations should be less than the expected minimum film thickness; otherwise, peaks on the surfaces will be in contact with one another. This results in higher friction and temperature increases.

In general, better surface finishes are required for hydrodynamic lubrication, and metal-to-metal contact must be avoided. Also, the harder the material the better the surface finish required. For boundary-layer lubrication applications, the surface finish requirements may be somewhat relaxed since "wear-in" will in time smooth the surface.

As a general guide to the surface finishes required, consider that smooth finishes are needed for harder materials, for high loads, and for high rotational speeds.

The recommended ranges of surface roughness obtained by various finishing methods are identified in table #14.

Grease Lubrication

Lubricating grease is normally a fine dispersion of an oil-insoluble thickening agent, usually a soap, in a fluid lubricant which is generally mineral oil. The nature and amount of the thickener, the characteristics of the mineral oil, whether additives are used, and the method used for making the grease account for its properties.

Grease is primarily used in applications where an oil lubricant would not work well. For example in applications where oil would easily leak out, could not properly seal the lubricated part, and would fall away or not reach the point of application.

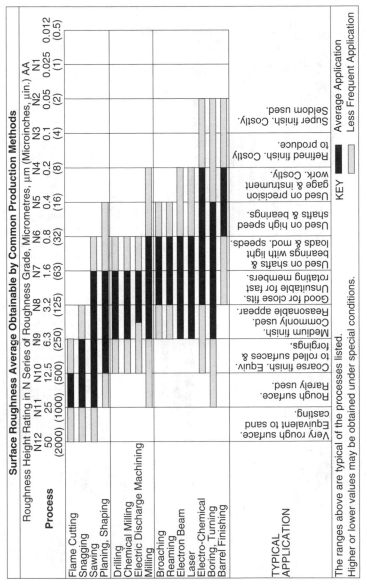

Table #14A - Surface Roughness

Lubrication Principles

Basic Lubrication Principles (cont'd)

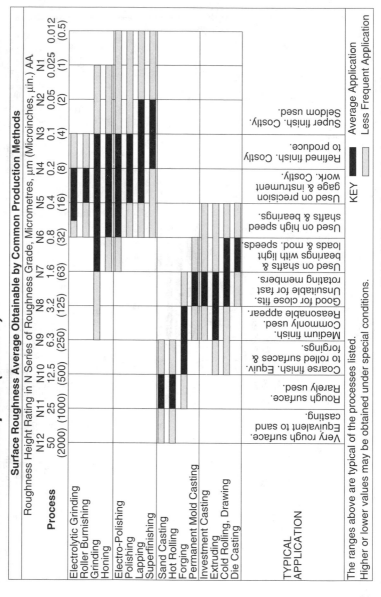

Surface Roughness Average Obtainable by Common Production Methods

Roughness Height Rating in N Series of Roughness Grade, Micrometres, μm (Microinches, μin.) AA

Process	N12 50 (2000)	N11 25 (1000)	N10 12.5 (500)	N9 6.3 (250)	N8 3.2 (125)	N7 1.6 (63)	N6 0.8 (32)	N5 0.4 (16)	N4 0.2 (8)	N3 0.1 (4)	N2 0.05 (2)	N1 0.025 (1)	0.012 (0.5)

Processes listed:
Electrolytic Grinding
Roller Burnishing
Grinding
Honing
Electro-Polishing
Polishing
Lapping
Superfinishing
Sand Casting
Hot Rolling
Forging
Permanent Mold Casting
Investment Casting
Extruding
Cold Rolling, Drawing
Die Casting

TYPICAL APPLICATION

Typical applications (bottom labels):
Very rough surface. Equivalent to sand casting.
Rough surface. Rarely used.
Coarse finish. Equiv. to rolled surfaces & forgings.
Medium finish. Commonly used. Reasonable appear.
Good for close fits.
Unsuitable for fast rotating members.
Used on shafts & bearings with light loads & mod. speeds.
Used on high speed shafts & bearings.
Used on precision gage & instrument work. Costly.
Refined finish. Costly to produce.
Super finish. Costly. Seldom used.

KEY   ■ Average Application   ▨ Less Frequent Application

The ranges above are typical of the processes listed.
Higher or lower values may be obtained under special conditions.

Table #14B - Surface Roughness (cont'd)

Grease Lubrication (cont'd)

The use of grease has certain advantages in the following applications:

a. When grease is used there is a decrease in drippage and splattering, as the grease acts as an additional seal to reduce leakage.

b. Grease is useful for those hard to get to lubrication points.

c. Using grease may decrease the frequency of lubrication application.

d. Grease helps to seal in the lubricant and assists in sealing out contaminants such as water and dirt.

e. In corrosive atmospheres, grease will help seal out damaging corrosives.

f. Grease has the ability to "cling" on to the lubricated part and this is an advantage in any type of intermittent operations where oil would drain away from the part.

g. Grease has the ability to suspend additional solids such as graphite and moly, as do some oils, but generally greases are better at doing this.

Grease Ingredients

A lubricating grease is usually defined as a semi-liquid to a solid dispersion of a thickening agent in a liquid. Grease consists of a mixture of 85-90% mineral or synthetic oil and a thickener. In most types of greases, the thickener is a metallic soap, which is formed when a metal hydroxide reacts with a fatty acid. The thickener functions as a container for the base oil (oil lubricant).

The most common types of grease use a calcium (Ca), sodium (Na), or lithium (Li) soap as a thickener.

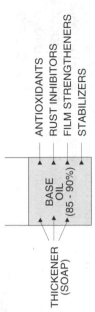

THICKENER (SOAP)

BASE OIL (85 - 90%)

ANTIOXIDANTS
RUST INHIBITORS
FILM STRENGTHENERS
STABILIZERS

Illustration #155 - Lubricating Grease Ingredients

Grease Lubrication (cont'd)

Note: Lithium soap greases are often called multi-purpose greases, and have been found particularly suitable for rolling bearings (anti-friction).

Greases may have several special properties if other ingredients are added, such as inhibiting rust and oxidation and improving the strength of the film. Film strength is important in bearings which rotate slowly or operate under heavy loads. Stabilizers constitute a further class of additive. They make it possible for the base oil to be thickened with soaps which do not easily form compounds. Refer to illustration #155.

Grease Types

Calcium Soap Greases: Calcium soap greases are sometimes called lime based greases. These greases have a smooth texture and good mechanical stability. This grease does not dissolve in water and is usually stabilized with one to three percent water for helping bind the soap with the oil.

Grease/Ingredients/Types

If the water is lost, the soap separates from the oil so the grease loses its normal consistency and becomes semi-liquid or liquid. This is why these greases have relatively poor high temperature properties. At about 176°F (80°C) calcium grease begins to lose its internal water, resulting in oil and soap separation.

Calcium soap greases are recommended in such applications as chassis lubrication which requires good water resistance, paper making machines and in certain marine environments where temperatures are not too high.

Sodium Soap Greases: Sodium soap greases, sometimes referred to as soda-base grease, have good high temperature properties, but are soluble in water and should not be used where it is exposed to any type of water washing action. Sodium soap greases have excellent anti-corrosion properties and provide good rust protection in humid atmosphere.

Grease Types (cont'd)

Lithium Soap Greases: Lithium soap greases combine good high temperature properties with good water resistance. The structure of lithium soap greases resembles that of calcium soap greases, that is smooth and butter-like texture.

Lithium soap greases are often referred to as multi-purpose greases. They have the positive properties of calcium and sodium soap greases, but none of the disadvantages. This grease has good adhesion qualities to metal surfaces, remains stable at high temperatures, is used over a wide range of temperatures, and have good water resistance.

Complex Soap Greases: Complex soap greases withstand higher operating temperatures than corresponding conventional greases. They contain salt and a metallic soap, usually of the same metal. Examples include lithium, sodium, barium and aluminum complexes.

Mixed Soap Greases: The thickeners of some grease are mixtures of various types of soap. These mixed soap greases usually take the advantages of various soaps to produce a quality and cost-effective product. For example, a grease thickened with a mixture of calcium and sodium soaps would combine some of the water resistance of the calcium soap grease and the high temperature resistance of the sodium soap grease.

Greases Thickened With Inorganic Substances: Inorganic substances such as bentonite and silica gel, can be utilized as thickeners instead of a metallic soap. The active surface utilized on particles of these substances absorbs oil molecules. Greases in this group are stable at high temperatures, suitable for high temperature applications and water resistant. A disadvantage of these greases is that their lubricating properties deteriorate at normal temperatures.

Grease Types (cont'd)

Synthetic Greases: A wide variety of other fluids, generally called synthetics, are made into grease for either general or specialized applications. Organic esters, polyglycols, silicone, and synthetic hydrocarbon are common products used in the manufacture of synthetic greases. These do not oxidize as rapidly as mineral oils.

Some of the characteristics of the more common synthetic products include:

1. Organic Esters: Used for low-or-wide-temperature applications such as aircraft lubricants.

2. Polyglycols: Very good for high temperatures but poor for wet applications.

3. Silicones: These do not contain any carbon atoms but rather a chain of alternating silicon and oxygen atoms. They are used in high temperature and wide-temperature range applications, and they are very costly and normally used in specialized applications.

Grease Types/Additives

4. Synthetic Hydrocarbons: Two basic types are used; (1) polyalphaolefins (PAO) and (2) alkylated aromatics. They are becoming more common in special and multipurpose applications; are used over a wide temperature range than mineral oils; are less volatile; more heat resistant; have high oxidation stability at high temperatures and are excellent for severe service application.

Various thickeners are used with synthetic greases, including lithium soap, bentonite and PTFE (polytetraflouroethylene). Synthetic greases have a wider range of applications than do mineral oil based greases. Synthetic greases often have very low frictional resistance at low temperatures, in certain applications down to minus 70°C.

Grease Additives, Fillers and Dyes

Some of the characteristics of various types of additives are listed below:

1. Sulfur, Chlorine or Phosphorus Compounds: Used as an EP (extreme-pressure) agent in EP greases.

Grease Additives, Fillers and Dyes (cont'd)

2. Molybdenum Disulfide (Moly), Graphite And Other Soft Metals/Minerals: Moly is probably one of the best known additives used in greases with concentration of 1-3% or more; moly and graphite reduce friction because of their low internal friction and by filling in the small voids in the bearing surfaces; moly, because of its high sulfate compound, can become corrosive in a bearing at high temperatures, just like sulfur in an EP gear oil; both moly and graphite provide excellent protection in sliding and oscillating motion types of applications; normal color of a grease containing moly or graphite is grey.

3. Powdered Zinc and Copper: These metals are suspended in the grease; they are often used as an "antiseize" compound on threads in order to lubricate the threads and to prevent the threads from binding or welding together under loads of extreme pressure.

4. Zinc Antiscuff Compounds: Help protect against shock loading or extreme pressures on a bearing surface.

5. Dyes And Other Fillers: Often added for cosmetic and marketing purposes.

Grease Properties

There are several properties common to greases. To meet specific grease lubrication applications, it is necessary to use a grease with properties which satisfy the prevailing operating conditions of the machinery. The following grease properties will be discussed in detail:

- Consistency
- Temperature range and load conditions
- Dropping point
- Miscibility (compatibility)
- Rust protection properties
- Mechanical stability and wear protection
- Sealing properties

Grease Properties (cont'd)

Grease Properties

Consistency: Consistency, as applied to grease, refers to the degree of stiffness which the grease possesses. Consistency depends on the type and quantity of thickener used, the operating temperatures, and the mechanical working conditions.

Consistency is commonly specified in accordance with ASTM standards and the NLGI index (National Lubricating Grease Institute). The NLGI index is based on the degree of penetration achieved by allowing a standard verified cone to penetrate into the grease at a standard temperature of 25°C over a period of five seconds, with subsequent measurement of the depth of penetration in tenths of a millimetre. The softer the grease is, the greater the depth of penetration and the lower the NLGI index.

Refer to illustration #156 for a demonstration of how the NLGI index is measured.

Table #15 identifies the NLGI index numbers and their corresponding depth of penetration in tenths of a millimetre.

NLGI Index for Greases		
NLGI Consistency Grades	ASTM Worked Penetration mm/10	Description
000	445-475	Semi fluid
00	400-430	Very soft
0	355-385	Soft - grease gun
1	319-340	Grease gun
2	265-295	Grease gun
3	220-250	Gun or cup
4	275-205	Grease cup
5	130-160	Grease cup
6	85-115	Block grease

Table #15 - NLGI Index for Greases

LUBRICATION

Grease Properties (cont'd)

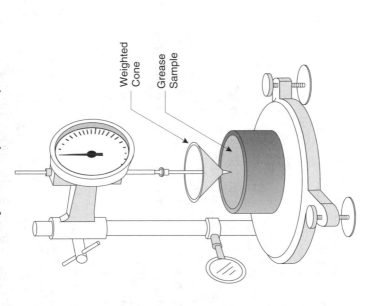

Weighted Cone

Grease Sample

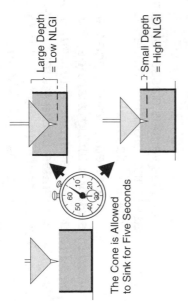

The Cone is Allowed to Sink for Five Seconds

Large Depth = Low NLGI

Small Depth = High NLGI

Illustration #156 - Measurement for NLGI Index

Lubricating greases used for rolling bearings are usually metallic-soap greases with consistency classes of NLGI 1,2, and 3, and in most industrial applications a grease of consistency class 2 is used.

Temperature Range and Load Conditions: It is important to select a grease which is suited to the relevant temperature the machinery operates in.

Grease Properties (cont'd)

At high operating temperatures many types of greases will soften like butter, and there is a risk of leakage. At constant high temperatures it is necessary to use a high-temperature grease. At extremely high temperatures, in the 266°F - 285°F (130°C - 140°C) range, lubricating greases oxidize rapidly, particularly metallic soap greases.

Note: The temperatures referred to are for mineral oil based greases. The upper temperature ranges for synthetic greases are much higher.

At very low temperatures, normal greases become so stiff that they lubricate poorly. For example, on roller bearings, the rolling elements rotate under resistance, and therefore slow down or almost stop in the unloaded section of the bearing. Upon getting back into the loaded section they are immediately forced to accelerate under the load.

Grease Properties

Heavy sliding occurs, the rolling elements break through the oil film and cause the surface damage shown in illustration #157.

At very low temperatures, normal greases become stiff and lubricate poorly. Any rolling element is prevented from rolling, instead it will slide and wear is set up, causing poor running and worn or failed rolling parts.

Note: The lower temperature limit for a normal mineral oil based grease is approximately -22°F (-30°C).

Table #16 identifies various classes of lubricating greases and provides temperature conditions for each class.

Note: Grease for heavy loads, ones supported by slowly rotating bearings, are required to provide a strong lubricating oil film. If unevenness in the metal surface comes into contact with the tips, the temperature increases quickly at these points. If this occurs there is risk that the surfaces will almost fuse or weld together momentarily.

Grease Properties (cont'd)

Illustration #158 shows where high spots of two uneven surfaces come into contact, therefore resulting in a temperature increase immediately around the tips of the high spots.

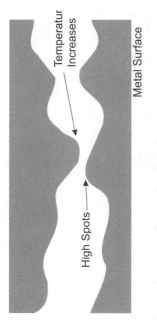

Illustration #158 - Contacting High Spots

Dropping Point: Dropping point, as defined under ASTM standards and prescribed conditions, is defined as the temperature at which the first drop of grease falls from an orifice in a standard test apparatus. This is the temperature at which the grease softens enough to flow. Dropping point is a factor for evaluating the high temperature capabilities of a grease.

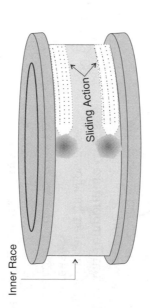

Illustration #157 - Sliding Action on Roller Element

Grease Properties

Grease Properties (cont'd)

Classes of Lubricating Grease by Temperature

Grease Classification by Temperature	Recommended Temp. Range	Base Oil Viscosity (mm²/s at 40°C)	Consistency (NLGI Index)
Low Temperature Greases – offer little resistance on start-up – low viscosity – recommended for cold, low temperature applications	-50°C to +70°C	15 mm²/s	May vary from NLGI 0 to NLGI 2, but consistencies 0 and 1 may require effective seals to prevent leakage
Medium Temperature Greases – often called "multipurpose" greases – recommended for roller bearings	-30°C to +110°C	75 to 200 mm²/s	Consistency is usually NLGI 2 or 3
High Temperature Greases – contain additives which improve oxidation stability – high viscosity – recommended for very high temperature applications – may become relatively stiff at low ambient temperatures and cause increased starting torque	+70°C to +150°C	normally about 110 mm²/s	consistency is NLGI 3

Table #16A - Lubrication Greases by Temperature

Grease Properties (cont'd)

Classes of Lubricating Grease by Temperature

Grease Classification by Temperature	Recommended Temp. Range	Base Oil Viscosity (mm^2/s at 40°C)	Consistency (NLGI Index)
EP Grease – contains film strengthening compounds such as sulfur, chlorine or phosphorous – compounds help increase the load carrying capacity of the film – intended for slow rotating bearings and where high sliding friction occurs	-30°C to +110°C	normally about 170 mm^2/s	consistency is usually NLGI 2
EM Grease – contains molybdenum disulfide which produces a stronger film than corresponding EP additives – graphite may also be used	-30°C to +110°C	200 to 500 mm^2/s	consistency is usually NLGI 2

Table #16B - Lubrication Greases by Temperature (cont'd)

Grease Properties (cont'd)

Because grease is a mixture of the lubricating oil and thickeners, there is no distinct melting point for the dropping point. Only at some elevated temperature the grease becomes fluid enough to drip.

Note: A grease with a dropping point below the operating temperature would not provide proper lubrication and the converse is not necessarily true: a dropping point above the operating temperature is no guarantee of adequate lubrication. In the selection of grease, the dropping point serves a useful purpose by eliminating certain greases from further consideration.

Miscibility (Compatibility): There are types of greases which are not at all compatible. The mixing of different grease types in service should be avoided if possible. The term "miscibility" is used in grease lubrication often and refers to the grease's capability of being mixed with other types of greases.

Where greases of different basis are mixed, there is a possibility of extreme softening, lots of leakage and subsequent loss of lubricant. It is recommended that grease packed bearings should be thoroughly cleaned of any old grease when a grease of a different soap base is to be used. In certain bearings it does not matter greatly if a grease mixture softens somewhat. However, it is recommended that regreasing be undertaken more frequently than normal until the old grease has been entirely replaced by the new.

Note: Greases with the same thickeners and a similar base oil can be mixed. If two greases which are not compatible are mixed, the consistency usually becomes softer. Do not mix greases with different thickeners.

Rust Protection Properties: The selection of a grease is most important where water contamination is involved.

Grease Properties (cont'd)

It is not enough for a grease to resist water "wash-out", but the grease must also prevent rusting of the metallic parts when water, or condensation and grease come into contact with each other. Rust inhibitors are often included in the grease formulation to enhance the natural rust protecting properties of a grease. As a general rule, sodium soap greases cannot resist water "washing-out", while calcium and lithium base greases are water resistant. The ASTM D-1743 rust test is one method of measuring resistance to rust under wet conditions.

Note: For roller bearings which may come into contact with a larger volume of water, the rust inhibitor in the grease should be insoluble and it should adhere to the bearing's metal surfaces providing a lubricating film even if the grease is saturated with water.

Mechanical Stability and Wear

Protection: Certain greases, in particular lithium soap greases of earlier types, have a tendency to soften during mechanical working, and this results in excessive leakage. In applications such as vibration screens, the working action within the parts and bearings is quite vigorous and the grease is being continuously vibrated. Therefore, for any vibrating applications, a grease must be chosen with good mechanical stability.

The combination of the lubricating oil and metallic soaps generally used to make greases gives a product with excellent lubrication qualities and anti-wear properties. Additional anti-wear additives can be added to overcome severe loading.

Wear generally results from excessive metal-to-metal contact, either from rolling or sliding action of the parts. It is important to select a grease which provides the necessary lubricant film required to minimize any contact.

Grease Properties (cont'd)

Sealing Properties: It is important for a bearing or gear assembly to be protected against the environment in such a way that no contaminants or moisture enters and damages the parts. The grease can provide this protection only if it remains secure within the parts. The effectiveness of the seal, is very important to the service life of the parts. The seal arrangement is important.

Grease lubricants may "soften up" as the operating temperature of the machine or the ambient air temperature increases. The sealing ability required is even more crucial in these situations. Check for the consistency of the grease and use only the recommended NLGI index for the temperature ranges encountered.

Two types of seals are commonly used for sealing in lubricants and for keeping out contaminants and moisture: non-contact seals and contacting seals.

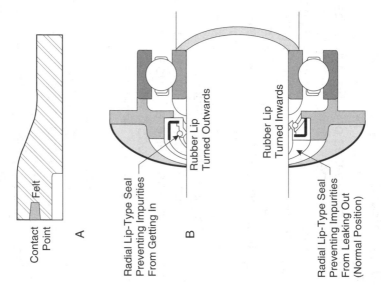

A — Contact Point / Felt

B — Radial Lip-Type Seal Preventing Impurities From Getting In / Rubber Lip Turned Outwards

Radial Lip-Type Seal Preventing Impurities From Leaking Out (Normal Position) / Rubber Lip Turned Inwards

Illustration #159 - Felt and Radial Lip Seals

Grease Properties (cont'd)

Contacting seals imply that a rotating member is in contact with a non-rotating member, this provides a seal which eliminates radial and axial clearance between mating parts. Illustration #159A shows a felt type contact seal.

In illustration #159B, the radial lip type seal, the lip is positioned inwards to prevent the grease from leaking out. This is the general mounting arrangement. The grease pushes against the lip and forces it down against the shaft. Illustration #159B also shows the radial lip seal mounted so that the seal lip is positioned outwards which helps the seal keep out any contaminants and moisture. A pair of radial lip seals can also be mounted back-to-back with the space between them filled with grease to stabilize the seals.

Illustration #160A shows a type of non-contact seal which consists of small circular grooves in the end cover shaft bore.

Illustration #160B and #160C identify two types of tongue and groove seals, commonly referred to as labyrinth seals. Closely maintained radial and axial clearances are essential in the effective sealing operation of labyrinth seals. The slinger ring, as shown in illustration #160C acts to keep out contaminants and moisture.

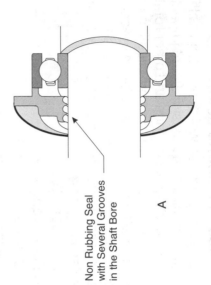

Non Rubbing Seal
with Several Grooves
in the Shaft Bore

A

Illustration #160A - Non-Contact Seal

Grease Properties (cont'd)

Grease/Properties/Selecting Factors

Grease Selection Factors

A lubricating grease which is not suitable for a given application has significant impact on the service life of bearings and other rotating and sliding parts. In most applications it is not too difficult to select a suitable grease, as the standard qualities relate to a wide variety of applications. Factors considered when selecting grease are:

- Load condition
- Speed range
- Operating conditions
- Temperature conditions
- Sealing efficiency
- External environment

Bearing Greasing

It is important in the greasing of bearings that the following conditions be met:

- Correct mounting methods
- Correct time
- Correct quantities
- Correct methods

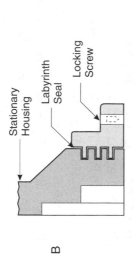

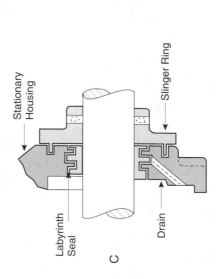

Illustration #160B,C - Axial and Parallel Labyrinth Seals

LUBRICATION

Bearing Greasing (cont'd)

Correct Mounting: All the care taken in the choice of a grease may be pointless if the correct method of mounting and suitable tools are not employed and if insufficient attention is paid to cleanliness. There are several key factors to remember when mounting bearings on shafts. These include:

a. Work should be carried out in a clean, dust free area.

b. The place of work should be away from chip-forming and dust-producing machines.

c. Shafts, sleeves and collars should be examined carefully, deburred where necessary, and cleaned.

d. Seals should be checked and changed if worn.

e. Clean the bearing and seals carefully.

f. Do not remove a new bearing from its wrapping until it is to be mounted.

g. Allow the rust inhibitor to remain except in the bore and the outside diameter surfaces.

h. Use only recommended solvents to clean the bearings.

i. Wipe and dry the metal surfaces with lint-free cloth.

j. If using compressed air to clean bearings, hold the inner and outer races and blow the air through the rollers, never spin the bearing with the air pressure as this is extremely dangerous

Correct Time: The later the bearing can be lubricated (packed with grease) the better it is protected from contamination during mounting and installation. There are several reasons for this. Some of them are concerned with the bearing type; for example, bearings with tapered bores, the reduction in the radial clearance when the bearing's preload is being set cannot be measured accurately if the bearing is lubricated. Others relate to the method of mounting, the bearing may possibly have to be heated, therefore any pre-greasing would be pointless.

Bearing Greasing (cont'd)

The most important reason, however, is the cleanliness requirement. The later the grease is applied, the better the chance of preventing contamination, which leads to premature bearing failure.

Note: Grease and oil contamination is one of the main causes of bearing failure in rotating equipment. To ensure long reliable service of any bearing, keep the lubricant free from contaminants - during bearing installation and while the machinery is in operation.

Correct Quantity: Bearings must never be over-greased as excessive lubrication may cause overheating. A general rule is to completely pack the bearing with grease and to leave some free space in the bearing housing to allow the grease to expand away from the bearing. This is very important during start-up. 30% to 50% grease in the bearing housing is often considered adequate.

Any high-speed bearing which is overfilled with grease will see a rapid increase in temperature. Bearings operating at slow speeds and those which require corrosion protection may have their housings completely full of grease.

Note: With many quality lithium soap greases, it is possible to fill up to 90% of the free space inside the bearing housing without risk of a temperature rise. This helps to keep out contaminants and extends lubricating application intervals. In machinery such as vibrating assemblies, the screens, shakers and wheel hubs, grease is packed to a maximum of 60%.

Correct Methods: The right method for applying grease largely depends upon the design of the bearing and its housing. Bearings can be divided into two categories: (1) non-separable and (2) separable bearings. The bearing housings are either split or one piece.

Bearing Greasing (cont'd)

Non-Separable Bearings: Are rigid in design. Deep groove ball bearings and certain angular contact ball bearings are non-separable types. These bearings should be packed with grease from both sides, as shown in illustration #161. Some types of deep groove ball bearings may be either shielded or sealed on one side. Sealed bearings are packed with grease by the bearing manufacturers. Some may recommend packing the grease from one side of the bearing only and stopping once the grease oozes out between the collars on the opposite side. This is a good practice for re-greasing used bearings, as the new clean grease pushes out the used grease.

Self-aligning bearings are considered to be non-separable as well. They differ from the rigid types because it is possible to swivel the inner ring so the rolling elements are accessible and grease can be packed into the free spaces in between them.

Illustration #162 demonstrates the packing of a self-aligning bearing.

Rigid bearings are filled with grease from both sides

Illustration #161 - Rigid Bearing Filled From Both Sides

It is possible to swivel the inner ring on the spherical bearing

Illustration #162 - Packing a Self-Aligning Bearing

Bearing Greasing (cont'd)

The best examples of self-aligning bearings include spherical roller bearings and self-aligning radial ball bearings.

Separable Bearings: These bearings include cylindrical roller bearings, taper roller bearings and various types of thrust bearings. These bearings can be greased while in their separate parts in the order determined by the mounting sequence.

As shown in illustration #163, after mounting the outer ring of the cylindrical roller bearing, completely fill the inner ring and roller assembly with grease. It is best to put a light film of grease on the inside surface of the outer ring as well.

Push the roller assembly into the inner bore of the outer ring.

Bearing Greasing

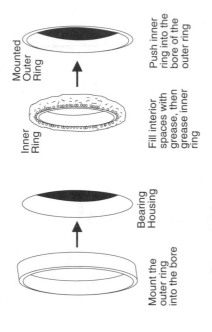

Mounted Outer Ring

Inner Ring

Bearing Housing

Push inner ring into the bore of the outer ring

Fill interior spaces with grease, then grease inner ring

Mount the outer ring into the bore

Illustration #163 - Packing a Separable Bearing

In thrust bearings, as shown in illustration #164, the cage assembly with the rolling elements is separate from the shaft and the housing washer.

LUBRICATION

Bearing Greasing (cont'd)

Split Bearing Housings: These types, often referred to as pillow blocks, are used to house various types of split bearings. Illustration #165 shows one type of split bearing housing. The roller bearing is mounted on the shaft first. The bearing is immediately packed with grease. For used bearings, it is best to pack the grease into the bearing, between the rollers, from one side only.

By using this method, any dirt or contaminants should be pushed through to the opposite side where the excess grease and dirt is wiped off. Once the bearing is placed into the bottom half of the split bearing housing, free spaces in the housing are now filled with plenty of grease. Do not forget to make sure these spaces are clean. Secure the top half onto the housing.

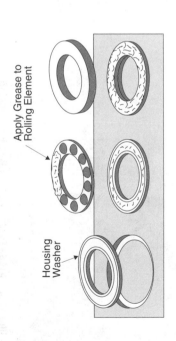

Apply Grease to Rolling Element

Housing Washer

Illustration #164 - Greasing a Thrust Bearing

Completely fill the rolling elements and cage assembly with grease, then fit it into the raceway of the housing washer. The other washer is fitted on top of the rolling element and cage and any spaces which are outside the washer rings must be filled with grease.

Bearing Greasing (cont'd)

It is best to keep the housing approximately half full of grease. Too much grease in the housing may cause the bearing to overheat. Ensure that the shaft seals are in proper position and the housing vent hole is not plugged.

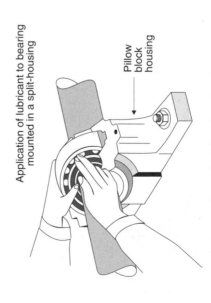

Application of lubricant to bearing mounted in a split-housing

Pillow block housing →

Illustration #165 - Packing a Split Bearing Housing

Bearing Greasing

One Piece Bearing Housings: Refer to illustration #166 for greasing the roller bearing mounted into the flange type one piece bearing housing. First, position the inner shaft seal and the internal space in the back, and then fill with grease in gradual amounts.

Second, pack grease through the rolling elements of the roller bearing, then mount the bearing, remove any excessive grease with a clean lint free cloth; fill again, clean the grease on the outside of the housing, and fill any free spaces. Fill the end bearing housing cap with grease and ensure that the gasket or shim is in place before securing the cap to the bearing housing. If the roller bearing is to be mounted without clearance to the shaft, complete the mounting before greasing the bearing.

Bearing Greasing (cont'd)

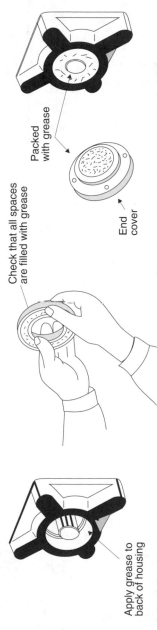

Apply grease to back of housing

Check that all spaces are filled with grease

Packed with grease

End cover

Illustration #166 - One Piece Bearing Housing

Replacing Grease In Anti-Friction Bearings

It is recommended to use the same grease on relubrication as that previously used in the bearing assembly. Some greases have poorer lubricating properties when mixed with another grease.

There are several ways to relubricate a bearing. When operating conditions are such that relubrication intervals are long, it may be best to have a bearing housing designed so that it can be opened and easily accessible.

If the bearing housing is split, as shown in illustration #165, with the top half lifted off, as much of the old grease as possible should be removed and new grease packed in, especially between the rolling elements.

If frequent relubrication is required, it is recommended to fit the bearing housing with a grease fitting. The grease is injected into the bearing assembly with a grease gun.

Bearing Greasing (cont'd)

The grease, while under pressure, is forced into the rolling elements by way of a lubricating duct in the housing. This is shown in illustration #167A and #167B. For the new grease to penetrate effectively into the interior of the bearing and for the old grease to be ejected, the duct should feed the grease immediately adjacent to the outer ring side face, as in illustration #167A; or directly into the lubricating groove of the bearings outer race as shown in illustration #167B.

After relubrication has occurred a number of times through the grease fitting, it is best to open the bearing housing and remove the old grease. Inspect the bearing and seals at this time for wear, contamination and fit. If all is okay, pack new grease into the rolling assembly.

Note: Wipe the grease fitting clean before new grease is added. This may prevent dirt and contamination from entering the bearing. See illustration #168.

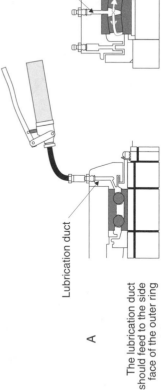

A

Lubrication duct

The lubrication duct should feed to the side face of the outer ring

B

Lubrication duct

The bearing is lubricated through holes in the outer ring while the labyrinth seals are lubricated through their own ducts

Illustration #167 - Lubrication Locations

Bearing Greasing (cont'd)

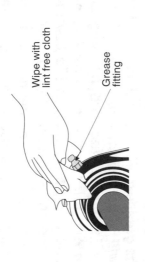

Wipe with
lint free cloth

Grease
fitting

Illustration #168 - Wipe Clean Before Greasing

Correct Amount Of Grease

There are several methods for determining the correct amount of grease for roller bearings. A common rule-of-thumb for roller bearings located in a bearing housing is to fill the bearing housing from one third to two thirds full of grease. This amount depends on speed and temperature.

Initially, it is the grease in the bearing itself which is replaced. The amount of new grease should therefore be suited to the size of the bearing. Its always good practice to completely pack grease between and around all the rolling elements of the bearing and cage assembly. If there are no specific lubricating instructions from the equipment manufacturer or from the bearing supplier, the quantity of grease for the bearing can be determined by using various bearing supplier tables or with the aid of a grease quantity formula. *The following formula can be used to determine how many grams of grease are required for a certain bearing based on the bearings width and outside diameter measurements in millimeters:*

$$G = 0.005 \times D \times B$$

where:

G = grease quantity in grams

D = bearing's outside diameter in millimeters

B = bearing's width, in millimetres

Correct Amount Of Grease (cont'd)

Note: Grease fill in a roller bearing is critical. It is important to never fill the bearing housing with grease, because when a greased bearing rotates, it is lubricated by a thin film of grease only and the excess is moved into the cavities of the bearing and housing. If these cavities are already filled with grease, the excess has nowhere to go and is recycled back into the bearing where it is "churned." In very little time the temperature will rise, causing the grease to liquefy and run out. Failure will soon follow. Fill the available space in the bearing and housing between one third and two thirds full, depending upon the speed of the bearing: the higher the speed, the less grease.

When a properly packed bearing starts up, there will be an initial rise in the temperature while the grease disperses throughout the bearing and housing, before falling off to a steady operating temperature.

Amount of Grease/Application

If the temperature does not lower then there is too much grease in the bearing, or there is a problem with the bearing fit.

Application Methods

Generally, bearings are greased at regular intervals by means of positive displacement pumps, either gear or piston type. For large grease volume requirements, gear or piston pumps are used to deliver fixed amounts of grease to various points on the machinery. The rate of delivery and amount delivered can be variable, depending upon need. A grease gun is a hand operated piston pump which is commonly used to relubricate bearings. Often suppliers will provide charts which indicate how much grease is required by the number of strokes provided by the hand operated grease gun.

"Packing" is a term used when applying grease by hand to a bearing. Over-packing accounts for many bearing failures.

Application Methods (cont'd)

Excess grease in the bearing increases internal friction, which can raise the temperature of the grease beyond its dropping point. The grease will then separate and lose its lubricating properties.

For bearings in housings without vents, gun greasing should be applied with care to protect the seals from rupturing. For example, hand operated grease guns can generate pressures up to 10,000 psi (68,970 kPa).

The procedure for greasing bearings with vents:

1. Remove vent plug with the shaft stopped from rotating.

2. Apply grease until new grease comes out the vent.

3. With the vent plug removed, rotate the bearing slowly for a short time so that it can expel any excess grease.

4. Close the vent and clean off the housing.

5. After several hours of operation, check to ensure that the bearing temperature is normal.

Greasing Intervals

Determination of the regreasing interval depends on the following factors:

a. severity of service
b. shock loading
c. condition of seals
d. contamination from the environment

If the bearing is running at a temperature above normal, with no indication of drippage, a small amount of grease should be applied. In approximately two hours the bearing should be running cooler.

However, if the bearing's temperature has increased, the grease fitting should be removed to determine if excess grease is present. If removal of the grease fitting does not release grease from the bearing, the grease may have oxidized and it should be thoroughly cleaned and refilled with new grease.

Greasing Intervals (cont'd)

Where there is a risk that the grease may be heavily contaminated in service, it should be regreased more frequently. The same applies to bearing assemblies where the grease has the function of sealing against water.

Note: Greases should not be mixed unless they have the same soap structure. If the grease type is changed, the bearing should be flushed out and cleaned thoroughly before new grease is applied.

Oil Lubrication

Much of the modern rotating equipment operates at high speed, heavy loads, or at extreme temperatures, and frequently under strict production requirements in automatic and precise process conditions. This equipment must be lubricated with the right oil in order to reduce friction, prevent wear or corrosion, and carry the loads needed to keep the machine components operating at top efficiency and at high rates of reliability.

When, for technical or economic reasons, a grease is not suitable for a given bearing, oil must be used as a lubricant. Oil lubrication offers the advantage of its suitability for high temperatures. The upper limit for commercial mineral oils is near 320°F (150°C) and of synthetic oils near 430°F (220°C).

High loads and high speeds leading to a prohibitive rise in bearing temperatures often make oil lubrication mandatory. The same applies in the case of high ambient temperature surrounding the machinery. Oil is capable of carrying off undesirable heat, thus reducing the bearing temperature to an acceptable level.

Industrial Oil Classifications

The international standard ISO 3448-1975(E), entitled "Industrial Liquid Lubricants - ISO Viscosity Classification," established a series of lubricant viscosity grades (VG) based on Kinematic Viscosties at 40°C.

LUBRICATION

Oil Classifications 307

Industrial Oil Classifications (cont'd)

Several related proposals which have also gained acceptance include:

a. use of 40°C and 100°C as the principle viscosity measuring temperatures for essentially all types of lubricants and a Viscosity Index system based on these temperatures.

b. use of centistokes (cSt) as the official viscosity unit for this system.

c. general use of whole degrees Celsius (Centigrade) for specifications, classifications, and various petroleum tests.

Note: The centistoke (cSt) was adopted instead of the official unit of the Systéms International d'Unités, square millimetres per second (mm²/S), in recognition of the convenience and long established use of the centistoke.

The new ISO system has been widely adopted by the petroleum industry as well as by many other industries throughout the world.

Note: The American Society for Testing and Materials (ASTM) has also committed to full implementation to the ISO system and have revised its method D2422, "Viscosity System for Industrial Fluids Lubricants", to conform to ISO3448. In addition, ASTM has developed charts and procedures required to implement the 40°C/100°C Kinematic Viscosity and Viscosity Index Systems. ASTM method D2270 (IP226), "Calculating Viscosity Index from Kinematic Viscosity", has been revised for 40°C/100°C. "Viscosity Index Tables Calculated from Kinematic Viscosity", DS39a has been revised to the 40°C/100°C system.

Table #17 identifies all of the ISO VG Classification with their limits provide by ISO 3448-1975 standards.

For convenience, table #18 provides equivalent viscosities in Saybolt Universal Seconds (SUS) at 100°F and 210°F, at 95 VI, for each ISO grade.

Industrial Oil Classifications (cont'd)

Industrial Liquid Lubricants - ISO Viscosity Classification (ISO 3448-1975)		
ISO Viscosity Grade	Mid-point Kinematic Viscosity cST at 40°C	Kinematic Viscosity Limits cSt at 40°C
		Minimum	Maximum
ISO VG 10	10	9.0	11.0
ISO VG 15	15	13.5	16.5
ISO VG 22	22	19.8	24.2
ISO VG 32	32	28.8	35.2
ISO VG 46	46	41.4	50.6
ISO VG 68	68	61.2	74.8
ISO VG 100	100	90.0	110
ISO VG 150	150	135	165
ISO VG 220	220	198	242
ISO VG 320	320	288	352
ISO VG 460	460	414	506
ISO VG 680	680	612	748
ISO VG 1000	1000	900	1100
ISO VG 1500	1500	1350	1650

Table #17 ISO Viscosity Classification

Industrial Oil Classifications (cont'd)

VISCOSITY CONVERSION CHART
ISO Viscosity Grades to SUS @ 100°F and 210°F

ISO Grade	Kinematic Viscosity Range cSt@40°C	Approximate Kinematic Viscosity Range SUS@100°F(95 VI)	Approximate Kinematic Viscosity Range SUS@210°F(95 VI)
10	9.00-11.00	57.6-65.4	34.6-35.7
15	13.5-16.5	75.8-89.1	37.0-38.3
22	19.8-24.2	105-126	39.7-41.4
32	28.8-35.2	149-182	42.9-45.0
46	41.4-50.6	214-262	47.1-49.9
68	61.2-74.8	317-389	53.0-56.9
100	90.0-110	469-575	61.4-66.9
150	135-165	708-869	74.0-81.9
220	198-242	1046-1283	90.3-101
320	288-352	1531-1878	112-126
460	414-506	2216-2717	139-158
680	612-748	3298-4046	178-202
1000	900-1100	4885-5994	227-257
1500	1350-1650	7385-9063	293-331

Table #18 - Viscosity Conversion Chart

Gear Oil Classifications

The American Gear Manufacturers Association (AGMA) has defined a system for describing gear oils in terms of AGMA Lubricant Numbers.

Oil Classifications

These numbers are often used in recommending oils for common gear operations. The viscosity ranges for the AGMA Lubricant Numbers conform to the ISO VG classification system, as shown in table #19.

AGMA LUBRICANT NUMBERS			
R&O (Rust & Oxidation Inhibitors)	EP (Extreme Pressure Loading)	Kinematic Viscosity Range cSt @ 40°C	ISO VG Grade
1	–	41.4-50.6	46
2	2 EP	61.2-74.8	68
3	3 EP	90-110	100
4	4 EP	135-165	150
5	5 EP	198-242	220
6	6 EP	288-352	320
7 Comp.[1]	7 EP	414-506	460
8 Comp.[1]	8 EP	612-748	680
8A Comp.[1]	8 AEP	900-1100	1000

[1] The oils marked "Comp." are those compounded with 3% to 10% acidless tallow or other suitable animal fats.

Table #19 - AGMA Lubricant Numbers

Gear Oil Classification (cont'd)

Note: In table #19 one set of specifications cover R&O (rust and oxidation inhibited) oil for gears under normal loading, and a separate list applies to oils used under mild EP (extreme pressure) loading. The severe EP conditions met in automotive hypoid gears are not included.

Engine Oil Classifications

Engine oils are classified by viscosity and performance. There are two classifications for engine oils:

a. SAE Viscosity Classification
b. API Engine Service Classifications (Performance).

SAE Viscosity Classification: The Society of Automotive Engineers (SAE) classifies engine oils by eleven SAE Viscosity Numbers, commonly called "viscosity grades" or SAE grades" shown in table #20.

The six "W" grades shown in table #20 are measured by "Cold Cranking Simulator" (CCS) viscosity.

This viscosity is commonly referred to as "absolute viscosity" and gives an indication of the ability of the oil to shear at low temperatures. The procedure is given by ASTM D2602 and the viscosity is reported in centipoise (cp) or poise.

This determines the ease of cranking an engine at low temperature. Therefore all "W" grades of oil are specifically tested under cold conditions to assure reliable cold temperature performance.

Pumpability Temperature defines the oil's pumpability after engine startup to provide the required lubrication during warm-up.

The SAE system of engine oil classification is based primarily on viscosity. Generally other factors of oil quality or performance are not considered.

Oil Classifications

Engine Oil Classifications (cont'd)

SAE Viscosity Grade	SAE ENGINE VISCOSITY GRADES PER SAE J300		
	Low Temperature Viscosity		Viscosity at 212°F** (100°C)
	Cold Cranking Temperatures °F (°C)	Pumpability* Temperatures °F (°C)	
0W	≤ 3.25 Pa•s at -22 (-30)	≤ 30.0 Pa•s at -31 (-35)	≥ 3.8 mm²/s
5W	≤ 3.50 Pa•s at -13 (-25)	≤ 30.0 Pa•s at -22 (-30)	≥ 3.8 mm²/s
10W	≤ 3.50 Pa•s at -4 (-20)	≤ 30.0 Pa•s at -13 (-25)	≥ 4.1 mm²/s
15W	≤ 3.50 Pa•s at +5 (-15)	≤ 30.0 Pa•s at -4 (-20)	≥ 5.6 mm²/s
20W	≤ 4.50 Pa•s at +14 (-10)	≤ 30.0 Pa•s at +5 (-15)	≥ 5.6 mm²/s
25W	≤ 6.00 Pa•s at +23 (-5)	≤ 30.0 Pa•s at +14 (-10)	≥ 9.3 mm²/s
20			≥ 5.6 mm²/s < 9.3 mm²/s
30			≥ 9.3 mm²/s < 12.5 mm²/s
40			≥ 12.5 mm²/s < 16.3 mm²/s
50			≥ 16.3 mm²/s < 21.9 mm²/s
60			≥ 21.9 mm²/s < 26.1 mm²/s

* Pumpability is a measure of the oil's ability to flow to the oil pump inlet and provide adequate oil pressure during start-up.

** All viscosity grades are tested for minimum viscosity at 212°F (100°C).

Table #20 - SAE Engine Viscosity Grades

Engine Oil Classifications (cont'd)

Oil viscosity is a measure of the fluidity of an oil at a given temperature. In the SAE viscosity test, a measured quantity of oil is brought to the specific temperature. The length of time (in seconds) required for a specified volume of oil to flow through a standard sized orifice in an instrument such as a Saybolt or Kinematic Viscometer is recorded.

Some engine oils are compounded to behave as light oils at cold temperatures, and as heavier oils at high temperatures. These oils are called "multigrade" or "multiviscosity" oils. Where recommended, one multigrade oil can replace as many as four or five single-grade oils. These oils give engine protection at both high and low temperatures. Oil changes viscosity with temperature. At low temperatures the oil is thick, and its viscosity is high. As the temperature rises, the oil becomes thinner and its viscosity decreases.

A thick sluggish engine oil makes engine cranking difficult and delays warm-up to the lubrication, while excessively thin oils result in poor lubrication qualities and high amounts of oil consumption.

Multigrade oils are formulated by starting with a base oil of the lower viscosity grade such as "5W" to which viscosity index improvers called polymers are added. Polymers do not significantly affect low temperature viscosity, but expand with increasing temperatures. This expansion effect causes an increase in viscosity at the higher temperature, producing multigrade oil such as 5W-30. Modern multigrade oils: 0W-30, 5W-30, 10W-30, 10W-40, and 15W-40 are common engine oils providing reliable engine service throughout Canada and many parts of United States and Europe.

Engine Oil Classifications (cont'd)

API Engine Service Classifications (Performance): The American Petroleum Institute (API) has classified and described engine oils in terms intended to aid machinery manufacturers in recommending proper oils and consumers in selecting them.

The API classification system is a joint effort of the American Petroleum Institute (API), American Society for Testing and Materials (ASTM), and the Society of Automotive Engineers (SAE) organizations.

Their goal was to clarify the engine oil specifications and better define oil qualities between engine manufacturers, the petroleum industry, and the consumer.

The two API classifications are "S" for service status, gasoline, or spark ignition and "C" for commercial, diesel or compression ignition. The various "S" and "C" classifications are listed in table #21.

The most common API service classifications are "SG" for gasoline engines and "CD", "CD-II", and "CE" for diesel engines. At the time of writing, the latest diesel classification, effective December, 1990, is currently "CF-4", which exceeds the "CE" requirements and will replace "CE" in some applications.

Note: The API Engine Service Classification of "SG" became more stringent in 1993 as the API tightened their formulations involving different base stock oils in the manufacturing process.

Engine Oil Classifications (cont'd)

API SERVICE RATINGS FOR ENGINE OILS

API "S" CLASSIFICATIONS	API "C" CLASSIFICATIONS
SA - Moderate service in older engines, with little or no additives and is not currently recommended by any engine manufacturer. This classification is obsolete.	**CA** - For mild-to-moderate duty diesel service with high quality fuel and not to be used unless the manufacturer recommends this grade. Used widely in the 1940's and 1950's. This classification is obsolete.
SB - Minimum duty and minimum protection, may contain antiscuff and rust oxidation additives and is not currently recommended by any engine manufacturer. This classification is obsolete.	**CB** - Similar to services provided by CA except for fuels which are not of the highest quality. Should not be used unless the manufacturer recommends this grade. First introduced in 1949. This classification is obsolete.
SC - Mild detergent-dispersant engine oil recommended for 1964 - 1967 engines which has become difficult to get in today's marketplace. This classification is obsolete.	**CC** - Introduced in 1961 for moderate duty diesel service, but is not recommended today for any current engines except perhaps by Detroit Diesel for their 149 series engine. The higher ash level in this class may be problematic. This classification is obsolete.
SD - Provides more protection than needed for 1968 - 1970 warranty for some engines. This classification is obsolete.	**CD** - Intended for severe service on naturally aspirated, turbo-charged, or supercharged diesel engines with high quality fuel. First introduced in 1955. This classification will soon be obsolete.
SE - Warranty engine oil in 1971 - 1972 which provides more protection from deposits, rust, wear, and oxidation. This classification is obsolete.	**CE** - Severe service typical of many turbocharged or super-charged high performance diesel engines: operation includes low speed/high load and high speed/high load conditions. Provides improved control of oil consumption, oil thickening, and piston assembly deposits and wear related to the performance of a CD oil. Introduced in 1983. Can be used when previous API engine service categories for diesel engines are recommended.

Table #21A - API Service Ratings

Engine Oil Classifications (cont'd)

API SERVICE RATINGS FOR ENGINE OILS	
API "S" CLASSIFICATIONS	API "C" CLASSIFICATIONS
SF - This classification greatly increases engine protection for 1980 and later warranty and may be used where SC, SD, and SE oils are recommended. It has improved performance in oxidation resistance and antiwear. May see this classification on some diesel engines which are also designed for severe diesel service. **SG** - This classification denotes service for 1989 gasoline engine warranty - service typical of present gasoline engines under manufacturers' recommended maintenance procedures. SG class includes the performance properties for CC diesel service and would replace SE and SF oils for gasoline engines. Provides protection against rust, oil thickening, valve train wear, sludge, piston varnish and piston deposits.	**CF-4** - This is the latest diesel classification adopted in December 1990 for services typical of high speed turbocharged or supercharged four-stroke diesel engines. CF-4 oils are particularly suited for on-highway heavy duty engines. CF-4 oils exceed the CE oils and will ultimately replace CE oils: also can be used in place of earlier CC and CD oils.

Table #21B - API Service Ratings (continued)

Automotive Gear Oils

Two gear oil classifications for automotive use include The American Petroleum Institute (API) lubricant service designations for automotive manual transmissions and axles and the Society of Automotive Engineers (SAE) viscosity grades for automotive gear oils.

API Service Designations for Automotive Gear Oils: The API lubricants service designations for automotive manual transmissions and axles are based on the type of gear unit and the degree of EP (extreme pressure) antiwear protection needed.

Table #22 provides a brief description of API gear oil service designations (GL identification).

A complete description of these oils can be obtained in API Publication No. 1560, February 1981 (5th Edition).

Note: Some equipment manufacturers may require an API category different from the usual recommendation or prohibit use of an API category that would appear satisfactory. In all cases, the manufacturer's recommendations for automotive gear oils should be consulted.

Note: API automotive gear oil designations apply only to axles and manual transmissions. Automatic or semi-automatic transmissions, fluid couplings, torque converters, limited-slip differentials and tractor hydraulic systems usually require special lubricants.

SAE Viscosity Classifications for Automotive Gear Oil: SAE viscosity grades are established for automotive gear oils in a similar manner to that used for engine oils. Grades better suited for cold-weather use are defined by viscosity limits at low temperatures and minimum viscosities at 100°C.

Automotive Gear Oils (cont'd)

API SERVICE CLASSIFICATION

API Designation	Service Type (General)
GL-1	Operation typical of spiral-bevel and worm gears under mild conditions, where straight mineral oil is suitable.
GL-2	Conditions normally associated with worm gears and axles, more severe than GL-1, calling for added anti-wear characteristics
GL-3	Service typical of spiral-bevel axles and manual transmissions operating under moderately severe conditions of speed and load, calling for a mild EP lubricant.
GL-4	Conditions, typical of hypoid gears, calling for the performance characteristics outlined by MIL-L-2105.
GL-5	Conditions, typical of hypoid gears, calling for the performance characteristics outline by MIL-L-2105C, D.
GL-6	Operation of high offset hypoid gears (above 2.0 inches offset and approaching 25% of ring gear diameter) under high-speed, high-performance conditions.

NOTE: GL-6 is an obsolete classification, but products meeting this performance level are available for severe service.

Table #22 - API Service Classifications

LUBRICATION

Automotive Gear Oils (cont'd)

High viscosity grades, which are not expected to have good cold fluidity properties, are defined by viscosity ranges at 100°C.

Table #23 identifies seven grades of SAE gear oil, all based on measured viscosity. The SAE number designations for gear oil grades were purposely chosen to be completely different from the SAE engine-oil grade numbers. This was to minimize the chances of using the wrong type of lubricant, particularly because they differ so much in composition and performance qualities.

Generally, lower viscosity gear oils have better cold fluidity characteristics, whereas higher viscosity oils give less gear noise, better oil-film wear protection (in low EP oils), and decreased tendency for leakage past oil seals. Higher viscosity oils tend to increase power loss in the gears and give higher oil temperatures, which can promote oxidation.

SAE J306 GEAR OIL VISCOSITY SYSTEM			
SAE Viscosity Grade	Maximum Temp. For Viscosity of 150,000 cP, °C	Viscosity at 100°C, cSt	
		Minimum	Maximum
70W	-55	4.1	–
75W	-40	4.1	–
80W	-26	7.0	–
85W	-12	11.0	–
90	–	13.5	<24.0
140	–	24.0	<41.0
250	–	41.0	–

Table #23 - SAE J306 Gear Oil Viscosity

Note: *Other factors which must be considered when choosing a lubricant for a given application include speed variations, loading, wet or dry conditions, clean or dusty/dirty conditions, and specific lubrication intervals.*

Lubricating Oil Types

All lubricating oils must be free of impurities which may cause wear and must have good resistance to oxidation and to deterioration.

Also, they must not allow bearing and part corrosion, whether the machine is in operation or at rest.

There are three main types of lubricating oils and the classifications are:

1. Mineral
2. Animal or vegetable
3. Synthetic

Mineral Oils

Refined crude oil produces many types of mineral type lubricating oils. Crude oil itself, before refining, can be found in a variety of types ranging from light colored grades which yield products such as gasoline, to black crudes which are almost like solid asphalt. The hydrogen carbon atom structures vary a great deal, as do the impurities, such as wax and sulfur.

There are three basic types of crudes: paraffinic; intermediate, naphthenic, or mixed-base; and asphaltic.

The different base crude stocks may be more suitable for one type of purpose than for another. For example, it would not be cost effective to use a light paraffinic crude oil to lubricate open gears where a heavier poorer quality asphaltic crude oil would work quite well. Likewise, producers wouldn't recommend using an asphaltic crude oil for applications requiring high performance and high speed.

Paraffinic and intermediate crude oil stocks tend to make up the majority of the modern lube oils. These stocks are carefully monitored, tested, and selected for certain applications, such as engine oil, hydraulic oil, gear oil, and grease applications.

Lubricating Oil Types (cont'd)

Animal and Vegetable Oils

Animal and vegetable oils are not normally used for typical roller and journal bearing applications, as there are concerns of quality, formations of acids, reduced temperature ranges and corrosion problems.

There are special oils which have a high percentage mineral oil base, and a maximum amount of animal or vegetable oil is added (compounded oils). If considering using these types of animal or vegetable oils - and compounded oil types, always be sure to check with the equipment manufacturer first.

Synthetic Lubricants

Synthetic lubricants are becoming more common in both industrial equipment and engine applications, as well as for gears, transmissions and hydraulic applications. There are many different types and many uses for specific synthetic lubricants.

The general categories of synthetic lubricants fall into the following ASTM classifications:

Synthesized Hydrocarbons:

- Olefin Oligomers
- Alkylated Aromatics
- Cycloalephatics

Organic Esters:

- Dibasic Acid Esters
- Polyol Esters
- Polyesters

Other Fluids:

- Polyglycols
- Phosphate Esters
- Silicates
- Silicones
- Polyphenyl Esters
- Fluorocarbons

Lubricating Oil Types (cont'd)

Note: Any of the above synthetics listed in the ASTM classifications can be blended and may also contain special additives to enhance performance. Specific amounts of mineral oil may be added to generate performance type synthetic lubricants.

Advantages of synthetic lubricants, in many cases, include:

● Provide superior performance at extremely low and high temperatures
● Operate well in conditions where there is a large range of operating temperature.
● Excellent in compressor applications.
● Fire resistant.
● Usually have longer service life.
● Greater protection from oil degradation.
● Can greatly reduce friction.
● Lower pour points.
● Natural detergency characteristics.
● A natural higher viscosity index.

Note: When conventional mineral oil lubricants are refined, the result is a complex mixture of different sized molecules which also contain impurities, such as wax, sulfur and silica compounds. It is difficult and expensive to refine these out of a conventional mineral oil lubricant.

Common Oil Additives

Additives are used generally to improve the performance and reliability of a petroleum type lubricant (mineral oil). Additives have permitted various lubricants to perform better and longer in severe applications. The advanced technology and the trend towards optimum machinery performance in modern rotating equipment and internal-combustion engines requires specific additives for the lubricants in order to function properly.

Common Oil Additives (cont'd)

Some of the most common additives for lubricants are as follows:

Oxidation Inhibitors: These types of additives decrease the rate of oil oxidation by reducing the tendency of the hydrocarbons to combine with oxygen molecules, otherwise, without the inhibitors, the oil would react with oxygen causing oil thickening, acidity problems, and causing bearing and part corrosion.

Oxidation increases a lubricant's viscosity and causes a chemical change which results in the formation of peroxides and organic acids. High temperatures, catalytic metals and exposure to air increases the oil's rate of oxidation. After the oxidation inhibitors are depleted, the rate of oxidation depends on the natural oxidation resistance of the base oil.

Pour Point Depressant Additives: Pour point is the lowest temperature at which the oil will flow when tested under prescribed conditions. Base oils, containing hydrocarbons, tend to solidify or form wax crystals at lower temperatures. The wax crystals prohibit the oil from flowing. This condition is undesirable in rotating equipment operating under low temperature start-up conditions, which are lower than the pour point of the oil.

Use of low temperature flow improvers in the oil formulation modifies the wax crystal structure resulting in better low temperature fluidity and a lower pour point.

Rust Inhibitors: Rust inhibitors improve the oil's ability to adhere to smooth metal surfaces in order to protect the surfaces from oxygen attack and prevent moisture from penetrating the protective oil film. Rust inhibiting additives are common in most oil formulation.

Common Oil Additives (cont'd)

Anti-Wear Additives: Wear due to adhesion (metal-to-metal contact), acidic corrosion and surface fatigues is best overcome by the use of film-forming compounds such as zinc dialkyldithicophosphate (ZDDP). ZDDP and other special anti-wear additives are recommended for oils used in engines and high pressure hydraulic systems.

Caution: ZDDP additives should not be used where journal bearings and other components are silver plated.

Extreme Pressure Additives: Oil film strength and extreme pressure characteristics may be required for protection against heavy sliding loads and shock loads.

Extreme pressure additives such as sulfur, phosphorous, and/or chlorine based additives are then added to the oil formulation.

A sulfur-phosphorous combination is one of the most commonly used extreme pressure additives, especially in automotive and industrial gear oils.

The extreme pressure additives chemically react with metal surfaces to form a film, or surface compound, which wears or polishes off rather than allowing the mating metal surfaces to weld and tear loose. They reduce friction, prevent galling, scoring, seizure and wear.

Foam Depressants: Detergent/dispersant type of oils tend to entrain air which, when rapidly released, causes foaming. Foam depressants are added to control the release rate of entrained air thus minimizing this problem. Air bubbles can restrict lubrication, so it is important to use oil with foam depressants which act to break up the bubbles, keeping the oil from foaming.

Common Oil Additives (cont'd)

Detergent - Dispersant Additives: Detergent - dispersant additives help keep metal surfaces clean and prevents deposit formation. Particles, soot, oxidized oils, etc. are suspended in the oil. This is common in internal combustion engines. These additives help to prevent too much build up of sludge and reduce the amount of varnish on metal surfaces.

Suspension of the contaminants is so fine that it passes through the oil filter and continues to be carried by the oil. Overextended drain intervals or excessive by-products of combustion can cause depletion of these additives and allow the contaminants to deposit themselves throughout the internal workings of the engine or machine. Detergent-dispersant additives are used more to keep an engine or machine's parts clean than to clean up deposits already in the engine or machine.

Viscosity Index Improvers

Petroleum oils "thin out" with increasing temperatures. Viscosity Index (VI) is a measure of the rate of viscosity change with temperature. The higher the Viscosity Index, the more resistant an oil is to thinning with increased temperature. The addition of a viscosity modifier in the oil formulation will slow down the rate of "thinning." Thus a high VI oil will resist thinning better than a low VI oil.

Viscosity Index Improvers are used extensively to formulate multigrade oils. An SAE 10W oil and an SAE 40, with the same VI, will thin at the same rate with increasing temperature. If a Viscosity Index Improver is added to SAE 10W oil, increasing its resistance to thinning, it could be as viscous as a SAE 40 weight oil at an increased temperature. That oil could then be called SAE 10W-40, behaving like a SAE 10W at low temperature and like a SAE 40 at high temperatures.

Viscosity Index Improvers (cont'd)

VI Improvers are used in hydraulic oils, transmission fluids, motor oils, and gear oils.

Load Carrying Ability Test Methods

For machine parts that encounter high loads, shock loads and sliding friction loads, the lubricant must be capable of maintaining a film that prevents metal-to-metal contact under the extreme pressures involved. Otherwise scoring and seizing of the surfaces and possible failure of the parts will result.

Several test machines have been constructed and standardized test procedures established for determining the types of conditions a lubricant will meet in field applications. Four widely used tests are:

1. Timken Machine Test

2. FZG Test

3. Four Ball Friction and Wear Test

4. Four Ball EP Test

Flash Point and Fire Point

The flash point and fire point of a petroleum liquid are measurements of flammability.

Flash Point: is the minimum temperature at which sufficient liquid is vaporized to create a mixture of fuel and air that will burn if ignited. As the name implies, combustion at this temperature is only an instant in duration.

Fire Point: is somewhat higher than flash point, and is defined as the minimum temperature at which vapor is generated at a rate sufficient to maintain combustion.

Note: In either case, combustion is possible only when the ratio of fuel vapor to air lies between certain limits.

The fire point of a lubricating oil is so closely associated with its flash point that it is generally omitted from inspection data. For most commercial lube oils, fire point runs about 30°C (86°F) above the flash point.

Flash Point and Fire Point (cont'd)

In general, the storage and operating temperatures of lubricating oils are low enough to preclude any possibility of fire. Among the exceptions are oils that come in contact with high-temperature metals, such as quenching and tempering oils and heat transfer oils.

Since flash and fire points are also related to volatility, they offer a rough indication of the tendency of lubricating oils to evaporate in service. Often though, oil comparisons are distorted because of differences in oil type and in the methods the oil is manufactured.

Flash and fire points of lubricating oils are determined by a standard procedure called the "open-cup method" (sometimes called Cleveland Open Cup (COC)) described in ASTM D 92. For relatively volatile oils, closed-cup methods may also be used.

Oil Analysis

Oil analysis is a valuable method for setting up a complete and comprehensive preventive maintenance program. Reliable methods for oil analysis can help:

- establish appropriate oil change intervals
- detecting contamination
- determining oil degradation
- identifying abnormal wear patterns
- indicate particular operational problems that would lead to equipment failure

Oil Analysis Program Fundamentals

Many of the lubrication characteristics, oil properties and various tests discussed in this section can be applied to oil analysis programs and can provide reliable information depending on the type of oil and its service. Three primary fundamentals are required in order to formulate reliable data from an oil analysis program. These are:

Oil Analysis Program Fundamentals (cont'd)

1. Sufficient care must be taken to obtain a representative sample of the oil and to sample it from a clean part of the machine and store in a clean container. In many cases incorrect conclusions have resulted from contamination of the oil sample prior to analysis.

2. It is important to work with the equipment manufacturers and lubricant supplier to design an oil testing program that is appropriate to the oil being used.

3. For drawing reliable conclusions from the oil analysis, it is important to understand the characteristics of quality lubricating oils and to establish a "base line" of the changes expected in normal service.

Only in this way can abnormal patterns be detected that can provide reliable conclusions for a preventive maintenance program.

Reasons for Oil Analysis

- to reduce maintenance costs
- to reduce equipment downtime
- to reduce labor costs
- to increase equipment resale value
- to help eliminate major failure by performing minor repairs

Periodic Oil Sampling

Periodic oil sampling is done primarily to detect the following faults in rotating equipment, for both automotive and industrial engines and drive units.

Oil sampling is used to detect:

- metallic wear rates
- additive levels
- leakage into the oil (water, glycol, etc.)
- oil condition
- overheating conditions
- part and component condition
- filter effectiveness
- contamination by foreign particles

Critical Stages Of An Oil Analysis Program

The four critical stages of an oil analysis program are:

1. Sampling of the oil
2. Laboratory analysis
3. Interpretation of accumulated data
4. Formulating a conclusion and/or decision

The accuracy of each stage is dependent on the accuracy of the one previous. Therefore, if the first step is done poorly, or the sample is clearly not representative of the oil system, the laboratory results will be inaccurate. Faulty results can lead to faulty interpretation followed by improper decision making and the end result could result in failures of major parts and components. The results of the oil analysis are only as accurate as the samples are representative.

To enhance oil sampling procedures, the following points should be considered:

a. Both the testing person and the maintenance supervisor need to be involved closely with the sampling procedures to make certain that all samples are taken in accordance to the guidelines.

b. Sample slips are recorded accurately and always attempt to provide extensive detail and information on your sample.

c. Consider organizing short seminars or toolbox meetings for the tradespeople and maintenance supervisors which focuses on taking samples, oil analysis interpretation, and the various procedures of the oil analysis program.

d. Look at where the oil samples are taken from and question whether the current method is truly a representative sample. Sampling locations include:

Oil storage tank/reservoir: probably one of the easiest places to take a sample, but not always the best.

Critical Stages Of An Oil Analysis Program (cont'd)

Take the sample at "mid tank" or at a point midway between the exit and entrance, not at the top or bottom of the tank.

Piping system: usually it is not too difficult to install a fitting, either with a plug or a valve, in the piping system so it is easier to take the sample.

Sample port: probably the most uncommon design for taking samples from, as the equipment manufacturer would have to design them; also, ports tend to accumulate sludge and crud.

Filters: probably one of the poorest locations to take oil samples from, as this is where lots of crud and contamination accumulate because the filter retains the contaminants entering the system

Tap/valve fittings: installed specially for sampling at key locations on the equipment;

these fittings are an inexpensive method for simplifying the sampling process.

Suction or sample pump: can be used to take representative oil samples from locations such as sumps, reservoirs, tanks and crankcase and gear box housings

Note: The sampling technique is probably the single most important step in the oil analysis program, therefore, spend the time and effort perfecting it.

Oil Sample Slip

Each laboratory that performs oil analysis for industry requires a "Sample Slip" which identifies information and details about the scheduled oil sample and subsequent analysis desired.

Illustration #169 identifies one example of an oil sample chart a tradesperson or maintenance supervisor would complete and would include this with the oil sample given to the laboratory.

Oil Sample Slip (cont'd)

OIL SAMPLE SLIP

Test Request:	Total Acid Number	Total Base Number	Particle Count	Other Test
Company Name	Attention:		Date:	
Company Address	Telephone:		Equipment Name/No.	
Unit Make:	Model:	Serial No.	Hours on Unit:	Hours on Oil:
Component Make:	Model:	Serial No.	Hours on Component:	Fuel Type:
IMPORTANT Include Make and Serial No. - This is required to match	Oil Changed? Yes No	Quantity of Oil Added:	Oil Brand:	Type: / Grade:

Illustration #169A - Oil Sample Slip

Oil Sample Slip (cont'd)

Oil Analysis

Sample Taken From:

Sample Taken From:

Engine ——————

Pump ——————

Hydraulics ——————

Compressor ——————

Automatic Transmission ——————

Gear Box ——————

Manual Transmission ——————

Mixer/Agitator ——————

Rear/Front Diff. ——————

Turbine ——————

Steering System ——————

Conveyor Drive ——————

Wheel Hub/Wheel Motor ——————

Clutch/Coupling ——————

Final Drive ——————

Other ——————

Complete this form and send Green Copy with Oil Sample

Purchase Order Number
for Special Tests: ——————

COMMENTS:

INSTRUCTIONS:
1. Fill Standard Sample Bottle with Oil.
2. Seal Bottle Tightly and Affix ID Label to Top of Lid.
3. Wrap Green Copy of Sample Slip Around the Bottle and Mail to Laboratory in White Box.
4. Keep Blue Copy for your Records.

Illustration #169B - Oil Sample Slip(cont'd)

Common Oil Analysis Tests

As mentioned in Section One, oil analysis should form part of any preventive maintenance program. There are various tests and analysis methods used for determining both the condition of the oil and the equipment - its parts and unit components. Generally there are several common tests performed in oil analysis which are part of any reliable preventive maintenance program. These include:

1. Basic Spectrographic Oil Analysis
2. Particle Count Analysis
3. Total Base Number Test
4. Total Acid Number

Basic Spectrographic Oil Analysis

Spectrographic Analysis is a series of tests performed under laboratory conditions commonly used to determine condition of lubricants. The tests identify the following conditions:

- wear metals
- contaminant metals
- base elements
- viscosity/grade of lubricant
- % of allowable soot (internal combustion engine)
- % of allowable sulfur
- % of allowable oxidation
- % of water
- % of glycol (internal combustion engine)
- fuel dilution (internal combustion engine)
- flash point
- consistency for greases

Table #24 shows an example of an oil analysis report where Spectrographic Analysis identified Wear Metals and Base Elements.

Table #25 identifies some of the common sources of contaminating elements in oil from wear metals, oil additive metals, antifreeze and contaminant metals. This table is not conclusive by any means, but it does identify some of the more common elements and their sources.

Basic Spectrographic Oil Analysis (cont'd)

SPECTROGRAPHIC OIL ANALYSIS			
WearMetals		**Base Elements**	
Silicon (Dirt)	98	Boron	154
Iron	56	Zinc	2
Aluminum	31	Calcium	22
Chrome	0		
Nickel	0		
Copper	0		
Lead	0		
Tin	0		
Silver	0		
Magnesium	5		
Molybdenum	7		
Sodium	4		

Table #24 - Spectrographic Oil Analysis

Spectrographic Oil Analysis (cont'd)

COMMON SOURCES OF ELEMENTS
(Wear Metals, Oil Additive Metals, Contaminant Metals)

TIN
- component in bronze and brass
- component of many types of solders
- component of babbitt metals
- used as an overlay on pistons to facilitate wear in

LEAD
- component of bronze and brass
- component of babbitt metals which is used as an overlay on bearings
- component of many solders
- certain types of lubricating oil additives contain lead
- some types of sealing gaskets contain lead
- some types of "anti-seize" compounds contain lead
- tetraethyl lead is an additive in some gasoline fuels

COPPER
- frequently used as an overlay on bearings
- main component in bronze and brass
- some mechanical parts are copper tubing
- some oils contain copper additives
- copper tubing may be used as cooling coils
- some gasket sealants and "anti-seize" compounds use copper
- some mechanical seals use copper parts

ALUMINUM
- can be found in certain greases
- sometimes used as a journal bearing material
- aluminum alloys, because they are light-weight, are used for parts and housings
- component of clay
- some filtering/reclaiming systems use aluminum
- some engine blocks/heads are aluminum
- supercharger/turbocharger blades are made of aluminum alloys
- can be the main component in piston material

Table #25A - Common Sources of Elements

Spectrographic Oil Analysis (cont'd)

SILICON

- principle component of dirt, dust and sand, these materials are abrasive and cause extra wear
- can be an oil additive
- frequent compound of antifoam additives
- some synthetic oils are silicon based oil
- some greases are made from silicon
- in oil filter analysis, the acid insoluble portion, after the carbon is removed, can be considered silica
- an additive in engine coolants
- often present in steel, but not used as an indicator of metal wear

IRON

- main component of steel - can vary over a wide range from soft to hard steel
- when reading iron results - see other metals such as chromium, nickel, vanadium, molybdenum, titanium, and manganese - as these metals have significant effect on the type of steel that is wearing
- most bearing parts are made of steel - shells, rings, rolling elements
- gearboxes and gears are often made of steel/iron
- some pistons are made of iron
- cylinder walls or liners are often made of iron alloy steel
- camshafts, crankshafts, shafting in general contain steel
- rust comes from iron

CHROMIUM

- used to make steels harder
- indicator of gear wear, roller or ball wear on bearings and shaft wear
- piston rings are often chrome faced
- chromium is main ingredient in chrome plating
- most stainless steels contain chromium
- sodium chromate and potassium dichromate are very good rust preventatives in cooling systems

SILVER

- sometimes used as a coating on bearings and bushings
- component of some solders

Table #25B - Common Sources of Elements

Spectrographic Oil Analysis (cont'd)

ZINC
- often an additive for engine oils
- component of bronze and brass
- used in "cathodic protection" in circulating water systems
- main ingredient for the "galvanization" process

MAGNESIUM
- can be an oil additive
- found in water - ground or city water supplies
- compound in aluminum and steel alloys
- can be in airborne dust, clay and sand
- material used in gearbox housings
- used in "cathodic protection" systems

NICKEL
- used with iron to make hard steels
- compound in stainless steels
- used for nickel plating
- is an indicator of shaft wear, gear wear, and roller and ball bearing wear

SODIUM
- can come from oil additives
- found in airborne dusts from salt/road salt

- present in many washing/cleaning compounds/detergents
- found in antifreezes
- rarely used as an indicator of metal wear
- some grease additives contain sodium

BARIUM
- can be an oil additive
- some types of greases contain barium
- can be found in fuel additives
- rarely used as an indicator of metal wear
- barium can be found in dust and water

CALCIUM
- can be an oil additive
- some types of greases contain calcium
- airborne dust and dirt frequently contain calcium, especially cement dust
- compounds of calcium that make pure water "hard water"
- rarely used as an indicator of metal wear
- calcium salts can be used as road salt

Table #25C - Common Sources of Elements

Spectrographic Oil Analysis (cont'd)

VANADIUM
- found in certain type of hard steels
- is a good indicator of contamination from crude oil
- residual fuels (bunker fuel) contain vanadium, thus frequently found in ash from this type of fuel

PHOSPHOROUS
- often a component of lubricating oil additives
- can be part of an engine oil's detergent-dispersant and anti-wear additives
- in gear oils can be part of the EP additives
- found in grease additives
- often part of the additive package for anti-freezes
- often found in steel, but not used as an indicator of metal wear
- dust, dirt, and clay contain phosphates
- some types of phosphates are in fertilizers

MOLYBDENUM
- used to make steels harder
- sometimes used in piston rings
- can be a component for lubricating oils and grease additives

BORON
- found in some types of lubricating oil additives, both engine and gear oils
- is part of the additives in most ant freezes
- can be found in dirt and water
- some types of washing detergents contain boron

MANGANESE
- some types of steels contain manganese
- may be used as a sacrificial coating to aid wear in
- used as an additive for unleaded gasoline

Table #25D - Common Sources of Elements

Spectrographic Oil Analysis (cont'd)

In summary, table #25 identifies elements according to wear metals, oil additive metals, antifreeze additives and contaminant metals.

Note: Some of the elements fit into more than one category.

Wear Metals: Tin, Lead, Copper, Aluminum, Iron, Chromium, Silver, Nickel, Vanadium, Molybdenum, Manganese

Oil Additive Metals: Lead, Copper, Silicon, Zinc, Magnesium, Barium, Sodium, Calcium, Phosphorous, Boron

Antifreeze Additives: Silicon, Chromium, Sodium, Phosphorous, Boron, Potassium

Contaminant Metals: Aluminum, Silicon (Silica), Magnesium, Nickel, Sodium, Calcium, Vanadium, Phosphorous, Boron, Potassium

Particle Count Analysis

This series of oil analysis tests is used to determine the range of larger particles not identified in the Spectrographic Analysis. Primarily, Particle Count Analysis is looking for particles larger than 5 microns.

This test is common when determining the oil's cleanliness typically in hydraulic and gear lubricants.

Table #26 provides an example of a report which could be used to count the number of particles in an oil sample.

Note: It is important in oil analysis to establish a "baseline" or "normal" reading. This can include an analysis of unused oil as well as representative samples from equipment in good operating condition

Total Base Number Test (TBN) and Total Acid Number (TAN)

The Total Base Number Test is useful to determine the oil's capability to neutralize acids formed during combustion in internal combustion engines.

Particle Count/TBN/TAN (cont'd)

The Total Acid Number test is used frequently to determine the amount of acid formed in the oil.

TBN and TAN is usually expressed in KOH units (milligrams of potassium hyroxide need to neutralize a gram of sample). Strong and weak acidic base numbers are discussed with TBN and TAN as well.

PARTICLE COUNT ANALYSIS REPORT		
Oil Sample Information:	Sample No. _____	Date: _____
	Oil Brand: _____	Oil Type: _____
Viscosity: _____	Hours on Oil: _____	Oil Changed: Yes No
PARTICLE SIZE (MICRONS)	CURRENT COUNT	PREVIOUS COUNT
>5 μm		
10 μm		
15 μm		
20 μm		
30 μm		
50 μm		
75 μm		
100 μm		

Table #26 - Particle Count Analysis

Total Base Number Test (TBN) and
Total Acid Number (TAN) (cont'd)

For TBN and TAN the strong acidic and base numbers may be determined by ASTM D 665 and ASTM D 4739 on the basis of the plateaus in the calomel/glass - electrode voltage curves during titration. Weak acidic and base numbers are the difference between the total acid or base number and the strong acid or base numbers.

Both TBN and TAN are classed as "neutralization" numbers, which are widely used criteria of used oil quality. The neutralization number of used oil tells little unless it is compared with the number for new oil.

Many additives used in automotive and industrial engine oils will give the new oil a high acid or base number. It is the amount and rate the neutralization number changes during service that is important for a guide to used oil quality, and the need for filter or oil changes.

A rise in acid number and/or drop in base number are generally indicative of increasing oxidation and may also be related to an additive, many of which are alkaline.

It is impossible to generalize about the limits to which neutralization values of an oil in service may safely be allowed to go. Each combination of oil, machine, and type of service follows a pattern of its own. Only through experience with a particular set of conditions can it be determined at what neutralization value an oil is no longer suitable for service.

Illustration #170 shows how the Total Base Number (TBN) is plotted in graph form over a period of net operating hours for two engines. A trend is shown here, as the operating hours increase for both engines, the Total Base Number (TBN) of the engine oil decreases. At some point a decision will have to be made about changing the oil as the oil's capability to neutralize acids formed during combustion is becoming less effective.

Total Base Number Test (TBN) and
Total Acid Number (TAN) (cont'd)

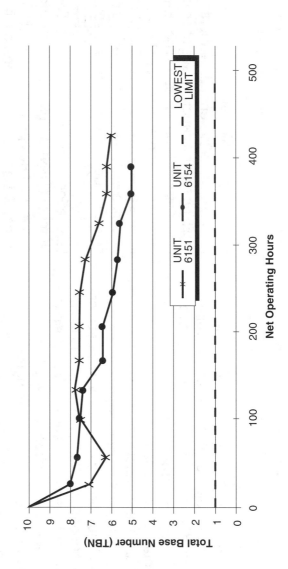

Illustration #170 - Total Base Number

Allowable Soot Test

Another oil analysis test commonly conducted in preventive maintenance programs for engines is a by-product allowable soot test. Soot is a by-product from combustion of fuels and oils and the soot deposits, which are carbon like materials, accumulate in the engine's lubricating oil.

Laboratory tests can easily determine and quantify the percentage of allowable soot found in the oil. Illustration #171 identifies two engines operating over a period of hours for each engine. In this example, each engine has exceeded the allowable limit set by the owner and it appears the value is increasing over time. This trend may indicate problems related to combustion and mechanical wear of both engine's internal parts.

Viscosity Test

A common oil analysis test is to determine the viscosity of the used oil over a period of operation.

Viscosity is a measure of the resistance of flow and it decreases with increasing temperature and increases with large increases in pressure (this latter property is not easily measured).

Viscosity is measured in two ways: kinematic and absolute. The most common measure is kinematic viscosity, which is measured by the time taken for a fixed volume of oil to flow through a capillary tube. The most generally accepted unit for measurement in the petroleum industry is the centistoke (cSt), which is numerically equal to the official SI unit of mm^2/s.

Allowable Soot Test (cont'd)

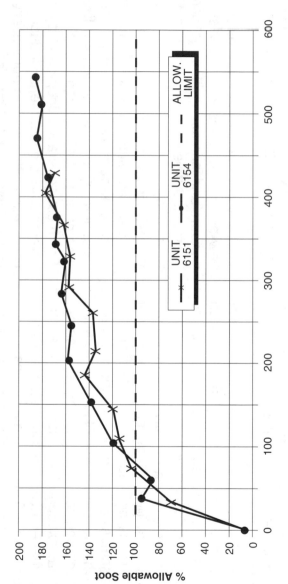

Illustration #171 - % Allowable Soot

Viscosity Test (cont'd)

Viscosity testing is useful for identifying oil grades and for following the performance of oils in service. An increase in viscosity usually indicates that the oil has deteriorated somewhat through oxidation. A decrease in viscosity usually indicates fuel dilution, contamination or the break up of polymers in the oil due to shear.

The permissible extent of viscosity increase or decrease before corrective measures need to be taken is largely a matter of experience and judgment on the part of the tradesperson and maintenance supervisor. Illustration #172 demonstrates how the oil viscosity of two engines vary as the operating hours increase over time. This identifies an upper and lower viscosity limit for this application as well.

Wear Metal - Iron (PPM)

Illustration #173 indicates how iron, a wear metal, is graphed in PPM over a duration of operating hours. Again two engines are tracked, each is similar in wear metal characteristics and both are well below the maximum upper limit for iron as a wear metal.

Allowable Oxidation

Oil reacting with oxygen causes oil thickening, acidity problems and leads to bearing and part corrosion. Oxidation is accelerated by high temperatures, catalysts (such as copper and iron), and the presence of water. The rate of oxidation increases with time. Oxidation also tends to raise the viscosity of an oil.

Reliable testing to determine a percentage of allowable oxidation in an oil is difficult as there are many operating variables that cannot be easily duplicated under test conditions. Moreover, results can be distorted by the presence of certain additives in the oil.

Viscosity Test (cont'd)

Oil Analysis

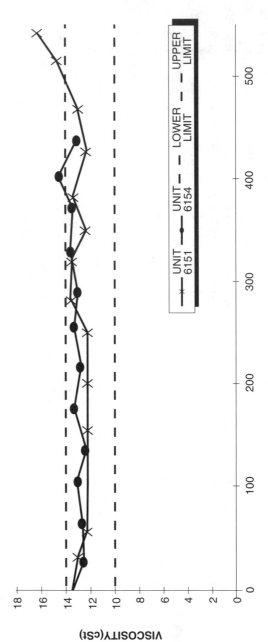

Illustration #172 - Viscosity Test

Wear Metal - Iron (PPM) (cont'd)

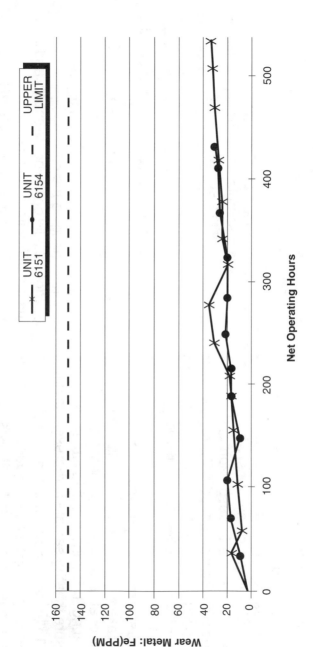

Illustration #173 - Wear Metal: Fe(PPM)

Sampling Procedures

Identified below are the basic sampling procedures to take for pressurized and non-pressurized oil systems. It is recommended that the tradesperson and maintenance supervisor periodically review their sampling procedures to ensure that representative oil samples are consistently being taken.

Pressurized Oil Systems

1. Take the sample while equipment is running or at its idle speed and while the oil is circulating throughout the system (this will ensure that the sample is representative).

2. Take the sample when the oil is at normal operating temperature (usually the equipment must be running for at least 30 minutes).

3. Wipe the valve fitting or tap with a clean lint free cloth.

4. Purge the port for a few seconds into a pail (approximately 0.2 litres).

5. Completely fill the proper oil sample bottle, then close the lid of the bottle snugly and label the container immediately.

Non-Pressurized Oil System

1. Take the sample while the equipment is running at its idle speed.

2. Take the sample when the oil is at normal operating temperature.

3. Wipe the valve fitting, tap, or plug area clean. Open the valve, tap or remove the plug slowly.

4. Drain a small amount of the oil into a pail before filling the oil sample bottle.

5. Close off the valve, or screw the plug back in if not changing the oil.

6. Close the lid on the bottle snugly and label the container immediately.

Note: Never use dirty funnels, bottles, sample needles or hose which may contaminate the oil and cause inaccurate results. Remember to thoroughly fill out the sample slip and attach a copy to the bottle. Keep a copy for the records.

Oil Sample Report Interpretation

Report interpretation is important because it tells the past, present, and future condition of the oil and of the equipment parts and components. Experience and training leads to proper reading and interpretation of the complex data a good oil analysis sample report contains.

In order to accomplish this task, one must also have the necessary knowledge of the equipment, its components and parts, operating conditions, oil properties and sound field experience. High quality report interpretation, in summary, depends on many factors:

● Quality of the oil sample
● Quality of the data on the sample slip
● Knowledge of the equipment
● Knowledge of lubricants
● Knowledge of testing procedures
● Field experience
● Access to reliable historical data

Illustration #174 exhibits one type of oil sample report which a laboratory would complete and return to the owner. Complete data would be given for the spectrographic analysis (PPM), physical properties of the oil, wear control values (accumulated wear metals - total PPM), and oil degradation as a percentage of allowable amounts.

Making A Conclusion and Decision

Drawing up a conclusion and deciding what to do is the final step and depends on the three previous steps: sampling, laboratory analysis, and interpretation. If any of these steps are not performed accurately, then the conclusion and subsequent decision(s) will not be dependable. This is the point where everything comes together and action is taken.

Oil Analysis

Oil Sample Report Interpretation (cont'd)

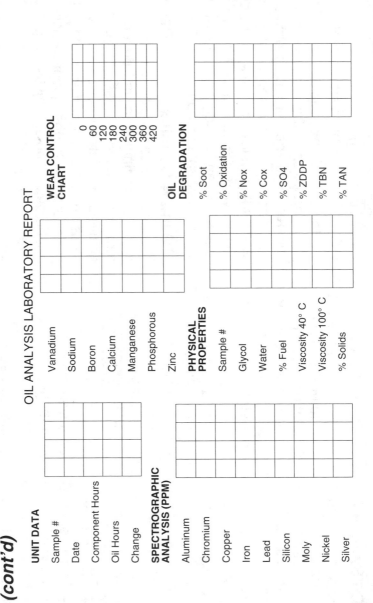

OIL ANALYSIS LABORATORY REPORT

UNIT DATA

Sample #

Date

Component Hours

Oil Hours

Change

SPECTROGRAPHIC ANALYSIS (PPM)

Aluminum

Chromium

Copper

Iron

Lead

Silicon

Moly

Nickel

Silver

Vanadium

Sodium

Boron

Calcium

Manganese

Phosphorous

Zinc

PHYSICAL PROPERTIES

Sample #

Glycol

Water

% Fuel

Viscosity 40° C

Viscosity 100° C

% Solids

WEAR CONTROL CHART

0
60
120
180
240
300
360
420

OIL DEGRADATION

% Soot

% Oxidation

% Nox

% Cox

% SO4

% ZDDP

% TBN

% TAN

Illustration #174 - Oil Analysis Laboratory Report

Making A Conclusion and Decision (cont'd)

The decision making should not be done alone. Use the knowledge of the lubrication specialists, equipment manufacturers and experienced field personnel to help formulate the necessary criteria for making the decision regarding what action(s) are planned to correct either or both the oil and equipment condition.

If one can continue to demonstrate that every oil sample taken meets the specified procedures, that the laboratory results are exact and that the oil sample reports are interpreted correctly, then the decision making process is assured to be fairly accurate.

Changing Lubricant

This is probably one of the most challenging questions facing the tradesperson and maintenance supervisor. The equipment manufacturer will usually specify the relubrication periods for the equipment.

However this should only be taken as a guide as they do not have control over operating conditions.

As a general rule, any increase in running temperature, pressure or speed, will result in more frequent relubrication periods. All lubricants, greases and oils, will deteriorate in service, to a greater or lesser extent, and will need replacement at some time. Certain additives are incorporated to retard deterioration, but these also deplete over time. Oxidation continues to be the most common form of oil degradation and hydrocarbons when oxidized, take the following path:

OIL - ALDEHYDE - ACID - SLUDGE - CARBON

Aldehydes have a characteristic pungent odor and once the anti-oxidant additives are depleted, the oil smells strongly and the acidity starts to rise. Petroleum is made up of hundreds of different molecules and each will oxidize at a different rate.

Changing Lubricant (cont'd)

In order to limit the formation of amounts of sludge and carbon which could interfere with the operation of the equipment, oil must be removed/changed out at the point where a certain acidly level has been reached. Research indicates that for petroleum oils an Acid Number of 2.0 to 2.5 means the oil should be changed. For engine oils, because of their high additive treatments, the Acid Number 3.0 to 3.5, and for synthetic oils, which comprise of single molecules, the level is an Acid Number of 5.0 to 5.5.

Primarily, with Acid Numbers in mind, the lubricant needs to be changed out under the following circumstances:

a. After a specified length of service.

b. If contaminated with moisture or dirt.

c. If wear metals are found to be in excess quantities.

d. If mixed with the wrong lubricant.

Oil Changing/Systems

Oil Lubrication Systems

Oil Bath System: The oil bath system is probably the simplest method for oil lubrication for bearings, gears and other rotating parts. It is suitable for low speed, as there is plenty of oil in movement.

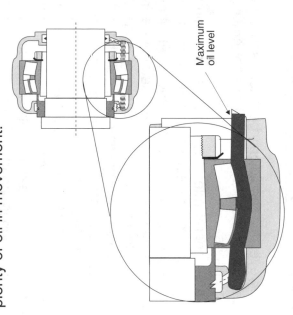

Maximum oil level

Illustration #175 - Oil Bath System

Oil Lubrication Systems (cont'd)

Illustration #175 identifies an oil bath system for lubricating a spherical roller bearing. When the bearing is at rest, the oil level should come to a level just below the center of the bottom (lowest) rolling element. On rotation, the oil is drawn up by the action of the rotating bearing parts causing the oil to run through the bearing and returning to the bath. Excess oil level would cause the bearing to overheat because of the extra friction produced by the swirling - moving oil.

Oil Circulation: Oil circulation is a closed system, where the oil is circulated to the bearings by a pump, under constant pressure and flow, and returns back to a reservoir before its pumped back to begin the circulation route again. The higher the operating temperature of the bearing, the more rapidly the lubricating oil begins to degrade. This is largely determined by the rate of oil flow through the bearing, and the size of the sump (also ambient temperature, cooling etc.).

To avoid excessively close oil - change intervals, oil lubrication is provided by maintaining the oil in circulation. In most systems like this, the oil runs through a filter before it returns to the bearing. Illustration #176 demonstrates one type of oil circulation system used for bearing lubrication.

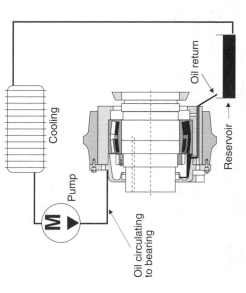

Illustration #176 - Oil Circulation System

Oil Lubrication Systems (cont'd)

This system uses a cooling system which serves to maintain the oil temperature at a pre-determined level. In cold operating environments, an oil heater may be used to keep the oil flowing smoothly and constantly throughout the circulation system.

Oil Injection Systems: At high speeds of equipment rotation, the lubricating oil must penetrate the interior sections of the bearing, gear teeth, or moving parts to provide an oil film and remove heat, because at high speeds oil can be easily forced out of these areas which results in serious damage.

As shown in illustration #177, an effective method for providing lubricating oil to high speed equipment is with an oil injection system.

Oil Systems

Oil is injected into the bearing or part and the speed of the oil jet must be high enough to ensure that sufficient oil penetrates the air vortex caused by the high speed of the rotating parts.

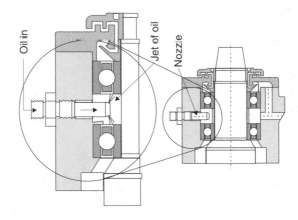

Illustration #177 - Oil Injection System

Oil and Grease Storage and Handling

Storage: Careless storage, handling, contamination, exposure to abnormal temperatures, and confusion of stocks/inventory all lead to waste, damage to equipment, deterioration of lubricants, higher maintenance costs and loss of production.

It is essential that careful consideration be given to setting up reliable and adequate storage and handling procedures for lubricating oils and greases.

Outdoor storage should be avoided if at all possible as:

a. Weathering can obliterate labels or stencils on containers, leading to possible mistakes in selection.

b. Widely varying outdoor temperatures, with consequent expansion and contraction of seams and seals on containers, may lead to leakage and waste.

c. The likelihood of contamination is increased.

d. Water can leak into even tightly closed drums.

e. Extremely cold or hot weather can also change the composition of some lubricants, making them useless.

When containers must be stored outside temporarily, the following precautions are advised:

a. Lay drums on their sides if possible.

b. Position the drums so that the bungs are at 9:00 and 3:00 o'clock position to ensure they are covered by drum contents, this minimizes moisture migration and drying out of seals.

c. If drums are stored upright, tilt them slightly to prevent water from collecting around the bungs.

d. Keep bungs tight.

e. Use drum covers or spread a tarpaulin over the drums to keep the weather out.

f. Before removing the bungs, dry the drum top off and wipe clean any contaminants.

Oil and Grease Storage and Handling (cont'd)

Note: Always remember the importance of keeping grit and sand out of oil used for bearings and rotating parts.

Indoor storage allows for more constant storage temperatures at all times.

a.   Lubricants in indoor storage facilities should be located away from sources of heat and ignition, or from possible sources of industrial contamination such as ash, dust, grit and other airborne contaminants.

b.   Storage areas should always be kept clean and free from debris and fire hazard materials.

c.   Regular cleaning schedules should be maintained.

d.   Any oil or grease dispensing equipment must never be allowed to become fouled.

e.   Orderliness in the storage area is essential to prevent contamination and confusion of oil brands.

Storage and Handling

f.   Avoid having partially filled containers and dispensing equipment laying around, open to the elements.

g.   Labels on all containers and equipment should be kept legible at all times.

h.   Be careful not to use the same dispensing equipment for non-compatible oils.

i.   Galvanized containers should never be used for transporting oil.   Certain additives may react with the zinc.

j.   Always know the fire protection procedures in and around the storage facility and have the proper type of fire extinguisher available for petroleum fires.

k.   Be prepared to handle spills and leaks, as environmental management is part of everyone's job; a clean work and storage area is a safe one.

l.   Have proper separate metal containers for storing clean wiping cloths and dirty contaminated cloths. Attempt to wash and reuse the dirty cloths.

Petroleum Product Handling Rules

a. Minimize skin contact with whatever product being used.

b. Remove oils and grease from the skin promptly, using mild non-abrasive soap and warm water or a skin cleanser and warm water.

c. Do not use gasoline, solvents, kerosene or similar products to remove oil and grease from the skin.

d. Do not wear oil soaked clothing, launder all work clothes frequently.

e. Wash hands and face before eating and take a shower before leaving work.

f. Clean up spilled oil and grease immediately and dispose correctly. Keep the product from going into sewers and waterways.

g. Get first aid treatment immediately for all cuts and scratches and report as required.

h. Be careful to not inhale oil mists or solvent vapors.

i. Obtain and read medical advice on all potential health hazards related to petroleum products.

Lubrication Scheduling

Well thought out schedules for lubrication plays an important part in preventive maintenance and in control of lubrication costs. Once a basic product line of lubricants has been selected, a program should be planned and organized to:

1. Ensure the right lubricant is applied to the right place.

2. Ensure the right machine gets the right amount of lubricant.

3. Ensure the right amount of lubrication is applied at the right time and that no point requiring lubrication is missed.

Note: Most lubricant manufacturers and suppliers have a lubrication survey system to help their customers set up scheduled lubrication programs. Contact the supplier for further information.

Plant Lubrication Department Functions

1. Collect and Record all Lubrication Requirements:

a. Usual source for this is the equipment supplier.

b. Both the type of lubricant and the method of lubrication should be recorded.

c. Develop an effective record keeping system for storing specific lubrication data and information.

2. Specify Lubricants For Each Machine:

a. Determine what lube products are available to meet specific machine requirements.

b. Responsibility and decision may be based on: purchasing policy; equipment manufacturer recommendations; past experiences; consultation with others with similar machinery; employ specifications based on oil analysis laboratory tests; own in-house performance test methods; considering brand name products.

3. Develop Lubrication Schedules:

a. Collaborate with the equipment manufacturer and lubricant supplier to determine the best schedule for re-lubrication.

b. Establish re-lubrication and change-out frequencies and inspection intervals where applicable.

4. Develop Methods of Lubrication:

a. Decide what type of lubrication system is needed for each piece of equipment.

b. Will the lubricant be applied internally or externally; intermittent or continuous; manual or automatic; once through or recirculating; by oil bath, oil mist, or spot lubrication?

c. Should grease or oil be used?

d. What environmental and safety conditions must be considered?

e. What is the dependability of the lubrication system selected?

5. Establish Standards For Lubrication Storage

Plant Lubrication Department Functions (cont'd)

6. Maintain Detailed Records of Consumption and Cost:

a. Collect consumption and cost information on a regular basis.

b. Record consumption and cost information on a data base.

c. Track and trend consumption and costs.

d. Use comparative reports for developing consumption and cost reduction programs.

7. Collaborate With Maintenance, Operations and Engineering Departments On Lubrication Problems:

a. Look at design inadequacies.

b. Determine if the equipment is operating at overload or too high of speeds.

8. Arrange For Testing of Lubricants:

a. Proper oil analysis programs greatly benefit any preventive maintenance program.

b. Collaborate with the laboratory that performs all the oil analysis tests.

c. Collect and record oil analysis test reports.

d. Work with the maintenance department to interpret the oil analysis test reports.

e. Aid in the decision making process.

f. Work with lubricant suppliers in developing improved lubricants.

9. Oversee New Installation And The Maintenance Of Lubricating Systems:

a. It is imperative that all related lubrication system equipment is correctly designed, installed, and above all serves to be fully reliable and trouble free.

b. Newly installed piping systems must undergo a precleaning and flushing procedure to prevent start-up problems.

c. Once in service, measures and checks must be taken to ensure systems are properly maintained.

Plant Lubrication Department Functions (cont'd)

d. It is good practice to develop a daily checklist for maintenance personnel to follow.

10. Monitor Lubricants In Service:

a. Perform regular checks of wear metals, particle counts, viscosity, water and sediment contamination and total base and acid numbers.

b. Review current oil sampling practices and regularly check to see that all sampling procedures are being followed.

c. Always strive to get a true representation of oil in each sample taken.

11. Monitor the Filtering Systems:

a. Ensure the correct micron rated filter is used.

b. Provide periodic filter inspections.

c. Develop regular filter replacement schedules.

d. Work with filter suppliers to develop improved filtering systems.

e. Develop appropriate methods for handling and storing used oil filters.

f. Periodically inspect the used filter elements for type of contaminants.

12. Provide On-Going Training:

An on-going training program must be provided to help keep servicemen, tradespeople, maintenance supervisors, operators and purchasing department personnel abreast of changes and specifications for oil and grease lubricants for such things as types, brands, grades, testing, applications and specific characteristics.

SECTION FIVE QUESTIONS
Lubrication Principles and Analysis

1. *The lubricant is required to form a film between rolling and sliding surfaces.*
   This serves best to:
   - ☐ seal out contaminants
   - ☐ prevent metal-to-metal contact
   - ☐ minimize corrosion
   - ☐ minimize clearances

2. *A lubricant should flow easily at low temperatures.*
   - ☐ true   ☐ false

3. *A lubricant is reacting normally if it foams and bubbles.*
   - ☐ true   ☐ false

4. *A lubricant should resist breakdowns even after prolonged use.*
   - ☐ true   ☐ false

5. *List four basic conditions to consider when selecting a lubricant.*
   Answer: _____

6. *The film strength of grease is particularly important in bearings which operate under:*
   - ☐ light loads and high speeds
   - ☐ heavy loads and rotate slowly

7. *Friction, in excess, causes:*
   Answer: _____

8. *Friction is required to have the lubricant film remain between two mating parts.*
   - ☐ true   ☐ false

9. *The friction between two rough mating surfaces is far _____ than two polished, flat surfaces.*
   - ☐ less   ☐ greater

10. *Friction is usually defined as:*
    Answer: _____

11. *Identify two types of friction common to components of rotating equipment.*
    Answer: _____

12. *Spur gear teeth display rolling or sliding friction at the gear tooth's pitch line:*
    ☐ rolling   ☐ sliding

13. *Oil viscosity is defined as the fluid's resistance to flow at a specific pressure.*
    ☐ true   ☐ false

14. *Oil becomes thinner or less viscous as it:*
    ☐ decreases in temperature
    ☐ increases in temperature

15. *Oil gets thicker or becomes more viscous as the temperature:*
    ☐ drops   ☐ increases

16. *If the ambient temperature is quite low:*
    ☐ a thinner oil, or low viscosity oil is needed
    ☐ a thicker oil, or high viscosity oil is needed

17. *Consistency is another fundamental principle of lubrication and is used to define:*
    ☐ the relative smoothness of machine part surfaces in contact
    ☐ the texture of the oil base
    ☐ the ability of the lubricant to mix with other lubricants
    ☐ the degree of stiffness which a grease possesses

18. *At low temperatures, normal greases become quite:*
    ☐ stiff, so they offer excellent lubrication qualities
    ☐ stiff, so they offer poor lubrication qualities
    ☐ thin, so they offer excellent lubrication qualities
    ☐ thin, so they offer poor lubrication qualities

19. _____ *lubrication refers to the thickness of the lubricant being approximately the same thickness as individual oil molecules.*
    ☐ boundary-layer
    ☐ hydrodynamic
    ☐ partial hydrodynamic

20. _____ *lubrication is obtained when two mating surfaces are completely separated by a cohesive film of lubricant.*
    ☐ boundary-layer
    ☐ hydrodynamic
    ☐ partial hydrodynamic

21. *The thickness of the lubricant film exceeds the combined unevenness of the mating surfaces for _____ lubrication.*
    ☐ boundary-layer
    ☐ hydrodynamic
    ☐ partial hydrodynamic

22. _____ lubrication occurs in heavily loaded contact surfaces which may change shape under heavy loads, but return to their original shape when the load is reduced.

☐ boundary-layer
☐ hydrodynamic
☐ partial hydrodynamic

23. Lubricating grease consists of two main components. These are:

Answer: _____

24. When grease is used there is an increase in drippage and splattering.

☐ true   ☐ false

25. Grease acts as an additional seal to reduce leakage.

☐ true   ☐ false

26. By using grease, there may be decreased frequency in lubrication application.

☐ true   ☐ false

27. Grease has the ability to _____ the machine part and this is an advantage of grease lubrication.

☐ flow from   ☐ cling to

28. In most common types of greases, the thickener is a/an:

☐ animal fat soap
☐ synthetic soap
☐ metallic soap
☐ mineral oil

29. Which type of soap greases are often referred to as "multi-purpose" greases?

☐ sulfur soap greases
☐ lithium soap greases
☐ calcium soap greases
☐ sodium soap greases

30. Which type of soap grease is soluble in water?

☐ lithium   ☐ calcium
☐ sodium   ☐ multi-purpose

31. Which type of soap grease contains bentonite and silica gel?

☐ metallic soap greases
☐ calcium soap greases
☐ lithium soap greases
☐ greases thickened with inorganic substances

32. One of the main advantages of synthetic greases is that they do not _____ as rapidly as mineral oils.

☐ deposit   ☐ demulsify
☐ oxidize   ☐ liquify

33. Synthetic greases often have very low frictional resistance at low temperatures.

☐ true   ☐ false

34. Which common compounds are used as agents in Extreme Pressure greases?

Answer: _____

35. Why are molybdenum and graphite probably the best known additives used in greases for bearings?

Answer: _____

36. Which metals are often used as "anti-seize" compounds for applications such as threads?

☐ powdered zinc and copper
☐ sulfur and sodium
☐ tin and lead
☐ lithium and chlorine

37. The NLGI index for grease is based on the degree of penetration achieved by allowing a standard verified cone to penetrate into the grease at a standard temperature of 25 degrees C over a period of 5 seconds.

☐ true   ☐ false

38. The softer the grease is, the greater the depth of penetration and the _____ the NLGI index.

☐ higher   ☐ lower

39. For most common industrial applications, a grease of consistency class of _____ is used.

☐ NLGI 1   ☐ NLGI 2
☐ NLGI 3   ☐ NLGI 6

40. The lower temperature limit for a normal mineral oil based grease is approximately _____.

☐ minus 10°C   ☐ minus 30°C
☐ minus 40°C   ☐ minus 55°C

41. The following definition is for which characteristic of grease? "The temperature at which the first drop of grease falls from an orifice in a standard test apparatus."

☐ fire point   ☐ flash point
☐ melting point   ☐ dropping point

42. The mixing of greases should be avoided if possible.
☐ true ☐ false

43. The term _____ refers to the grease's capability of being mixed with other types of greases.
☐ consistency ☐ miscibility
☐ dropping point ☐ stability

44. For roller bearings which may come into contact with a large volume of water, the rust inhibitor in the grease should be _____.
☐ insoluble ☐ soluble

45. Rust inhibitors used in grease should adhere well to the bearing metal surface providing a lubricating film even if the grease is saturated with water.
☐ true ☐ false

46. Greases selected for machinery such as vibrating screens should have which essential characteristic?
☐ miscibility
☐ consistency
☐ mechanical stability
☐ sealing properties

47. If grease remains secure within the machine parts it can provide sealing protection.
☐ yes ☐ no

48. A felt type is seal is an example of a:
☐ non-contact seal ☐ contact seal

49. A radial lip seal is an example of a:
☐ non-contact seal ☐ contact seal

50. Axial and parallel labyrinth seals are examples of:
☐ non-contact seals ☐ contact seals

51. The later the grease is applied to the bearing during mounting procedures, the better the chance of preventing:
☐ overloading ☐ clearance problems
☐ axial end play ☐ contamination

52. A general rule is to completely pack a bearing with grease, but leave some free space in the bearing housing to allow for the grease to expand.
☐ true ☐ false

53. Name two types of non-separable roller bearings.
Answer: _____

54. A self-aligning bearing is considered to be a:
☐ separable bearing ☐ non-separable bearing

55. A cylindrical roller bearing is considered a:
   □ separable bearing □ non-separable bearing

56. Why is the amount of grease fill in a roller bearing housing critical?
   Answer: _____

57. "Packing" is a term used when applying grease by hand to a bearing.
   □ true   □ false

58. Determination of the regreasing interval depends on four factors. List these factors:
   Answer: _____

59. Oil lubrication is capable of carrying away undesirable heat.
   □ true   □ false

60. The established viscosity grade for oil lubrication is based on Kinematic Viscosities at 40 degrees C.
   □ true   □ false

61. The centistoke (cSt) is the official viscosity unit.
   □ true   □ false

62. The Society of Automotive Engineers (SAE) classes engine oils by SAE Viscosity Numbers, commonly referred to as SAE Grades.
   □ true   □ false

63. Three types of lubricating oils and their classifications are:
   Answer: _____

64. One major advantage of synthetic oil is that it can operate well in conditions where there is a wide range of operating temperatures.
   □ true   □ false

65. Are synthetic oils generally regarded as being fire resistant?
   □ yes   □ no

66. Additives in mineral oil are used generally to:
   □ change the oil's color
   □ improve the temperature range of the oil
   □ improve the performance and reliability of the oil
   □ improve the viscosity index of the oil

67. *Oxidation inhibitors in oil:*

☐ decrease the rate of oil oxidation
☐ increase the rate of oil oxidation
☐ decrease the rate of oil degradation by the effects of temperature changes
☐ none of the above

68. *The lowest temperature at which oil will flow when tested under prescribed conditions is commonly called:*

☐ flash point   ☐ fire point
☐ dropping point   ☐ pour point

69. *Extreme pressure additives help to reduce friction and can prevent galling, scoring, seizure and wear.*

☐ true   ☐ false

70. *Foam depressants in oil serve to:*

☐ promote foaming and bubbling of the oil
☐ allow air bubbles to form in the oil
☐ control the release rate of entrained air in the oil
☐ distribute the air molecules freely throughout the entire system

71. *The measure of the rate of viscosity change with temperature is called:*

☐ consistency   ☐ viscosity index
☐ pour point   ☐ miscibility

72. *The minimum temperature at which sufficient liquid is vaporized to create a mixture of fuel and air that will burn if ignited is called:*

☐ fire point   ☐ flash point

73. *Reliable methods for oil analysis can help identify five facts about the oil lubrication system. List these:*

Answer: _____

74. *List three primary elements which are required in order to formulate reliable data from an oil analysis program.*

Answer: _____

75. *List five primary reasons for performing an oil analysis.*

Answer: _____

76. *List four critical stages of an oil analysis.*

Answer: _____

77. *The accuracy of each stage of the oil analysis is _____ on the accuracy of the one previous.*

☐ independent   ☐ dependent

78. *Take the oil sample at mid-tank or at a point midway between the exit and the entrance, not at the top or bottom of the tank.*

☐ true ☐ false

79. *The filter is one of the best places to take the oil sample from.*

☐ true ☐ false

80. *Each laboratory that performs an oil analysis requires a:*

☐ written report from the owner describing the sample taken
☐ manufacturer's recommendation which identifies machinery oil data
☐ purchase order number
☐ sample slip

81. *A test called _____ is commonly used to determine several conditions of lube oils and greases.*

☐ total base number test
☐ total acid number test
☐ spectrographic analysis
☐ radiography

82. *Basic spectrographic analysis identifies wear metals and base elements in lubrication oils and greases.*

☐ true ☐ false

83. *Tin is a component of babbitt metals used for friction bearings.*

☐ true ☐ false

84. *Lead is not a component in solders.*

☐ true ☐ false

85. *Copper is often used as an overlay on friction bearings.*

☐ true ☐ false

86. *Some types of filtering and reclaiming systems use aluminum.*

☐ true ☐ false

87. *Silicon is the principle component of:*

☐ dirt, dust and sand ☐ brass and bronze
☐ iron and steel ☐ cement

88. *Chromium is often used to make steels softer.*

☐ true ☐ false

89. *Nickel is often used to make steels harder.*

☐ true ☐ false

90. *Manganese is classed as a:*

☐ oil additive metal ☐ wear metal
☐ antifreeze additive ☐ contaminant metal

91. Primarily, _____ is looking for particles larger than 5 microns.

☐ spectrographic analysis
☐ particle count analysis
☐ total base number test
☐ total acid number test

92. The _____ is useful to determine the oil's capability to neutralize acids formed during combustion in internal combustion engines.

☐ spectrographic analysis
☐ particle count analysis
☐ total base number test
☐ total acid number test

93. The Total Acid Number Test is used frequently to determine the amount of acid formed in the oil.

☐ true   ☐ false

94. Soot is a by-product from:

☐ mixing of oils
☐ mixing of oils and fuels
☐ combustion of fuels and oils
☐ burning metal parts inside the engine

95. Explain what the purpose of "Viscosity Testing is for lubrication oils.

Answer: _____

96. Iron, a wear metal, is usually reported in Parts Per Million (PPM).

☐ true   ☐ false

97. Oxidation of oils is generally _____ by high operating temperatures.

☐ not accelerated   ☐ accelerated

98. For pressurized oil systems, take the oil sample when:

☐ the machine is shut down
☐ while the machine is running

99. For non-pressurized oil systems, take the oil sample when:

☐ the machine is shutdown
☐ while the machine is running a full speed
☐ while the machine is running at its idle speed

100. High quality report interpretation of the oil analysis performed requires seven key factors. These are:

Answer: _____

101. Oxidation continues to be the most common form of oil degradation.

☐ true   ☐ false

102. The recommended oil level for a spherical roller bearing when at rest in the bearing housing is:

☐ completely fill the bearing housing
☐ half-way up the top most roller
☐ half-way up the lowest/bottom roller
☐ to the mid-point of the bearing's overall outside diameter

103. An oil circulation system which uses a pump to circulate the oil to the bearings and seals is classed as:

☐ an open system   ☐ a closed system

104. An oil injection system is generally recommended for _____ because the oil can better penetrate the interior sections of the bearings.

☐ slow speed equipment
☐ high speed equipment

105. The likelihood of contamination is greatly increased if the lubricating oil is stored outside.

☐ true   ☐ false

106. When oil drums are stored upright it is best to:

☐ tilt them slightly
☐ keep them as vertical as possible

107. It is okay to use galvanized containers for storing and handling lubricant oils.

☐ true   ☐ false

108. It is okay to use gasoline, solvents, or kerosene to remove oil or similar products from the skin.

☐ true   ☐ false

109. Once a basic product line of lubricants has been selected, a program should be planned and organized for ensuring three main things. These are:

Answer: _____

110. The Plant Maintenance and/or Lubrication Department(s) is responsible for several key functions in order to maintain an effective lubrication program. List as many of these functions as possible:

Answer: _____

SECTION SIX

SIX

NON-DESTRUCTIVE TESTING

NDT Purpose

Non-destructive testing (NDT) or non-destructive examination (NDE) is used throughout industry to reduce the rate of machine failures. Testing and examinations are carried out without damage to parts or machines to determine:

a. If there are any defects that may cause a part to fail when in service.

b. That a part is within its specified tolerances.

c. That a machines condition will allow it to operate at its maximum efficiency.

This testing may be carried out during production of parts and also after a machine is commissioned and in service.

The types of faults and damage that may be found on rotating equipment include:

- Cracks
- Erosion
- Wear

- Loss of coating
- Reductions in thickness or wall size
- Weld integrity

An assembled machine can also be checked for:

- Correct assembly
- Loose parts
- Damage
- Blockages

Predictive and preventive maintenance programs are playing an increasingly larger role in the maintenance field. NDT is being used as one of the tools to increase plant safety and reliability.

The types of testing or examinations discussed in this section include:

1. Visual
2. Liquid Penetrant
3. Magnetic Particle
4. Ultrasonic
5. Eddy Current
6. Radiography

NDT Purpose (cont'd)

Although eddy current and radiography are listed here, only a brief description has been included on these two topics. This is because more extensive training is required to use these methods effectively and safely. Radiography also requires specific training, testing and certification of operators. With all NDT methods, well trained and experienced personnel will provide the most accurate and reliable results.

Before any testing, the tester should know what the problem(s) may be. More than one type of test may be required to ensure that the test piece is free of flaws.

Direct Visual Inspection

Direct visual inspection is the oldest and most common method of NDE. On plant shutdowns, when a machine is being dismantled, parts that are observed to be damaged can be put aside for replacement if the damage is obvious enough to be seen with the unaided eye. Further testing of apparently sound parts may also be carried out. This depends on the importance of that particular part. When a machine is being assembled, each part should be scrutinized visually before it is installed to ensure there is no obvious damage.

Direct visual is the simplest method of non-destructive examination. All that is required is adequate light, good eyesight, the ability to get close enough to carry out the examination, plus the experience and knowledge necessary to determine whether an imperfection is, or is not a problem.

Direct visual examination can be taken a step further with the use of magnification instruments such as magnifying glasses or microscopes.

Visual Inspection

Remote Visual Inspection (RVI)

Probably the simplest tool used for RVI is a swivel type mirror, which should be in every Millwright or Industrial Mechanics tool box. RVI allows the detection, observation, and analysis of defects inaccessible to the eye. Problems inside complex machines and machine parts can often be documented, photographed and sometimes repaired without costly dismantling of the machine.

The three main tools for accomplishing this are:

a. Videoimagescope
b. Fiberscope
c. Borescope

These three instruments share one common design feature, and that is a small diameter probe (of various lengths) which is attached to a control handle, to access the inner parts of a machine. The Videoimagescope and the Fiberscope have a flexible probe, which makes it easier to reach obscure places.

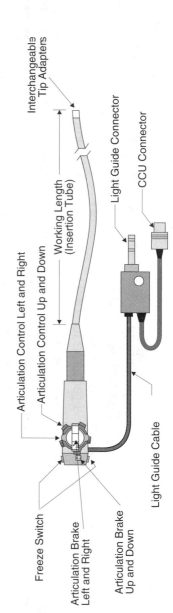

Illustration #178 - Videoimagescope

NON-DESTRUCTIVE TESTING

Visual Inspection (cont'd)

The Borescope has potentially the smallest diameter, but has a rigid probe. Because the Videoimagescope transmits the image via electrical impulses, it can reach longer distances than the Fiberscope.

Videoimagescope: This has a miniature color television camera built into the end of a flexible probe. The light is provided via fiberoptics through the probe. See illustration #178. The probe is flexible (illustration #179) and the tip can be articulated with the control at the handle. Interchangeable tips provide for various options such as changes in direction of view (directly ahead or sideways), and change in fields of view (magnification, depth of field or near/far focus).

The Videoimagescope image is viewed on a video monitor and can be stored and retrieved as required. The probe diameter may be as small as a quarter inch (6 mm) and over 65 feet (20 m) long.

Illustration #179 - Articulating Tip

Fiberscope: Uses a fiberoptic image bundle to carry the image back to the eyepiece. As with the Videoimagescope, the light source is also provided with fiber optics. The complete insertion tube is flexible, has an articulating tip and is usually waterproof.

Fiberscopes differ from Videoimagescopes in that a live image is seen at the eyepiece. The resolution and size of the image will depend on the number of fibers used in the image bundle. The diameter of the Fiberscope will determine this number. See illustration #180.

Visual Inspection (cont'd)

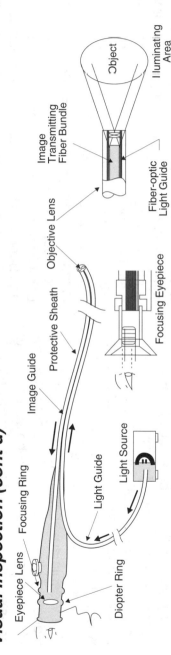

Illustration #180 - Fiberscope

Normal diameters range from 0.24 to 0.48 inches (6 - 12 mm). Although ultra thin Fiberscopes may go down to less than 0.04 inches (1 mm). Lengths with the larger diameters may go to over 20 feet (6 m).

Optical tip adapters are available to allow for various fields of view (10° to 100°) and directions of view (side and direct). See illustrations #181 and #182. Various adapters allow video or photographic cameras to be attached to the eyepiece to record inspections.

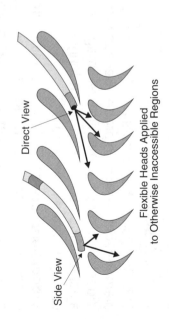

Illustration #181 - Inspecting Turbine Rotor Buckets

NON-DESTRUCTIVE TESTING

Visual Inspection (cont'd)

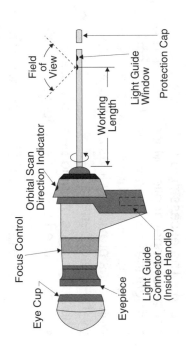

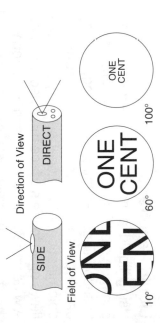

Illustration #182 - Direction & Fields of View

Illustration #183 - Direction of View and Borescope

Borescope: Is another instrument for remotely inspecting the inside of a machine by optical means. The insertion tube is rigid and the image is transmitted from the objective lens via relay lenses to the eyepiece. Again the light source is usually accomplished using fiber optics. Diameters range from approximately 0.06 to 0.63 inches (1.5 mm to 16 mm). Maximum lengths available are up to 90 inches (2.3 m) for the larger diameters.

Visual Inspection (cont'd)

The larger diameters will provide a larger and brighter image. Standard directions of view are shown in illustration #183 and are:

a. Direct
b. Fore-oblique
c. Side
d. Retrospective

As with the Fiberscope, various adapters are available to connect still and video cameras to the Borescope

Liquid Penetrant

Using liquid penetrant is one of the more common methods of checking for cracks due to such things as: fatigue, grinding, welding, casting, shrinkage, lack of bonding, delamination, etc. Local porosity and other flaws open to the surface may also be found. A wide variety of materials can be tested with this method (metals, ceramics, plastics and glass).

Visual Inspection/Liquid Penetrant

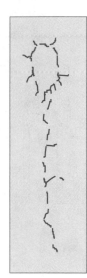

Illustration #184 - Crack in Pipe

The liquid penetrant method uses a special liquid to penetrate the flaw due to capillary action. The excess fluid is then cleaned off and a developer applied which is designed to highlight the flaw by drawing the liquid from it. Illustration #184 shows a surface crack which was previously invisible, made visible by the use of penetrant.

The advantages of liquid penetrant are:

● Can be used on a wide variety of materials.
● Simple to use and does not require extensive training.
● Does not require expensive and dedicated equipment.

Liquid Penetrant (cont'd)

The disadvantages of liquid penetrant are:

- Does not detect sub-surface faults.
- Does not indicate the width or depth of a crack.
  - Cannot be used on porous materials or materials that do not have a smooth surface.

Using liquid penetrant requires the following five steps. See illustration #185.

1. Surface preparation
2. Penetrant application
3. Removal of the excess penetrant
4. Developing
5. Inspection and interpretation

1. Surface Preparation: Not only is a clean surface essential, but if the crack or flaw is filled with dirt, grease or other matter the penetrant will not be able to penetrate and fill the flaw.

Preparation methods include: mechanical brushing and etch cleaning to remove rust and scale and the use of solvents and detergents to remove oil and grease.

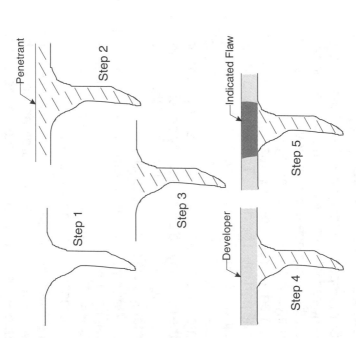

Illustration #185 - Five Steps of Liquid Penetrant

Liquid Penetrant (cont'd)

Some special cleaning substances may be required if there are certain coatings or paint on the test piece that may cover the discontinuity. A thorough washing may then be required to remove any residual chemicals. The part must be dried. Toweling and heated air will ensure that all moisture is removed.

Before applying the penetrant, the intermediate step of opening up any flaw by stressing the part may be performed by either bending, heating, or ultrasonic vibration. Choose the method which is applicable.

2. Penetrant Application: The penetrant is a liquid that exhibits good capillary characteristics. To make it visible it will contain a dye, fluorescent material, or both.

Dye penetrants produce a contrasting color with the developer under ordinary light. The fluorescent penetrant will require the use of an ultraviolet (black) light in a darkened room.

The penetrant is either brushed or sprayed on to the part, or the parts may be immersed in the penetrant. The penetrant is left on the part for a sufficient time (up to 30 minutes) to penetrate any flaws.

3. Removal of Excess Penetrant: The method of penetrant removal will depend on the type of penetrant used. Water washable penetrant can be simply wiped or rinsed off with water. The emulsifiable penetrant will require the application of an emulsifying agent before rinsing. The solvent type will require the application of a solvent to remove the excess.

After removal of the excess penetrant the part must be thoroughly dried before applying the developer.

4. Developing: The developing agent has four functions to accomplish:

a. Provide contrast to help identify the flaw.

b. Spread the penetrant over a larger area as it bleeds back.

Liquid Penetrant (cont'd)

c. Act as a "blotter" for the trapped penetrant.

d. Control the penetrant bleed out.

There are four types of developers:

1. Dry developer which is a powder like substance that may be brushed or air sprayed on. This is most suitable for rough surfaces.

2. Wet aqueous developers which are water based. Application is by spraying, dipping or pouring. Some heating may help to dry the part after application.

3. Wet non-aqueous developer which uses a volatile solvent base. Application is the same as #2 but drying is not necessary as the solvent evaporates rapidly.

4. Film type developer which contains a plastic powder and a solvent. As the solvent evaporates it draws the penetrant from the flaw. The penetrant combines with the plastic to harden into a removable plastic strip.

5. Inspection: After application of the developer, observe the part for bleed back. Large flaws will indicate almost immediately, while smaller flaws will require more time. Unless care is taken to clean off all of the excess penetrant, it may be impossible to obtain an accurate interpretation.

Magnetic Particle

When ferromagnetic material is magnetized, lines of magnetic flux run through the material in a uniform manner, in a direction depending on the method of inducing the magnetism. See illustration #186A.

If there is a discontinuity such as a crack or casting flaw the magnetic flux will be distorted as shown in illustrations #186B and #186C.

Magnetic Particle

Magnetic Particle (cont'd)

When a test piece is magnetized, any discontinuities that are oriented transverse to the magnetic field will distort the field, producing a flux leakage pattern directly above it. When finely divided magnetic particles are applied to the surface there will be a concentration of particles at the leakage point as they provide a path to bridge the gap. See illustration #187.

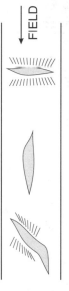

Diagonal Crack   Longitudinal Crack   Transverse Crack

Illustration #187 - Magnetic Particles & Flux Leakage

Flux Lines ➞

A   Uniform Flux Lines

Leakage from
Surface Flaw

B   Distortion by a Surface Crack

Leakage from
Subsurface Flaw

C   Distortion by Internal Flaw near the Surface

Illustration #186 - Magnetic Flux and Leakage

NON-DESTRUCTIVE TESTING

Magnetic Particle (cont'd)

The advantages of the Magnetic Particle method are:

- sensitive to flaws of almost any size shape and composition.
- can detect flaws that are just below the surface.

The disadvantages of the Magnetic Particle method are:

- can only be applied to ferromagnetic material.
- if the magnetic flux is parallel to the crack it will not show, therefore perhaps requiring two or more tests.

Using the Magnetic Particle method takes three major steps:

1. Magnetization of the part
2. Application of the particles
3. Inspection and interpretation

1. Magnetization of the Part: Magnetization is accomplished by the use of low voltage electric currents.

Permanent magnets produce magnetic fields but they are usually too weak and are seldom used.

The four types of current available are: alternating currents (AC), direct currents (DC), rectified AC and pulsed DC.

Alternating currents produce fields close to the surface and are best for locating surface flaws. Direct currents, rectified AC and pulsed DC produce magnetic fields that penetrate deep into the metal and are best for locating subsurface flaws.

There are four main methods to induce magnetism in the part:

a. Coil around the test piece. The test piece should be in the exact center for best results. On large pieces the coil may have to be moved to several positions. The magnetic field will be oriented as shown in illustration #188. Transverse cracks will cause flux leakage, longitudinal cracks will not.

Magnetic Particle (cont'd)

Magnetic Particle

Indirect Circumferential Magnetization

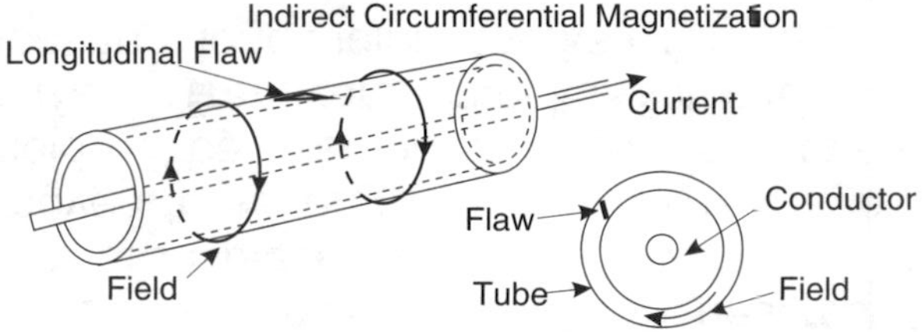

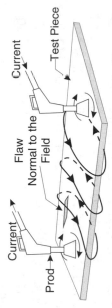

Illustration #190 - Current Through Conductor & Test Piece

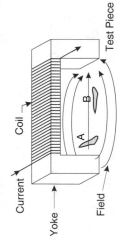

Illustration #191 - Use of Prods

Illustration #192 - Yoke Method

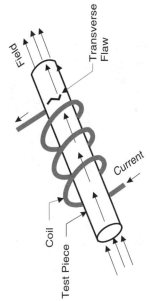

Illustration #188 - Coil Around Test Piece

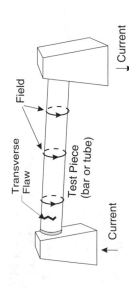

Illustration #189 - Current Through Test Piece

Magnetic Particle (cont'd)

b. Pass a current through a test piece (either directly through a solid piece or with a conductor through a hollow pipe) as shown in illustrations #189 and #190.

Transverse flaws oriented parallel to the resulting magnetic field (illustration #189) may not be detected. Flaws longitudinal to the test piece and oriented across the magnetic field (illustration #190) can be detected by flux leakage.

c. Pass a current through a portion using prods. When a test piece is large, selected suspect areas may be tested by this method. When using prods, the magnetic field is as shown in illustration #191. If a crack is normal to the field then flux leakage will be produced. Large currents may be required with this method so care must be used to avoid electric shock or arcing due to poor contact.

d. Electro-magnetic Yoke. This method is also used when only a portion of a large test piece is to be checked. The Yoke method produces a magnetic field as shown in illustration #192. Again it will depend on the orientation of any flaws whether it produces flux leakage. In illustration #192, flaw (A) will be detectable while flaw (B) may not.

2. Application of the Particles: The particles consist of a fine iron oxide powder that are elongated to assist in polarization and lubricated to enhance their mobility. There are two main forms of particle:

Dry particles are applied by sprinkling or spraying onto the magnetized surface. The particles should float down to the surface so that they are free to form an indication if there is a leakage flux. The dry powder is preferable for rougher surfaces and sub surface defects.

Wet particles are suspended in a fluid such as oil or water and are applied by spray or by dipping.

Magnetic Particle (cont'd)

The iron oxide particles may be a natural black color, dyed a brighter color, or treated with a fluorescent material. If the latter is used an ultra-violet (black) light will be required.

Usually the dry particles are dyed and the wet particles are fluorescent.

3. Inspection and interpretation: Whether or not a flaw is detected will depend on a number of factors. The strength of the magnetic field (too strong or too weak), the orientation of the fault with regard to the flux lines (which may require two or three tests to be conducted), and the depth of the flaw below the surface.

The strength of the current used will be determined by trial and experience. If the current is too weak, no pattern will develop. If the current is too strong then an accumulation of particles will obscure the pattern making it difficult to distinguish.

Magnetic Particle/Ultrasonic

Experience will also determine the placement and location of the prods, yoke or coil depending on the method of producing the magnetic field.

Ultrasonic

The application of high frequency sound waves is used to detect internal flaws in materials and also for thickness gaging.

Ultrasonic Sound Waves

Sound waves are audible in the range of 20 Hz to 20 kHz. If these long wavelengths were used to detect flaws they would merely bend around the flaw. When sound waves are produced at a higher frequency than the audible, they are referred to as ultrasonic. Ultrasonic sound waves used for NDT range to over 20 MHz. These high frequency waves interact with imperfections and help to reveal them.

Electrical energy is used to generate mechanical vibrations which are transferred to the material being inspected.

Ultrasonic (cont'd)

If the material is elastic the ultrasonic waves will propagate through the material by the displacement of successive molecules through the material.

Types of Waves

The three types of waves that are used in ultrasonic testing are:

1. Longitudinal waves in which the particles vibrate in the same direction as the wave is being propagated.

Illustration #193 - Longitudinal & Shear Waves

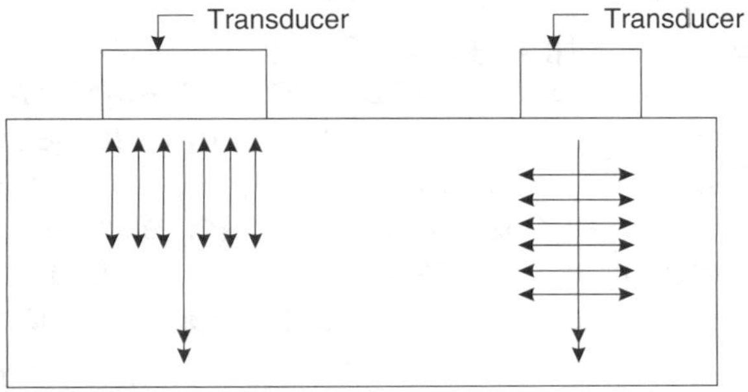

2. Transverse waves (sometimes referred to as shear waves), in which the particles vibrate at right angles to the direction of wave propagation.

3. Surface waves (Rayleigh waves are the most common type used) which travel close to the surface, following any curvature, and are used to detect surface cracks.

See illustration #193 for an example of longitudinal and shear waves. The advantages of ultrasonic testing are:

- Can reveal minute imperfections.
- The sensitivity does not change much over a wide range of thicknesses.
- No harmful radiation.
- Data or results are electronic and can be stored and retrieved as needed.
- Can reveal deep sub-surface flaws.
- Can be used on various materials types.

Ultrasonic Requirements

The instruments used for ultrasonic testing will depend on the method being used, but items common to most tests are as follows:

Illustration #193 - Longitudinal & Shear Waves

378   NON-DESTRUCTIVE TESTING

Ultrasonic (cont'd)

A high frequency pulse generator, a transmitting probe, a receiving probe, a signal amplifier, and a CRT or oscilloscope for the display. The transmitting and receiving probes are often referred to as transducers (any device that converts one type of energy to another is a transducer). For this test the electrical energy is converted to mechanical energy and vice versa). In some cases the sending and receiving transducer will be the same unit.

Transmitting the sound wave from the sending transducer to the test piece cannot be accomplished simply by holding the transmitting probe to the surface. Efficient energy transfer is accomplished by providing a thin layer of fluid. This is usually a mixture of glycerin, oil, grease or petroleum jelly, depending on the type of surface. This is referred to as the couplant. The non-drip type couplant (grease and petroleum jelly) would be used on vertical or overhead surfaces.

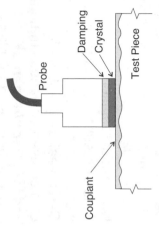

Illustration #194 - Couplant and Test Piece

The most common couplant is oil. Very smooth and flat surfaces would use a low viscosity oil, and rougher surfaces would use higher viscosity oil. The average viscosity is in the range of an SAE 30 oil.

One other method of transferring the ultrasonic waves is by immersion. The probe(s) and the test piece are immersed in a liquid, usually water and the ultrasonic waves travel through the water and then the test piece. See illustration #195

Ultrasonic (cont'd)

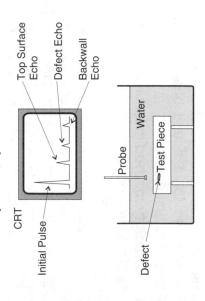

Illustration #195 - Immersed Test Piece

Surface Preparation

The surface condition can effect the reliability of the ultrasonic test procedure. Having a uniform surface is more important than concentrating on a high quality polished surface. All dirt, loose scale and sand, etc. should be removed, as particles can effect or vary the depth of the couplant. A very rough surface may be scraped or sanded.

Larger surfaces may be sand or bead blasted. If mechanical sanding is use beware of creating concave spots which will give an erratic coupling.

Ultrasonic Testing Methods

There are many techniques used in ultrasonic testing, but if the variables being measured are considered then there are four primary categories. These four are:

1. Resonant frequency method
2. Transit time method
3. Intensity method.
4. Intensity and transit time method.

The last two methods are used to measure material thickness.

The resonant frequency method is probably one of the older NDT methods if one considers the "ring" test where an item to be tested was lightly struck and the resultant ringing sound compared to other similar items. If a flaw is present the natural frequency of the object is changed resulting in a different tone.

Ultrasonic (cont'd)

Using the resonant frequency method with ultrasonics involves varying the frequency of the applied sound wave until standing waves are set up causing an increase in energy consumption which is read on a meter or CRT. The actual thickness is calculated by formula or read on a calibrated CRT screen.

The transit time method is used to determine thickness by measuring the length of time required for a sound beam to travel through the test piece.

The intensity method measures the amplitude of the ultrasound after being propagated through the test piece.

The intensity and transit time method is widely used and measures both the amplitude of the ultrasound after it has traveled the test piece and the time that it takes. The following is a description of some of the more common methods of ultrasonic testing beginning with the most common:

Ultrasonic

1. Intensity and transit time method: the pulse echo procedure is the most common intensity and transit time method, and is probably the most important. It can be used where it is not possible to reach both sides of the test piece. The test piece can be any shape and the distance that the defect is located from the probe can be measured. A variety of pulse echo procedures are available for detecting flaws. Some of these are:

a. normal probe or straight beam

b. angle beam

c. surface wave

The echo method is similar in principle to radar or sonar. A signal is sent out and the intensity and time of any echo that bounces back is measured. This is indicated on the CRT.

With normal probe or straight beam testing the ultrasonic wave is directed straight through the material so that its echo is reflected back to the signal transducer from the opposite surface.

Ultrasonic (cont'd)

Illustration #196A shows the signal observed on the CRT if there is no flaw, and illustration #196B shows the signal when there is a flaw.

The large blip on the left hand side is the initial pulse, any further blips are signal echoes received. The scale from left to right is a time scale and can be adjusted to suit the thickness of the material.

The height of the echo gives an indication of the size of the reflecting surface, but is somewhat effected by the thickness of the material and the effect the material has on reducing the signal.

Illustration #197A-E indicates various types of signals that may be observed when other faults are present. Illustration #197A has two small flaws; illustration #197B has a large flaw that is masking the flaw behind it and the back wall; illustration #197C has a large angled flaw that reflects the beam to the side with no echo; illustration #197D has a small flaw producing an echo but the angled back wall reflects the beam to the side; illustration #197E has porosity causing attenuation of the beam due to scattering, with no solid echo, only what is referred to as "grass."

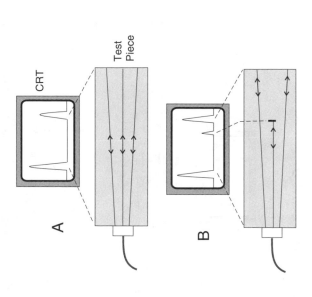

Illustration #196 - CRT Signal

Ultrasonic (cont'd)

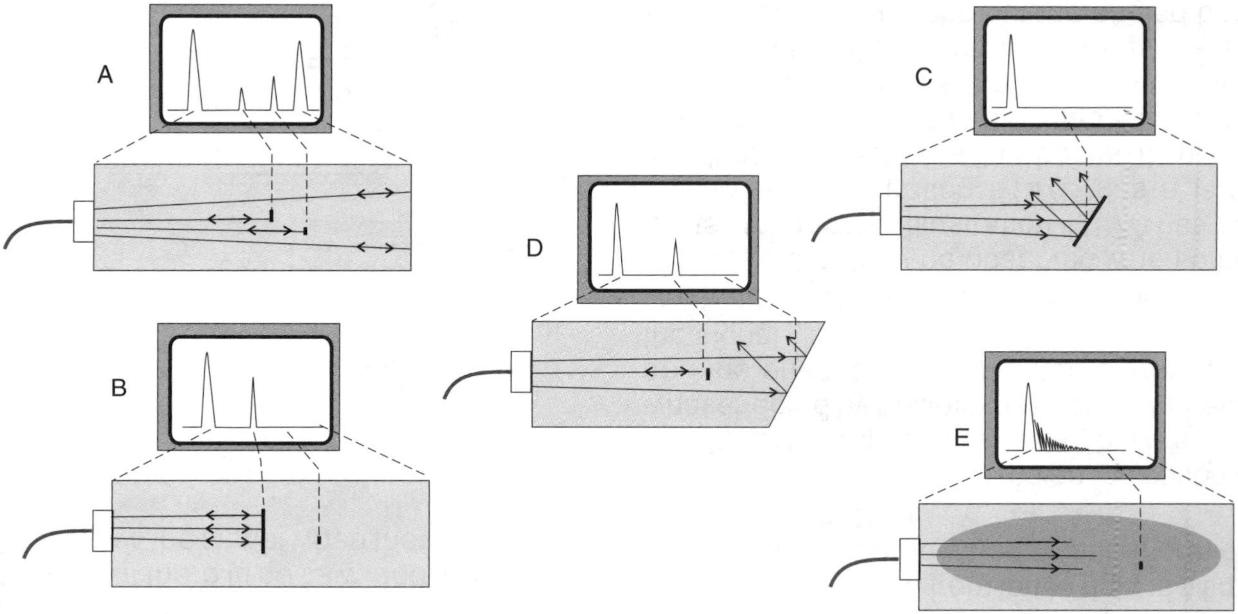

Illustration #197 - Various Faults on CRT

Ultrasonic (cont'd)

Note: On illustration #197A-E, the location of the fault can be estimated by observing the location of the blip compared to the top and bottom surfaces.

The main limitation of the pulse echo method using the straight beam when testing very thin materials is that it becomes inaccurate due to the speed at which the ultrasonic wave travels. There is not enough time between the initial pulse and the back wall echo to detect an echo from a flaw.

Angled beam testing using reflection to transmit transverse or shear waves is another version of the pulse echo procedure. Heavy machine rotors such as those from turbines, generators, compressors, etc., and heavy pipe and tubing can be inspected for flaws.

Because sound waves can be reflected in a similar manner to light waves, any sound wave that is introduced at an angle in a suitable part can reflect repeatedly at the surfaces and travel long distances.

This happens provided there is not a flaw to echo it back. See illustration #198 for an example of angled beam.

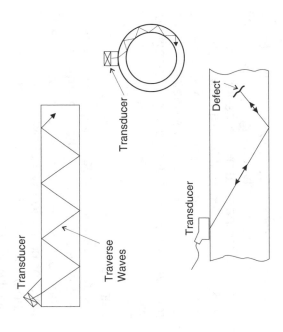

Illustration #198 - Angle Beam Examples

Ultrasonic

Ultrasonic (cont'd)

The radio frequency applied to the transducer is continually changing. When an echo arrives back at the transducer, its frequency will be different from that being transmitted at that moment. The difference between the two frequencies (the echo being received and the signal being transmitted) will give an indication of the depth of the flaw. Thickness testing can also be accomplished using the pulse echo technique. This uses the transit time method (the intensity component is not required). After calibration, any reduction in the thickness of a part due to wear or corrosion will show up on the CRT (the back wall echo will become closer to the initial pulse).

2. Intensity Method: The intensity method requires separate sending and receiving transceivers. If the straight beam method is used, then the transmitter and receiver will be on opposite sides of the test piece. See illustration #200.

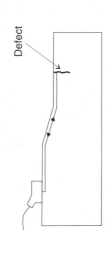

Defect

Illustration #199 - Surface Wave Crack Detection

The surface wave probe is another type of pulse echo procedure. Surface waves will follow the contour of the test piece surface and is therefore useful for detecting surface cracks in such parts as turbine rotor blades and axial flow compressor rotor blades, etc. See illustration #199.

Frequency Modulation is another intensity and transit time method. One transducer sends and receives ultrasonic energy continuously.

Ultrasonic (cont'd)

One most important application of this method is for testing sheet metal for laminar flaws. It is also suitable for the automatic testing of large numbers of similar test pieces.

If a reflective beam is used, as in illustration #201, the distance between the probes is critical and, in practice, a jig would have to be used to maintain the distance between the probes as they are moved to scan a particular area.

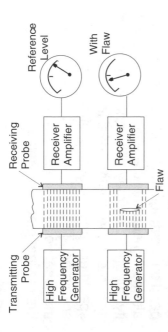

Illustration #200 - Intensity Method - Transmission

Using two transceivers poses a number of disadvantages over the reflection method:

- The test piece is required to have parallel sides and access to both sides is required.
- The probes must be positioned exactly opposite one another.
- Two probes double the chance of having problems with the fluid coupling.
- The location (depth) of the fault is not indicated.

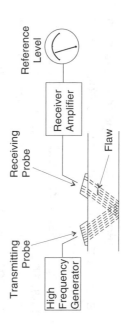

Illustration #201 - Intensity Method - Reflection

Eddy Current Testing

Eddy Current techniques can be used to inspect electrically conducting specimens for defects, irregularities in structure, and determining coating thickness. Eddy Current tests are most effective for locating irregularities near the surface of the specimen.

When a coil carrying AC is brought near a metal specimen, Eddy Currents are induced in the metal by electromagnetic induction. The magnitude of these induced currents depend on the magnitude and frequency of the alternating current; the electrical conductivity, magnetic permeability, and shape of the specimen; the relative position of coil and specimen; and presence of defects in the specimen. The Eddy Currents induced in the metal set up a magnetic field, which opposes the original magnetic field.

This magnetic field affects the impedance of the exciting coil, or any pickup coil close to the specimen.

A defect causes the path of the Eddy Currents, and thus the magnetic field, to be distorted. This results in an apparent change in coil impedance that can be measured.

Most Eddy Current applications are high speed testing of small diameter tube, bar, and wire. Sensitivity is set by means of referencing artificial defects in a test specimen and specimen handling. Data collection, data interpretation, and defect marking are automated operations.

NON-DESTRUCTIVE TESTING

Radiography

Radiography is one of the most popular and widely used processes of non-destructive testing to detect sub-surface defects and faults. A permanent record is produced in the form of an image created on a film that was exposed to a source of radiant energy.

Radiation has a very short wave length which allows it to pass through solid and opaque material. The radiation intensity is reduced in relation to the absorption rate of the structure it passes through.

Example: When radiation passes through a material which has an internal void such as porosity or slag the amount of absorption is reduced in that area, allowing a greater amount of radiation to reach the film directly behind the void. Unexposed film will darken when exposed to radiation and the degree of darkening is dependent upon the amount of radiation which reaches the film in a given area. See illustration #202.

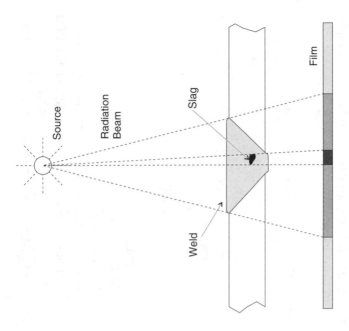

Illustration #202 - Differential Absorption Recorded on Film

Radiography Sources

There are two sources of penetrating waves which are suitable for radiography:

1. X-ray
2. Gamma Ray

Advantages of X-rays

- No residual radiation is generated or retained when the power is switched off.
- Penetrating power is adjustable through varying the high voltage (kV) input.
- Can be used on all materials (including aluminum).
- Provides radiographs with good contrast and sensitivity.
- Sufficient size machines exist to radiograph through 20 inches (500 mm) of steel.

Disadvantages

- High initial cost.
- Requires source of electrical power.
- Equipment not very portable, also relatively fragile.

- Tube head usually large in size; unusable in tight locations.
- Electrical hazard from high voltage.

Advantages of Gamma Rays

- Small initial and low maintenance costs.
- Rugged construction, more suited to industrial locations.
- No electric power required or concern of electrical hazard.
- High penetrating power.
- Portable with access into small areas with source tube.

Disadvantages

- Radiation hazard and radiation emitted continuously.
- Penetrating power cannot be adjusted.
- Radioisotope decays in strength requiring recalibration and replacement.
- Radiographic contrast generally less than X-ray.
- Cannot be used on all materials (eg. aluminum).

Radiography Safety

The process of radiography can be performed safely and without risk to the operator and personnel in the surrounding areas provided safety precautions are strictly followed.

It is the responsibility of the licensed operator to assure that all persons are kept a safe distance from the exposure area by the use of rope barricades and warning signs placed at all access points to the area.

Upon completion of the radiograph exposure and safe storage of the source, the barricades and signs should be removed immediately to avoid the development of a complacent attitude toward the warnings.

Note: Ionizing radiation can be very damaging to the human body depending on the concentration of the exposure. Illness produced from ionizing radiation ranges from nausea, vomiting, headache, and diarrhea to loss of hair and teeth, reduction in red and white blood cells, hemorrhaging, sterility, and death.

A safe distance in the use of Iridium 192 is at least 50 feet (15 m) from the source in all directions.

SECTION SIX QUESTIONS
Non-Destructive Testing

1. List six types of faults or damage that may be detected by using NDT or NDE methods.
   Answer: _____

2. Name six different non destructive examinations that may be used in predictive and preventive maintenance programs.
   Answer: _____

3. Which type of NDT method requires the operators to have specific training and certification?
   Answer: _____

4. What three tools or instruments are used for remote visual inspection?
   Answer: _____

5. Which of the three instruments used for remote visual inspection does not have a flexible probe?
   Answer: _____

6. Which of the three instruments used for remote visual inspection has potentially the longest reach?
   Answer: _____

7. Which of the three instruments used for remote visual inspection uses a miniature television camera to produce an image on a video monitor?
   Answer: _____

8. Liquid penetrant testing can only be used on metallic materials.
   ☐ true   ☐ false

9. One advantage of liquid penetrant testing is that it does not require expensive equipment.
   ☐ true   ☐ false

10. Liquid penetrant testing would be a suitable for checking for sub-surface cracks.
    ☐ true   ☐ false

11. Liquid penetrant testing is the most suitable test if the material being tested is porous or has a very rough surface.
    ☐ true   ☐ false

12. List the five steps that are followed when using liquid penetrant.
Answer: _____

13. When preparing a surface that has been painted for liquid penetrant testing, the paint should be:
☐ removed   ☐ left on

14. After washing a part with solvent in preparation for liquid penetrant testing, the excess solvent should be:
☐ left on to assist the penetrant application
☐ thoroughly dried

15. Sometimes before applying the penetrant, a part is stressed to open up any potential flaws. List three methods of stressing a sample.
Answer: _____

16. Dye penetrants:
☐ will require the use of an ultraviolet (black) light
☐ do not require the use of an ultraviolet light

17. Fluorescent penetrants:
☐ will require the use of an ultraviolet (black) light
☐ do not require the use of an ultraviolet light

18. Some penetrants contain both a dye and fluorescent material.
☐ true   ☐ false

19. After the penetrant is applied, it is left on long enough to harden.
☐ true   ☐ false

20. Any excess penetrant is removed after enough time has elapsed for it to penetrate the flaw.
☐ true   ☐ false

21. List the four functions of the developer used in liquid penetrant testing.
Answer: _____

22. The type of developer that would most likely require heating to assist in drying would be the:
☐ dry developer
☐ wet aqueous developer
☐ wet non aqueous developer
☐ film type

23. One advantage of the magnetic particle test is that it can detect sub-surface flaws.
☐ true   ☐ false

31. Ultrasonic testing is used for detecting flaws but cannot be used for thickness gaging.

☐ true ☐ false

32. What is the frequency range of audible sound waves?

Answer: _____

33. Ultrasonic sound waves used for NDT range up to what frequency?

Answer: _____

34. A device that converts one type of energy to another is often referred to as a/an:

☐ oscilloscope ☐ transducer
☐ CRT ☐ signal amplifier

35. The couplant used in ultrasonic testing provides an efficient method of transferring energy from the probe to the test piece.

☐ true ☐ false

36. On rough surfaces, a very low viscosity oil would be used as a couplant for ultrasonic testing.

☐ true ☐ false

37. List four primary categories of ultrasonic testing methods.

Answer: _____

24. List the three main steps in completing a magnetic particle test.

Answer: _____

25. One advantage of the magnetic particle test is that it can be used on virtually all types of materials.

☐ true ☐ false

26. Magnetization of a part is accomplished using:

☐ high voltage currents
☐ low voltage currents

27. Both alternating and direct currents can be used in magnetic particle testing.

☐ true ☐ false

28. After a test piece is magnetized, any discontinuities that are oriented _____ the magnetic field will distort the field.

☐ parallel to ☐ across

29. Wet particles are preferable for rough surfaces when magnetic particle testing.

☐ true ☐ false

30. The iron oxide particles used in magnetic particle testing come in three forms, which are:

Answer: _____

38. The transit time method can be used for measuring material thickness.

☐ true   ☐ false

39. The pulse echo procedure is the most common intensity and transit time method.

☐ true   ☐ false

40. The pulse echo procedure relies on the sound wave being bounced back to the transceiver.

☐ true   ☐ false

41. Thickness testing can be accomplished by the pulse echo method.

☐ true   ☐ false

42. Surface waves are used to test for:

☐ porosity   ☐ material thickness
☐ deep flaws   ☐ surface defects

43. The intensity method is ideal for locating the depth of a fault.

☐ true   ☐ false

44. The intensity method using a reflected beam would require only one transceiver.

☐ true   ☐ false

45. The most common use of eddy current testing is for high speed testing of small diameter tubes, bar and wire.

☐ true   ☐ false

46. Eddy current techniques can be used to determine coating thickness.

☐ true   ☐ false

47. Radiography provides a permanent record of any flaws in the piece being tested.

☐ true   ☐ false

48. What are the two usual sources of waves used in radiography?
Answer: _____

49. X-rays used in radiography require no electrical source.

☐ true   ☐ false

50. Gamma rays used in radiography require no electrical source.

☐ true   ☐ false

51. Radiography is potentially harmful to personnel if the required safety precautions are not strictly adhered to.

☐ true   ☐ false

SECTION SEVEN

BEARING FAILURE ANALYSIS

Bearing Problems

When attempting to find the cause of a bearing failure, ensure that none of the evidence is destroyed. For example, if a bearing has failed prematurely, do not immediately wash off the grease or pour all of the oil away to have a closer look at the bearing as some of the failure clues may be with the lubricant. If close examination at the site does not reveal any clues, laboratory testing of oil or grease samples may indicate such things as additive depletion, abrasive contamination, corrosive contamination, oxidation, viscosity changes etc. This information can be invaluable in determining the cause of a bearing problem and in deciding what corrective action should be taken.

Anti-friction Bearing Life

In a properly designed rotating machine using anti-friction bearings, the bearings are selected as to type and size so that they will last for an expected amount of time or number of revolutions.

This calculated life expectancy is based on five assumptions, which are:

1. Correct lubrication is supplied at all times.

2. The bearing will be installed correctly without damage.

3. The shaft and housing will be of the correct dimensions.

4. No inherent defects in the bearing.

5. The operating parameters such as load, speed and temperature will be within that assumed by the desigrer.

Even when correctly designed, installed and operated, a bearing will eventually be subject to fatigue failure.

Anti-friction Bearing Life (cont'd)

Normal fatigue will show up toward the end of a bearing's life as a flaking or spalling of the raceways and rolling members. This spalling starts below the surface where it is invisible, and cracks eventually show up on the surface. The spalling progresses as the metal starts to flake away.

The inner raceway of a deep groove ball bearing at the end of its life may look similar to illustration #203. Long before the bearing approaches this condition a predictive maintenance program would have detected bearing problems. If the bearing was allowed to reach the condition shown, excessive noise and high temperatures would indicate the serious damage sustained by the bearing. If operation of the machine is continued due to remoteness or lack of attention, then total destruction of the bearing and possible damage to the machine will result.

Illustration #203 - Spalling on Inner Ring

Load Path Patterns

Knowledge of the normal patterns produced by a load on a bearing is useful when determining the cause of premature bearing failure. When a rolling element bearing is used under load, the appearance of the contacting surfaces (the rolling members and the raceways) will change from being polished to becoming dull. This change in appearance shows where the loading is taking place in the bearing.

Load Path Patterns

Load Path Patterns (cont'd)

The following is a description of the expected load paths that may be found on a deep groove ball bearing for some of the common loading possibilities.

A **rotating inner ring load** occurs when the outer ring is held stationary in a housing and the inner ring rotates with the loaded shaft.

Illustration #204 shows the load distribution on a deep groove ball bearing that has a rotating inner ring load. The inner ring becomes loaded for 360 degrees while the outer ring carries the load on less than 180 degrees. Illustration #205 shows the load pattern on the raceways of the two rings.

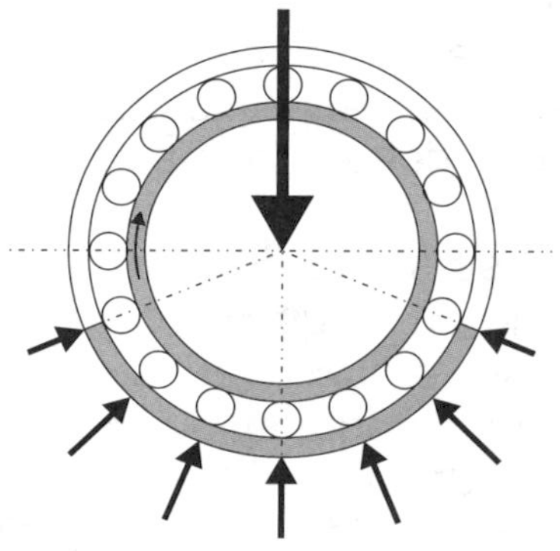

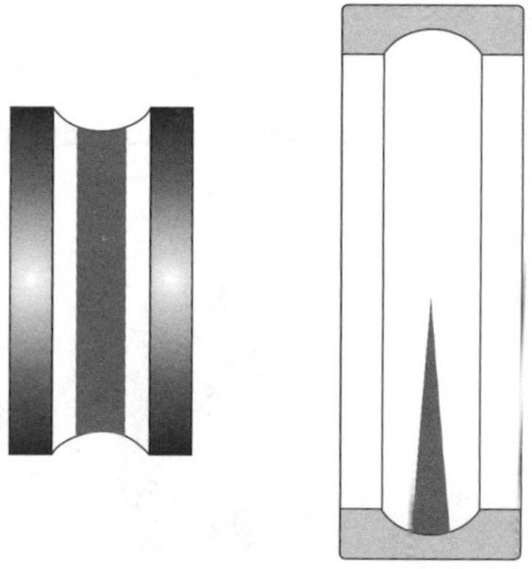

Illustration #205 - Normal Load Pattern
Rotating Inner Ring Load

Illustration #204 - Rotating Inner Ring Load

Load Path Patterns (cont'd)

A rotating outer ring load occurs when the inner ring is held on a stationary shaft and the rotating outer ring is loaded in one direction.

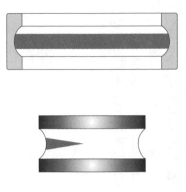

Illustration #206 - Load Distribution Rotating Outer Ring Load
Illustration #206 shows the load distribution on a deep groove ball bearing that has a loaded rotating outer ring and a stationary inner ring. The outer ring becomes loaded for 360 degrees while the inner ring carries the load on less than 180 degrees. Illustration #207 shows the load pattern on the raceways of the two rings.

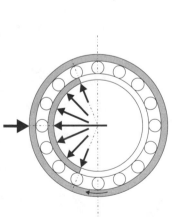

Illustration #207 - Normal Load Pattern
Rotating Outer Ring Load

Note: The load path patterns shown assume that there is no relative movement between the bearing rings and the shaft or housing. In most cases the stationary ring is installed with a slight clearance, and will slowly rotate (creep) around the shaft or housing. This will distribute the wear around the whole circumference of the stationary raceway.

Load Path Patterns

A deep groove ball bearing subjected to an axial load with little or no radial load would have a load pattern as shown in illustration #208A. As the amount of axial load is increased the contact would beccme closer to the sides of the rings. Excessive axial load is shown in illustration #208B. This is one example of both rings having a continuous 360 degree path.

If the normal axial load is combined with a radial load, the resulting pattern will be a combination of illustration #205 and #208A, as shown in illustration #209. The radial load in this example is from a rotating inner ring load.

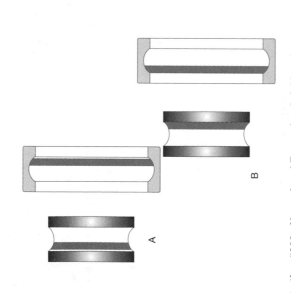

Illustration #208 - Normal and Excessive Axial Load

Load Path Patterns (cont'd)

A preload condition may exist if a bearing is mounted on a shaft or in a housing that has incorrect dimensions and all the clearance is taken out of the bearing. Illustration #210 shows the pattern of a preloaded deep groove ball bearing with a rotating inner ring load (depending on the application, some bearings are intentionally preloaded).

If the shaft housing is out of round the outer ring will become oval when installed. This would produce a pattern similar to illustration #211.

Some bearings will tolerate only small amounts of misalignment. The load path on a deep groove ball bearing which is mis-aligned will depend on which ring is station-ary and which is rotating. The load path from the misalignment is shown in illustrations #212A and #212B.

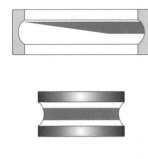

Illustration #209 - Axial and Radial Load

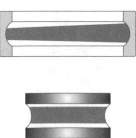

Illustration #210 - Preload With Radial Inner Ring Load

Load Path Patterns (cont'd)

Load Paths/Premature Failure

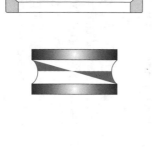

Illustration #211 - Out of Round or Pinched Outer Ring

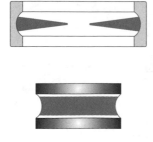

Illustration #212A - Misalignment (Inner Ring Rotating)

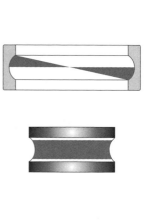

Illustration #212B - Misalignment (Outer Ring Rotating)

Premature Anti-friction Bearing Failure

Other types of bearings such as cylindrical roller, angular contact, taper roller, etc. will also have load path patterns depending on the type of loading. Illustrations #203 through #212 should help when determining if a load path pattern is normal or abnormal. When antifriction bearings fail prematurely, the cause can usually be attributed to one of the following problems:

Premature Bearing Failure (cont'd)

1. Lubrication failure
2. Lubricant contamination
3. Incorrect tolerances on shaft and housings
4. Incorrect mounting procedures
5. Vibration
6. Misalignment
7. Passage of electric current

Lubrication Failure

Lubrication failure will cause surface damage to the bearing as it operates under normal loads and operating conditions.

All bearings require an adequate supply of the correct type of lubricant to operate reliably for full life expectancy. The amount and properties of the lubricant will depend on the intended service. The manufacturer of the bearing is the best source of information on lubricants.

Lubrication failure is due to either an incorrect supply or the lubricant not having the required properties (lubrication contaminants causing bearing problems is referred to later in this section).

The primary purpose of the lubricant is to keep the sliding or rolling surfaces separated however there are other functions. See Section Five on Lubrication). When the lubricant is unable to do this function, surface damage will occur. This damage rapidly progresses to spalling which will then make it difficult to determine the reason for the premature failure.

Look for the following to determine if the surface is becoming damaged due to inadequate lubricant:

a. A highly glazed or glossy appearance, this later changes to gray or silvery finish as fine slivers of metal are pulled away from the metal surface. Spalling will then take place. See illustration #213A,B.

Lubrication Failure

Lubrication Failure (cont'd)

b. A slight roughness or waviness, followed later by fine cracks and then spalling.

c. Discoloration due to high temperatures. If temperatures become high enough, the metal properties will become damaged and softened.

d. Smearing of surfaces. This is due to the metal surfaces sliding instead of rolling and the lubricant is unable to prevent the surfaces from contacting. Metal to metal contact under load causes high points to momentarily to weld together and then immediately become torn apart. Smearing on rollers is shown in illustration #214. When a bearing is loaded in one direction only smearing may occur when the rolling members slide as they move from the unloaded to the loaded zones. See illustration #215. This may happen when oil viscosity is too high or the grease is too thick. This may be caused by using the wrong grade of lubricant or when the machinery is operated in low temperature conditions, especially on start ups.

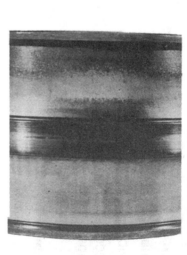

Illustration #213 - Glazed Roller/Metal Particles Pulled Away

Lubrication Failure (cont'd)

If lubrication failure is suspected, one of the first checks should be the operating conditions. An adequate supply of the correct lubricant may be available to the bearing but if the load, speed or operating temperatures are too high then the lubricant will not be able to do its job.

If the operating conditions are normal then the supply and type of lubricant should be considered. Overheating may be caused by either excessive or insufficient amounts of lubricant. Check with bearing and machine manufacturers if considering the possibility that the oil or grease specifications should be changed.

Lubrication Contamination

Contamination of the lubricant may come from a number of sources. Defective or inadequate sealing, poor installation practices and incorrect lubricant handling procedures are the most common.

Illustration #214 - Smearing on Cylindrical Rollers

Illustration #215 - Skid Smearing

Lubrication Contamination (cont'd)

Contamination of the lubricant will cause either corrosion or abrasion damage.

Corrosion occurs when moisture and/or acids in the oil overcome the anti-corrosion properties of the oil and damage the bearing. Corrosion usually starts as a dark etching of the surface. The area of etching may coincide with ball or roller spacing if the bearing was stationary. This will later develop to a pitting of the surface. See illustration #216.

Illustration #216 - Corrosion on Spherical Rollers

Lubrication Contamination

Abrasive wear will occur when dirt and other abrasive matter contaminates the lubricant. Abrasion will score both the raceway and the rolling members. See illustration #217. The bearing will become noisy, vibration levels will increase, and temperatures will be elevated due to the increased amount of friction.

Illustration #217 - Advanced Abrasive Wear

Lubrication Contamination (cont'd)

Abrasive wear combined with corrosion causes the bearing damage to accelerate. If abrasive wear or corrosion is apparent, the source of contaminant must be found and corrected before new bearings are installed and the machine operated. Check for component wear, gasket and seal problems, relubrication intervals and lubricant handling practices.

Incorrect Tolerances on Shaft and Housings

Most anti-friction bearings (angular contact and taper roller are an exception) have a specified amount of internal clearance before installation. This internal clearance will be reduced when the bearing is installed. When an inner ring is installed on a shaft that has an interference fit, the inner ring is expanded. Similarly when an outer ring has an interference fit in the housing the ring diameter is reduced.

This change in ring diameter directly effects the residual clearance of the bearing.

A ring will have an interference fit if it rotates relative to the load, if the ring is stationary relative to the load then it will normally be fitted with some clearance. The amount of interference will depend on the amount of load, speed, and whether vibration or shock loads are present.

A bearing that is used in heavily loaded vibrating applications will require more interference than normal on one or both rings. This may require that the original internal clearance of the bearing be greater than normal, to ensure that there will be sufficient internal clearance after the bearing is installed. If the ring size is changed to the extent that all the internal clearance is removed then the bearing will become preloaded (see illustration #210 for the load pattern). Preloading the bearing effectively increases the overall load, and fatigue failure will occur prematurely.

Incorrect Tolerances (cont'd)

Excessive motion between a bearing ring and the shaft or housing may cause damage (there should be no movement between a ring and the shaft or housing if there is an interference fit, a ring with a clearance fit may have some relative rotation referred to as creep). The cause of the excessive motion may be too much clearance between the shaft or housing and the bearing ring, or an increase in the internal friction within the bearing. Illustration #218 shows an inner race damaged by this. The shaft would also have been scored and damaged.

Illustration #218 - Excessive Motion Between Inner Ring and Shaft

Incorrect Tolerances

An excessively tight fit on an inner ring may stress the ring to the point that it will crack. If the shaft or housing is out of round, the installed ring will assume that oval shape. Excessive loading will take place where the ring has the smaller dimension. See illustrations #219 and #211.

In these examples fatigue and spalling will start on the pinched areas of the outer ring. The inner ring will also be subject to premature fatigue.

Illustration #219 - Outer Ring Pinched by Housing

Incorrect Tolerances (cont'd)

Before a bearing is mounted, the shaft and housing should be measured for size, out of round and taper. Checking these with tables supplied by bearing manufacturers will ensure that the correct amount of interference or clearance will be present when the bearing is installed.

Incorrect Mounting Procedures

Many failures can be attributed to the incorrect mounting of the bearing. Taper roller or angular contact bearings that are mounted in opposition will require the correct setting for a specified amount of axial clearance or preload.

Taper bore bearings such as spherical roller and self aligning ball bearings will require the correct amount of drive up on the taper to leave the required amount of internal clearance. Too much preload or preload when it is not required will result in reduced bearing life due to premature fatigue.

Illustration #220 - Fatigue Damage From Brinelling

Impact damage from faulty handling or mounting may result in brinelled depressions in the raceways. If mounting forces are transmitted through the rolling members to push on the tight ring, or if the bearing is subject to shock loads, as when a coupling hub is driven onto the shaft, then brinelling may be the result.

Incorrect Mounting (cont'd)

The raceway depressions will be spaced at ball or roller spacing, and when the bearing is used, flaking and spalling will occur first at these points See illustration #220.

Cylindrical rollers which have a separable inner or outer ring are often damaged when the separated ring is installed and then the rest of the bearing, which is mounted on the shaft or in the housing, is assembled.

The rollers may tilt slightly and if force is used to push the parts together the rollers may cut grooves in the raceway.   See illustration #221.   To avoid this problem a tapered sleeve is used to prevent the rollers from hanging up on the race as they slide over.

Vibration

A stationary machine that is subject to vibration may eventually have bearing damage due to the rolling members wearing small indentations into the raceways as well as damage to the balls or rollers.   This is referred to as false brinelling.   See illustration #222.

False brinelling will be characterized by depressions in the raceways that either have a polished appearance or are stained with the products of oxidation. Corresponding marks on the balls or rollers will also be present. The depressions will be spaced at intervals corresponding to the rolling element spacing.

Illustration #221 - Grooves From Tilted Rollers When Mounting

BEARING FAILURE
Vibration (cont'd)

Illustration #222 - False Brinelling

If the machine is operated after false brinelling has occurred the minute particles of metal which may be oxidized will act as an abrasive. False brinelling can occur during the transportation of machines and when machines are stationary for periods of time in a plant where vibration is present, such as standby machines.

Illustration #223 - Wavy Pattern From Vibration and Abrasive

If vibration and abrasive contamination is present in a rotating bearing a wavy pattern of wear may occur on the raceways. See illustration #223. This can be similar to the fluting caused by the passage of electric current and it may be difficult to distinguish between the two.

The difference between brinelling and false brinelling can be difficult to distinguish without microscopic examination.

Vibration (cont'd)

Note: True brinelling is a plastic flow of metal and the grinding marks will still be present. False brinelling is a wear condition and metal is removed from the indentations and the grinding marks will not be visible.

Misalignment

Misalignment causes an increase in the load in certain areas of the bearing (see illustration #212 for an example of the load path pattern of a deep groove ball bearing). This causes premature fatigue and spalling in the area that is subject to the extra loading. Misalignment may be caused by:

a. Bearing housings that are not on the same centerline.

b. A housing shoulder is not square to the housing bore.

c. A shaft shoulder is not square to the journal.

Vibration/Misalignment

d. An inner ring not square to the shaft or an outer ring not square to the housing bore. Roller bearings (cylindrical or taper) will show serious edge loading if the misalignment is significant. See illustration #224.

Illustration #224 - Spalling of Inner Ring on Taper Roller Bearing

The use of self aligning bearings (when possible) is sometimes utilized to correct misalignment problems.

BEARING FAILURE

Misalignment (cont'd)

Using self aligning bearings will not help if the rotating ring is off square. The rotating ring will wobble, causing smearing and early fatigue.

If a floating outer ring is off square in the housing it may be unable to float axially and may be subject to excessive axial load. It may also be out of round. See illustration #211 and #219.

Electric Current Passage

When an electric current seeks ground, the easiest path may be through the bearings. This could happen whether the machine is rotating or stationary. The current could be from static electricity being generated from moving belts or other processes that involve cloth, leather, paper, etc.

Another common source of electric current is from welding. If the ground is not correctly placed the electric circuit may pass through the bearings.

When welding on any machine that has bearings it is imperative that the ground be attached as close as possible to the weld and that there are no bearings between the weld and the ground attachment.

Illustration #225A,B - Pitting From Large Electric Currents

Electric Current Passage (cont'd)

The damage occurs when the current path is broken and arcing momentarily occurs. If relatively large amounts of current are involved then pitting may occur as shown in illustration #225.

If small amounts of current are passed over a long period of time when the machine is running then fluting may occur as shown in illustration #226.

Premature Journal Bearing Failure

Failure of journal bearings can usually be attributed to one or more of the following reasons:

- Unsuitable bearing design
- Unsuitable operating environment
- Lack of or unsuitable lubrication
- Misalignment
- Overloading/fatigue
- Electric current
- Improper assembly

Unsuitable Bearing Design

Bearing design is an important factor when considering the longevity of a machine. Most industrial machine designers supply suitable bearings for their machines. The exception to this is when the service of the machine is changed. If the loads, speeds and temperatures are changed it will make the OEM bearings more susceptible to early failure.

Illustration #226 - Fluting From Small Electric Currents

Unsuitable Bearing Design (cont'd)

When journal bearings are replaced or re-lined it is important to ensure that the correct bearing material is used. Load carrying ability, fatigue resistance, embedability, conformability and corrosion resistance are just some of the factors to be considered regarding the bearing material. Another factor sometimes overlooked when changing bearing material or type is the required hardness of the journal surface.

Faulty relining practices can result in premature failure of journal bearings. One or any combination of the following may cause a problem.

a. Improper preparation of the backing surface.

b. Improper preheating the backing and mandril.

c. Incorrect pouring temperature of the babbit.

d. Overheating the babbit causing excessive oxidation.

e. Contaminated babbit.

f. Improper set up causing air pockets to form while pouring.

Unsuitable Operating Environment

Dirt Contamination on Assembly: If dirt or other particles are inadvertently left between the bearing insert and the housing, the insert will deform and possibly rub the journal, thereby damaging the surface. The heat generated within the bearing is removed in two ways; part is carried away with the lubricating oil and part is dissipated through the bearing insert to the housing or bearing cap. A tight fit between the insert and the housing is required to transfer heat from the insert to the housing. The dirt behind the insert will cause a hot spot on the bearing because of the loss of metal to metal contact in that area and will cause premature failure. See illustration #227.

Journal Bearing Environment

Dirt Contaminating the Lubricating Oil:

Larger hard particles will embed themselves into the bearing material. This in effect protects the bearing assembly from the scoring effect of the dirt, however a bearing can only tolerate a limited amount of dirt.

Eventually dirt contaminated oil will reduce the bearing life with the result being scored journals and bearings.

Illustration #228 - Failure From Embedded Dirt

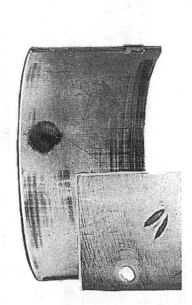

Illustration #227 - Localized Heat From Dirt Behind Insert

Careless assembly practices can also allow dirt to be introduced between the bearing surface and the journal. Journal bearings are more dirt tolerant than the anti-friction bearings, but dirt should not be permitted to contaminate the surface, and embedability of some journal bearings is also quite low depending on the construction of the bearing insert.

Unsuitable Environment (cont'd)

When inspecting bearings check for embedded particles in the bearing material (with a microscope if possible). Also check for scoring and abrasion on both the journals and bearings. Illustration #228 shows damage due to foreign material embedded in a bearing.

High Operating Temperatures: The operating temperature of a journal bearing will affect the service life and the type of bearing. Most industrial bearings are held at around 150 - 160 °F (65 - 71 °C). The major problem associated with high temperature is the effect on the oil, which includes: reduced viscosity, reduced load capability and rapid oxidation. In addition, the metallurgical characteristics of the bearing material are affected.

Corrosion: Corrosion of the bearing material can occur if acidic conditions are allowed.

Tin base babbits are resistant to corrosion, whereas some alloys such as lead-copper and cadmium-silver are much more susceptible to corrosive attack.

The corrosion shows up as large pitted areas of the bearing. In the case of a bearing of lead-copper alloy, the lead is eroded away leaving what looks like a very porous copper surface which will quickly break up. Corrosive conditions can be prevented if the oil temperature is controlled, contamination is kept to a minimum and regular oil monitoring is carried out.

Illustration #229 - Pitting from Corrosion

Lubrication Problems

The lubricant has a number of functions. See Section Five on lubrication for more details.

If the lubricant does not keep the bearing and journal separated from the bearing then rubbing will result. See illustration #230. This may be caused by a reduction or loss of the oil supply, supplying an oil that has too low a viscosity, or overloading the bearing.

A loss of oil supply may occur when filters or strainers become restricted, pumps become worn or fail, or when bearings become so worn that the pump cannot supply a sufficient quantity of oil to maintain the required pressure.

Another cause of rubbing is when the oil supply pump is driven by the machine that it is supplying oil to. On start up there is a period when the bearing is running dry. The amount of time will depend on the pump, the temperature and viscosity of the oil, and machine design. It is especially important to remember this after maintenance has been carried out and oil lines, galleries and filters may be empty. Considerable time will be required for the oil pump to make up this oil and lubricate the bearings on start up. It is prudent in this case to make sure that the system is fully primed before start up.

Illustration #230 - Damage from Rubbing

Lubrication Problems (cont'd)

To eliminate this start-up lack of oil, many machines are supplied with prelube pumps or a separate pump drive system so that lubricating oil can be supplied before the machine is rotated. With this design, the machine rotor should not be rotated, even for maintenance purposes, unless the lubrication pump or the prelube pump is supplying oil to the bearings.

Taking this a step further, some machines, such as large generating turbines that have heavily loaded bearings, are supplied with a system that provides static full film lubrication. This is sometimes referred to as jacking oil. The jacking oil is supplied at a high enough pressure to the underside of the journal to raise the journal from the bearing before rotation is started. When starting or rotating the machine for maintenance the jacking oil must be available to ensure that there will be no rubbing on the initial rotation.

Correct oil viscosity is extremely important to the life of the bearing. If viscosity is too high, then internal friction will increase temperatures and the bearing will run hotter than normal. There will also be some power loss to overcome this friction. If the viscosity is too low then bearing to journal contact may take place due to the reduction in the film thickness and load carrying capacity.

The oil viscosity varies with temperature change, if the oil temperature fluctuates then it is important to select an oil with a high viscosity index. If the machine is sometimes started from very cold ambient conditions some means of heating the oil should be considered.

Misalignment

Misalignment occurs when the axes of two bearings supporting a rotor or shaft are not parallel to the shaft axis. See illustration #231. Either one or both bearings will be carrying the load on a smaller area.

Misalignment (cont'd)

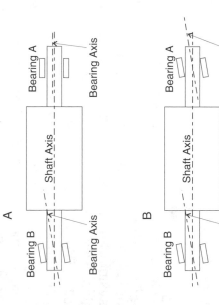

Illustration #231 - Bearing Misalignment

In illustration #231A only bearing B will have misalignment damage, whereas in #231B both bearings will be effected.

Journal Bearing Misalignment

This will in effect cause an overload on that area, the result being lubrication breakdown, rubbing, heat build up, and possibly complete failure depending on how severe the misalignment is. Illustration #232 shows the effect of rubbing due to misalignment.

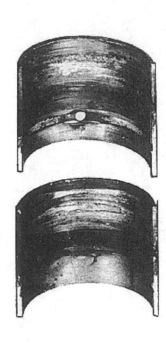

Illustration #232 - Effects of Misalignment

To ensure that the bearings are not misaligned the bearing/shaft contact should be checked on assembly. If one or more bearings indicate that misalignment is present it must be corrected.

Misalignment (cont'd)

Shimming the bearing housings or scraping the bearing may be required depending on the design of the machine. Some machines that have self aligning bearings with spherical seats on the housings should not have this type of problem. If they do, checks should be made for correct assembly including checking the clearances on the spherical seat to ensure that it is not binding.

Overloading and Fatigue

Each bearing will have an expected life which will be dependent on the service it is subjected to. If run long enough a bearing will eventually fail due to fatigue.

This fatigue may show up as hairline cracks and then flaking. As overloading occurs, the onset of fatigue will happen faster due to the increase in pressure on the bearing and the probable rise in temperature.

If overloading is more severe then metal to metal contact will occur as the oil film becomes too thin and lubrication breaks down.

Electric Current Passage

As with anti-friction bearings, journal bearings are also susceptible to damage if electric currents pass through the bearing. The arcing of the current between the journal and the bearing while running, causes microscopic pits in the bearing surface and the journal. The damage is shown in illustration #233 and appears as a frosted area in the loaded zone of the bearing.

If large currents are passed while the bearing is stationary the bearing may "weld" to the journal. When the machine is then started up the welded area of the bearing will pull out leaving large pits in the surface.

Electric Current Passage (cont'd)

Improper Assembly

Correct assembly not only involves fitting all the parts together in the correct sequence, but also, as mentioned before, cleanliness is essential. Parts must be meticulously cleaned before being installed, and an opened bearing should never be left uncovered. A bearing should not be assembled if there is a danger that it will be contaminated from other work occurring in close proximity, such as grinding, welding or cutting.

Confirmation of the journal to bearing clearance should be correctly carried out. Micrometer readings, plasti-gauge, feeler gages or bridge gages are all methods that may be used. After assembly a lift check may be the final confirmation. Bluing the bearing to check the shaft contact may also be required to ensure that the bearing is not misaligned and that it is supporting the shaft across its entire length.

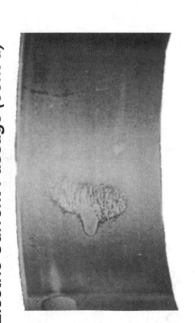

Illustration #233 - Damage from Electric Current

SECTION SEVEN QUESTIONS

Bearing Failure Analysis

1. When first checking a failed bearing, wash off all the grease and dirt so that the bearing can be inspected thoroughly.

   ☐ true   ☐ false

2. Only the raceways or rolling members will give any indication as to the cause of an anti-friction bearing failure.

   ☐ true   ☐ false

3. When a bearing is selected, what are the five assumptions that the bearing life expectancy is based on?

   Answer: _____

4. When a correctly designed, installed, and operated bearing is reaching the end of its life, what type of failure is to be expected?

   ☐ scoring   ☐ fatigue
   ☐ heat cracking   ☐ grooving

5. The load path pattern that is evident on a bearing will depend on whether the rotating load is on the outer ring or inner ring.

   ☐ true   ☐ false

6. What will be the effect on the load path pattern of the bearing stationary raceway if it is subject to creep?

   Answer: _____

7. When a bearing has a rotating inner ring load, the complete circumference of the inner raceway will be subject to load.

   ☐ true   ☐ false

8. When a bearing has a rotating outer ring load, the complete circumference of the inner raceway will be subject to load.

   ☐ true   ☐ false

9. The load path pattern on a deep groove ball bearing that is subject to an axial load will depend on whether the rotating load is on the outer ring or inner ring.

   ☐ true   ☐ false

10. Preload on a bearing will not effect the load path pattern.

☐ true   ☐ false

11. A bearing with a pinched outer ring and one with a misaligned bearing bore (outer ring rotating) may have similar load path patterns.

☐ true   ☐ false

12. Which two factors are responsible for lubrication failure?

Answer: _____

13. The primary purpose of the lubricant is to separate the sliding or rolling surfaces.

☐ true   ☐ false

14. Metal to metal contact under load may cause the high points to momentarily weld together and then immediately be torn apart again.

☐ true   ☐ false

15. Describe three visual indications that may be produced by lubrication failure.

Answer: _____

16. Smearing may occur as rolling members move from the unloaded to the loaded zone, this could be caused by:

☐ lubricant viscosity too low
☐ lubricant viscosity too high

17. Contamination of the lubricant will cause either _____ or _____ damage.

Answer: _____

18. A bearing effected by corrosion will eventually develop a _____ surface.

☐ scored   ☐ pitted
☐ brinelled   ☐ cracked

19. A bearing effected by abrasive particles will develop a _____ surface.

☐ scored   ☐ pitted
☐ brinelled   ☐ cracked

20. If contamination is found to be the cause of premature bearing life, what checks should be made before installing new bearings and running the machine?

Answer: _____

21. When only one ring on an anti-friction bearing is to have an interference fit, it is usually the one with the:

 ☐ rotating load ☐ stationary load
 ☐ largest load ☐ smallest load

22. If a large interference is required on both rings of an anti-friction bearing, what may be required to prevent pre-load taking place?
Answer: _____

---

23. It would be impossible to install the inner ring of an anti-friction bearing with enough interference to crack or break the ring.

 ☐ true ☐ false

24. When mounting anti-friction bearings where would one obtain the correct dimensions for the housing and shaft?

 ☐ measure a new shaft and housing
 ☐ the dimensions will be satisfactory if there is no evidence of wear
 ☐ from the box that the bearing came in
 ☐ tables supplied by the bearing manufacturer

25. Once an anti-friction bearing has been installed correctly it would be impossible for it to sustain damage from shock loads (brinelling).

 ☐ true ☐ false

26. Taper bore bearings such as spherical roller bearings are usually driven up until all the internal clearance is removed.

 ☐ true ☐ false

27. False brinelling in an anti-friction bearing may cause abrasive damage to occur.

 ☐ true ☐ false

28. False brinelling only occurs when the machine is operated at high speed.

 ☐ true ☐ false

29. Spalling on one edge of a cylindrical or taper roller bearing will probably have been cause by:

 ☐ misalignment
 ☐ brinelling
 ☐ abrasive wear
 ☐ lubrication failure

30. Self aligning bearings such as spherical roller or self aligning ball bearings may be used when it is suspected that the housing is misaligned.

 ☐ true ☐ false

31. Self aligning bearings such as spherical roller or self aligning ball bearings may be used to correct all types of misalignment.

 ☐ true ☐ false

32. When welding on a machine, where should the welding ground cable be attached?
Answer: _____

33. Name five properties that would be important to consider when considering which babbit material to use.
Answer: _____

34. Identify two ways heat is removed from the surface of a journal bearing.
Answer: _____

35. What is the usual operating temperature of industrial journal bearings?
Answer: _____

36. What effect would high temperatures have on lubricating oil?
Answer: _____

37. One property of journal bearings is embedability, therefore abrasive particles will never be a problem.
☐ true   ☐ false

38. Corrosion is more likely to effect copper than lead in a journal bearing.
☐ true   ☐ false

39. What design feature is sometimes used to eliminate a lack of lubricating oil to the bearings at start up?
Answer: _____

40. If a journal bearing insert shows signs of contact at one side, the probable cause would be:
☐ overloading
☐ misalignment
☐ oil viscosity breakdown
☐ contamination

41. What feature might be incorporated into a journal bearing design to eliminate misalignment problems?
☐ wider bearings
☐ increased oil supply
☐ softer bearing material
☐ spherical seats

42. List four methods of checking journal bearing clearance.
Answer: _____

SECTION EIGHT

PERFORMANCE MONITORING

Monitoring Methods

This section discusses other methods for measuring the performance of rotating equipment and diagnosing whether the machine is reliable and efficient. In previous sections, methods such as vibration analysis, lubrication analysis and non-destructive testing were identified as excellent methods for determining the overall condition of machinery and machinery parts.

This section will focus primarily on methods commonly used by maintenance personnel such as millwrights, electricians, machinists, and technicians to determine machinery performance and reliability including:

● Measuring Electrical Performance
● Measuring Fluid Performance
● Measuring Temperature
● Measuring RPM

It is common to use any of the above methods of performance measurement on a continuous basis, or also during routine equipment checks and inspections.

Monitoring Methods

With modern process controls becoming very sophisticated, it is possible to monitor and measure performance of the total machine, or specific components within the machine. This can be done continuously and automatically 24 hours/day. For high speed, complex and costly equipment, this type of continuous monitoring and measurement is very necessary. For periodic inspections and checks there are many portable instruments now available for measuring the electrical, fluid, and temperature conditions of most rotating equipment found in industry. To use these instruments efficiently requires time, training and possibly some type of specialized fittings or test points mounted to various sections of the machinery

Establishing Comparative Standards

Without comparative standards or normal values, which serve as benchmarks, performance measurement, just as condition monitoring, would not be particularly valuable.

Comparative Standards (cont'd)

Thus, comparative standards must be established to serve as a basis for indicating performance and condition. Generally, there are two types of comparative standards used in performance and condition measurement and monitoring:

1. Standards which represent absolute values.

2. More qualitative type of comparative criteria commonly used in vibration monitoring. Manufacturer's design limits, fluid and gas pressures, electrical measurements, temperature, speed, and clearances are examples of "absolute values" utilized for comparative standards. More specifically, manufacturer's operating and instructional manuals usually list normal, minimum and maximum values for a variety of things. Examples would include: normal and maximum bearing temperatures; maximum oil pressure; differential pressures on seals - inlet and outlet; and speeds at which a machine

may be safely operated. As well, design, assembled and operating clearances and limits are classed generally as absolute values.

Limits and comparative criteria for vibration, especially structural or casing vibration, are more qualitative types of comparative values, as they are often based on experience. Standards for judging vibration, can be obtained from a number of sources, such as manufacturer's data, guidelines published by vibration instrument manufacturers, and the experience and knowledge of others operating similar machinery under similar conditions.

Note: When establishing vibration limits, those required for performing qualitative comparisons, be aware that some machinery manufacturer's limits may be too high if the goal is to supply uninterrupted, trouble free machine operation for two to three years.

Comparative Standards (cont'd)

Conversely, the vibration limits supplied by the manufacturers of vibration instruments may be too low for certain types of machinery operating under specific conditions. Some machines may find those limits much too low, as the machine seems to perform reliably at higher levels.

Whether one is using absolute or qualitative comparison standards, and assuming that it is known which measurement(s) to make, where and how to make them, and what limits to set, consider the following points in order to judge the performance and condition of the machinery:

a. What seems to be out of its limit or has changed?

b. By how much have the limits changed?

c. Are the changes occurring slowly or rapidly?

d. Are there any other changes which either confirm or contradict the initial observations?

Measuring Electrical Performance

The ability to make safe and accurate electrical circuit measurements is an integral part of measuring performance and diagnosing faults of electric drives common to most rotating equipment.

Everyone involved must exercise caution in order to remain insulated from low and high voltage circuits being worked on. Before attempting to measure any electrical circuit for current, voltage or resistance, be aware of the various Federal, Provincial, State or any other regulatory body which may have rules and regulations identifying what is allowed in the trade area when it comes to performing electrical work.

The following procedures are recommended to avoid electrical shock or accidents:

a. When possible, turn the circuit off and verify it is off before working on it.

b. Make sure that all components which are capable of storing electric energy have been discharged.

Measuring Electrical Performance (cont'd)

c. Keep tools and test equipment in good condition. Repair or replace frayed leads, damaged probes and handles, and worn or cracked insulation.

d. Do not work around electric equipment if clothing is wet or damp. Water makes clothing and skin a better conductor. Avoid damp floors located around electrical equipment.

e. Never place both hands into a circuit. A hand-to-hand shock is particularly dangerous because the current can pass through the chest and heart.

f. Never place one hand on a metal cabinet, a chassis or frame, or any other grounded object while working in a circuit with the other hand.

g. Do not work with rings, bracelets, or other metal items on the hands or wrists.

h. Make sure there is adequate lighting around the work area.

i. Do not work on electrical circuits if taking any type of medication that could cause drowsiness or impair vision or concentration.

j. Do not remove equipment grounds or use adaptors that defeat a ground connection.

k. Do not modify circuits or equipment unless knowing exactly what the effects of the modification will be.

l. Always follow prescribed procedures. Use relevant literature and when in doubt, ask for help, research and study the equipment before proceeding.

m. Know the applicable Federal, Provincial, State or other rules and regulations which identify what can and cannot be done by you, the specific individual, on electrical systems.

Basic Instruments

Voltage, current, resistance and power measurements are routinely made in electrical circuits of those electric drives and switching components for rotating equipment. Electrical instruments are used to measure and monitor these circuit values. The most common field instruments used by tradesmen and technicians to test and/or troubleshoot electrical circuits are voltmeters, ammeters, ohmmeters, megohmmeters, and occasionally wattmeters.

Often three instruments are combined into one single instrument known as a VOM, volt-ohm-milliammeter, as shown in illustration #234. Multimeters are designed to allow the user to choose the type of electrical unit (current, voltage, resistance) to be measured by means of a selector switch. Multimeters are available in analog type (needle movement), or in digital type (DMM - digital multimeter), as shown in illustration #234.

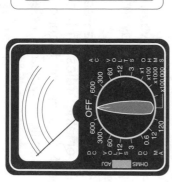

VOM (Volt-Ohm-Milliammeter)

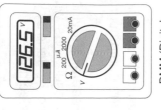

DMM (Digital Multimeter)

Illustration #234 - Multimeters

Ohm's Law

The amount of current flowing in an electrical circuit (I - Measured in amperage) is dependent upon the value of electrical pressure (E - measured in volts) and the amount of opposition to the flow of current (R - measured in ohms). The mathematical formula representing this relationship is:

$$I = E/R$$

Ohm's Law (cont'd)

Note: This formula is known as Ohm's Law and serves as the basic formula for determining the behavior of an electrical circuit.

Ohm's Law Example 1:

Calculate the current flowing in a circuit having 12 Ω resistance and 120 V of pressure.

$I = E/R$
$I = 120/12$
$I = 10$ AMPS

The amount of current flow in this circuit is 10 amps.

Ohm's Law Example 2:

Calculate the resistance of a circuit that allows only 0.5 A to flow when a voltage of 120 V is applied.

$R = E/I$
$R = 120/0.5$
$R = 240$ Ω

The amount of resistance in this circuit is 240 Ω

Ohm's Law Example 3:

Calculate the voltage in the circuit when the current flow is 10 A and the resistance in the circuit is found to be 12 Ω.

$E = R \times I$
$E = 12 \times 10$
$E = 120$ V

The voltage in this circuit is 120 V.

Measuring Voltage

To measure voltage, a voltmeter (either AC or DC) is connected across an electrical component. Remember to observe polarity marks when measuring DC. This connection is known as a parallel connection and is shown in illustration #235.

Note: The polarity of the voltmeter connections in illustration #236: positive is connected to positive and negative to negative. In this illustration, the voltage of the battery is measured. Note that the leads of the voltmeter are directly connected across the battery terminals.

Measuring Voltage (cont'd)

Voltmeter connected in parallel
with circuit load

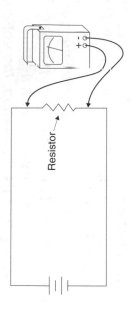

Voltmeter Connection

Illustration #235 - Parallel Connection

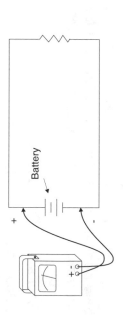

**Illustration #237 - Voltmeter Connection:
Measuring Voltage Drop**

In illustration #237, the voltage drop across the resistor is measured. The resistor is considered the "load" in this type of circuit. Once again, the circuit is not broken, and the voltmeter leads are connected directly across the resistor leads.

In many cases there is no practical difference between the two voltmeter connections shown in illustrations #236 and #237.

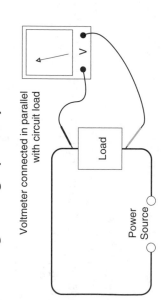

Illustration #236 - Voltmeter Connection: Note Polarity

Measuring Voltage (cont'd)

Illustration #238 shows an example which might be encountered when there is a difference. In this example there is significant conductor resistance and the motor is drawing a substantial current. In this case the voltage at V_L will be less than at V_B.

Note: It is very important that the right scale be selected in order that the meter movement not be subjected to voltage higher than it is capable of safely handling.

Note: Voltmeters are always connected across (parallel to) circuit components, never in series.

Measuring Current

A device used to measure current in a circuit is called an ammeter. A multimeter will also have the ability to measure current in amps as well. Usually there are several ranges that can be selected for measuring current.

An ammeter is always connected into the electrical circuit (series connection) as shown in illustrations #239A if of the lead type (either AC or DC); or placed around the circuit conductor as shown in illustration #239B if of the clip-on type (also known as the long test ammeter).

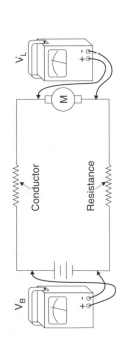

Illustration #238 - Voltmeter Connection: Different Connection-Different Reading

Electrical Performance

Measuring Current (cont'd)

Ammeter connected
in series
with the load

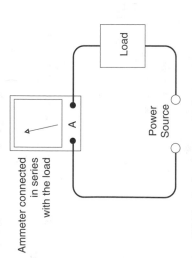

Illustration #239A - Series Connection

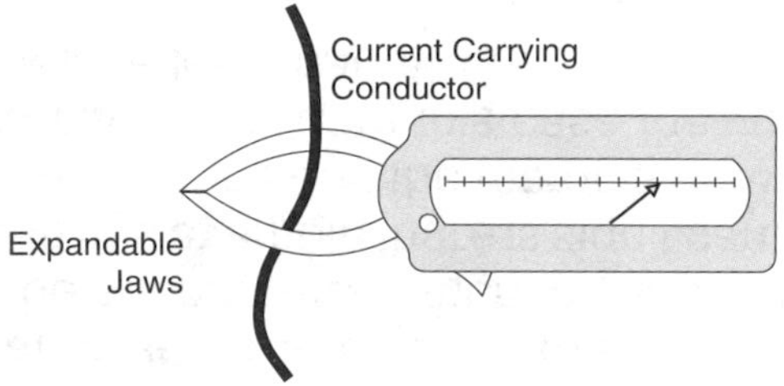

Current Carrying
Conductor

Expandable
Jaws

Illustration #239B - Clip-On Ammeter

When inserting a two lead ammeter into an electrical circuit first open the circuit at the point where the current measurement is desired and then insert the ammeter. Remember to observe polarity marks when measuring DC values.

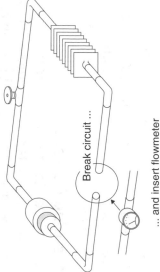

Break circuit ...

... and insert flowmeter

Illustration #240 - Measuring Flow Rate

Measuring Current (cont'd)

Measuring current flow is similar to measuring liquid flow. Illustration #240 shows that fluid flow is measured by breaking the piping at some point and installing a flowmeter. Current measurement is shown in illustration #241. Note that the circuit must be broken, and the two ammeter leads are then connected across the break. The current now flows through the meter as well as through the circuit.

Note: To avoid spillage, the fluid circuit in illustration #240 would be stopped before cutting into the piping. The same practice applies when measuring current flow. Connecting an ammeter to a live high-energy circuit is very dangerous. Use safe work practices with all circuits, and dangerous habits will not develop.

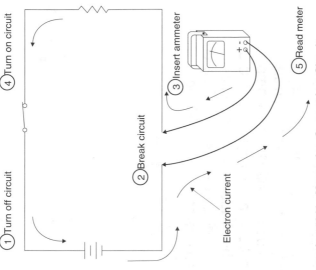

① Turn off circuit   ④ Turn on circuit

③ Insert ammeter

② Break circuit

⑤ Read meter

Electron current

Illustration #241 - Measuring Current in a Circuit

Illustration #242 shows that it is possible to measure the current flow in a part of a circuit. Again, break the circuit. The ammeter is installed to measure the current.

Electrical Performance

Measuring Current (cont'd)

If the circuit was not broken, serious damage could result to the ammeter and circuit. In illustration #242 for example, if the circuit is not broken and the ammeter is connected across R₁, an abnormally high current will result and the meter could be severely damaged.

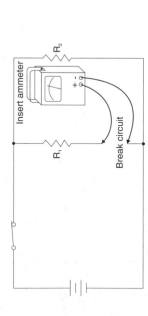

Illustration #242 - Measuring Current in Part of a Circuit

Note: Ammeters are always connected in series with electrical circuit components and must never be connected across the electrical circuit.

Measuring Resistance

Resistance is an opposition to the flow of current. If the resistance of a circuit is doubled, the current is reduced to one-half.

Resistance can be very useful in rotating equipment drives when the flow of current must be controlled. For example, in illustration #243 a component called a "rheostat" has been added to a motor circuit. A rheostat is an adjustable resistor. The current flow must overcome the resistance in the circuit.

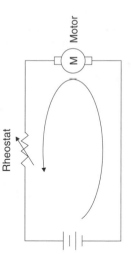

Illustration #243 - Resistance to Control Circuit

Measuring Resistance (cont'd)

As the rheostat is adjusted for more resistance, less current flows and the motor slows down. As the rheostat is adjusted for less resistance, the current flow increases and the motor speeds up. Resistance can also be used to control illumination, loudness, and many other useful circuit functions.

In some cases resistance is undesirable, as shown in illustration #244, where the conductors used to carry the motor current have excess resistance. If the motor is used where it must develop maximum output at all times, the conductor resistance is resistance that prevents the motor from developing its full output, and some electrical energy is wasted since heat is produced by the current flowing in the wires. In severe cases the wires could be damaged by the heat or a fire could result. Conductor resistance becomes a significant problem when the wires are very long and high currents must flow.

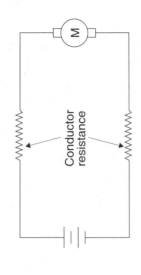

Illustration #244 - Undesirable Resistance

The instrument commonly used to measure resistance is an ohmmeter. An ohmmeter is shown in illustration #245. It consists of a battery and a variable resistor connected in series with a basic meter movement. The variable resistor is used to calibrate the meter to obtain a full scale deflection (zero ohms showing on the meter) when the two terminal leads are shorted together.

Measuring Resistance (cont'd)

Calibration is done to compensate for changes in the internal battery voltage due to aging (only needs to be done on analog type ohmmeters).

Note: Each time an analog ohmmeter's scale is changed the meter must be recalibrated.

When the ohmmeter leads are open, the pointer is located at the far side of the scale indicating infinite resistance (open circuit). This is shown in illustration #246A.

When the two leads are connected together, as shown in illustration #246B, the pointer deflects completely to the right indicating zero resistance (short circuit).

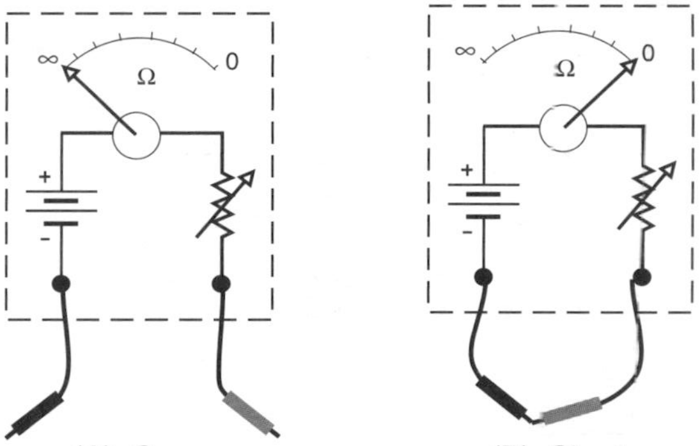

Illustration #245 - Basic Ohmmeter

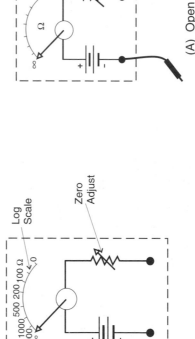

(A) Open
(Infinite Resistance)

(B) Short
(Zero Resistance)2

Illustration #246 - Ohmmeter Indications

Measuring Resistance (cont'd)

Note: An ohmmeter has its own power supply (battery) and therefore must never be connected into a circuit that is energized or being acted on by another voltage source. If an ohmmeter is connected into an energized circuit there is a high risk of damaging the meter and/or the electrical circuit being measured. Resistance must never be measured in a circuit that is energized.

Components should be isolated for ohmmeter tests. If they are not, the ohmmeter may provide a current to more than one device. This will cause an erroneously low reading. Refer to illustration #247. The resistance of R_3 is to be measured. At least one of its connections should be opened to separate it from R_2. This prevents the ohmmeter from sending a current through both devices.

A megohmmeter, popularly known as a "megger", is an instrument that is used for measuring very high resistance values. The term megohmmeter is derived from the fact that the device measures resistance values in the megohm range.

The megohmmeter's primary function is to test insulation resistance of power transmission systems, electrical machinery (motors, generators), transformers, and cables. A basic megohmmeter insulation tester consists of a hand-driven generator and a direct-reading true ohmmeter.

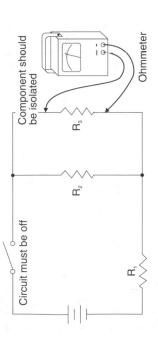

Illustration #247 - Measuring Resistance

Measuring Resistance (cont'd)

Megohmmeter models are available which produce different levels of test voltage (100, 250, 500, 1000, 1500, 2500. 5000 or 10,000 volts).

Illustration #248 shows how a megohmmeter is connected to measure the unknown resistance in the cable. The unknown resistance is connected between the terminals marked line and earth. The hand crank is turned at a moderate speed (approximately 120 RPM) and a DC voltage is generated. The scale is calibrated so that the pointer directly indicates the value of the resistance being measured (all values shown are in megohms). The purpose of "G" terminal (guard ring) is to eliminate surface current leakage across exposed conductors and or ground.

Note: The guard ring terminal is at the same potential as the line terminal.

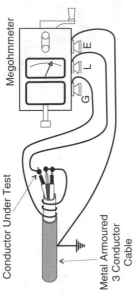

Conductor Under Test

Megohmmeter

Metal Armoured 3 Conductor Cable

Illustration #248 - Cable Testing With Megge˙

Note: Because the amount of power that the megger can produce is small, the test is considered to be non-destructive, meaning permanent damage is not likely to be caused in the insulation system of the device being tested. However, the level of output voltage is high enough to present a personal safety hazard if incorrect testing procedures are used. Never connect a megger insulation tester to energized lines or equipment.

MEASURING PERFORMANCE

Measuring Power

Power is defined as the rate of expending energy or rate of doing work. The watt (w) is the SI unit of power. A wattmeter measures the true power of an electrical circuit and is effective in both AC and DC circuits.

A wattmeter consists of two electromagnetic coils with one coil connected across (parallel) the electrical circuit being measured, and the other coil being connected into (series) the electrical circuit. The interaction of the magnetic fields of these two coils will result in a net value of power ($P = V \times I$). Illustration #249 shows a wattmeter measuring power in a single-phase circuit.

Wattmeters have polarity marks which must be observed to ensure connections are made correctly. Remember that the current should (normally) enter at the polarity mark and leave at the nonpolarity mark for both the voltage and current coils.

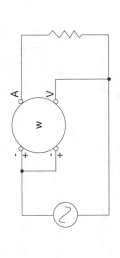

Illustration #249 - Using a Wattmeter

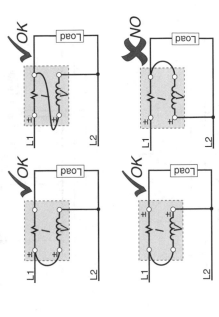

Illustration #250 - Wattmeter Connections

Measuring Power (cont'd)

Power in three phase circuits may be measured by using two or more wattmeters.

Illustration #251 shows the proper connections for measuring the power in both a three phase three wire system and a three phase-four wire system. The power readings obtained by the connections are correct for both balanced and unbalanced loads that are operating at power factors of 50% or better. The total power of the circuit is obtained by adding the values shown on the wattmeters.

Note: Energy measurement is accomplished by the use of watthour meters. Indicating dials are rotated by the action of the watthour meter and a kWHr value is displayed.

Note: The potential (voltage) coil of the wattmeter must always be connected across (parallel) to the electrical circuit being measured and the current coil must always be connected into the electrical circuit (series).

Electrical Performance

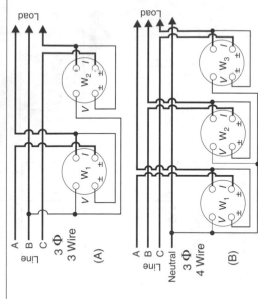

Illustration #251 - Three Phase Power Measurement

Protective Devices

Protective devices, such as fuses and circuit breakers are standard safety requirements for any electrical circuits used for domestic or industrial service. Fuses and circuit breakers are used to safeguard against short circuits and overloads.

Protective Devices (cont'd)

A short circuit is defined as being current that is out of its normal path and may be caused by faults in the insulation or faulty connections. During the short circuit, current by-passes the load and the only limiting factor is the impedance of the distribution system up-stream from the fault.

If this short circuit is not cut off within a matter of a few thousands of a second, then serious damage and destruction can occur. The consequences would be severe insulation damage, melting of conductors, vaporization of metal, arcing and fires, and huge magnetic field stresses that warp or distort electrical equipment.

An overload is defined as being low level faults that are caused by temporary surge currents that occur when motors are started up, transformers are energized, or they may be continuous overloads due to overloaded motors, transformers, etc.

Note: Despite the magnitude of over-loads being between one to six times the normal current level for motors and eight to twelve times for transformers, removal of the overload current within a few sec-onds will generally prevent equipment damage. Short circuits are much more serious, because fault currents may be many hundreds of times larger than the normal operating current.

Fuses are intentionally weakened circuit components that open when the current reaches a dangerous level. Refer to illustration #252A,B,C to see how a fuse works. There is an element inside the fuse that has resistance. When the current flow is normal, it is not high enough to melt the element.

Protective Devices (cont'd)

The short circuit in illustration #252B causes an abnormally high flow of current. The power dissipation in the fuse element increases and it reaches a high enough temperature to eventually melt, as shown in illustration #252C, and the circuit opens. When a fuse melts, it is said to have "blown."

Circuit breakers are also used to protect against overcurrent. Circuit breakers have the advantage of being able to open a circuit by "tripping." A tripped breaker can be reset by pushing a button or by throwing a toggle. Also available are automatic circuit breakers that reset themselves after they cool down. Illustration #253A and #253B shows the principle of operation of a thermal circuit breaker. The circuit current flows through a special bimetallic strip. Bimetallic strips are made up of two different metal alloys, each having a different coefficient of expansion.

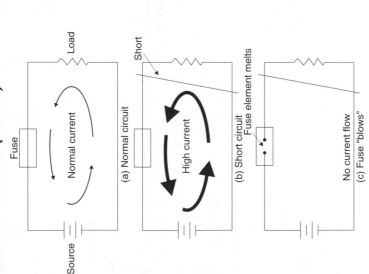

(a) Normal circuit

(b) Short circuit

(c) Fuse "blows"

Illustration #252 - Fuse Protecting a Circuit

Protective Devices *(cont'd)*

When a piece of metal gets hot, it tends to increase its physical dimensions. The metal that makes up the bottom of the bimetallic strip, as shown in illustration #253B, has a larger coefficient of expansion and it increases in length more than the piece that makes up the top of the strip.

When the strip gets hot, it bends upward and opens the contacts. The spring loaded hold-lever then moves into a position to catch the strip and prevents it from remaking contact when it cools down. A reset button must be pushed to move the hold-lever aside and allow the contacts to close again. If the hold-lever is eliminated, the breaker resets automatically when the bimetallic strip cools.

Measuring Fluid Performance

The ability to make safe and accurate fluid flow measurements is an integral part of measuring performance and diagnosing faults within fluid flow systems. It is important to maintain fluid flow, in both flow rate and pressure, at some predetermined constant. In order to maintain this its important that the rotating equipment is monitored and checked either continuously or periodically for correct fluid flow rates and pressures.

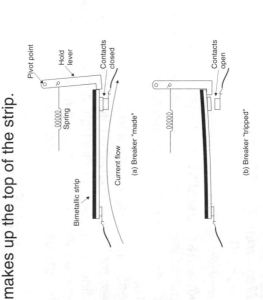

Illustration #253 - Bimetallic Circuit Breaker

MEASURING PERFORMANCE

Measuring Fluid Performance (cont'd)

A physical law that applies to fluid flow is known as Pascal's Law. Pascal's Law simply stated says: "Pressure applied on a confined fluid is transmitted undiminished in all directions, and acts with equal force on equal areas, and at right angles to the surface." For example, a pressurized fluid confined in a pipe, as shown in illustration #254, will act equally in all directions and at right angles to the inside surface of the pipe.

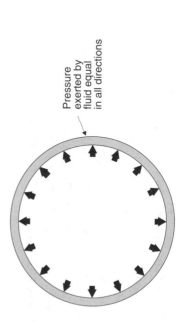

Pressure exerted by fluid equal in all directions

Illustration #254 - Fluid Reaction in a Pipe

Fluid Performance

Measuring Fluid Pressure

Pressure results in any fluid system whenever the flow of a fluid is resisted. The resistance may come from load or a restriction. Therefore, measuring fluid pressure, whether this is in the process of a pumping system or the oil pressure of a lube system, is an effective way for determining the performance of the machinery and system.

An inherent characteristic of fluids is that they will always take the path of least resistance. Thus, when parallel flow paths offer different resistances, the pressure will increase to the amount required to take the easier path.

In illustration #255, the hydraulic fluid has three possible flow paths. Since valve "A" opens at 100 psi, the fluid will go that way and pressure will build up to only 100 psi. If the flow was blocked beyond "A", pressure would build up to 200 psi; then hydraulic fluid would flow through "B" unless the path through valve "B" should also become blocked.

Measuring Fluid Pressure (cont'd)

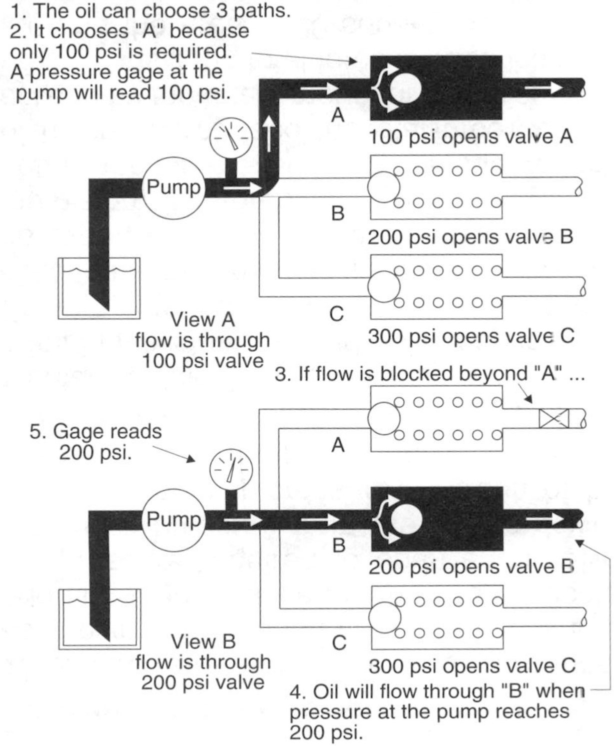

1. The oil can choose 3 paths.
2. It chooses "A" because only 100 psi is required. A pressure gage at the pump will read 100 psi.

3. If flow is blocked beyond "A" ...

View A
flow is through 100 psi valve

100 psi opens valve A

200 psi opens valve B

300 psi opens valve C

A

B

C

Pump

5. Gage reads 200 psi.

4. Oil will flow through "B" when pressure at the pump reaches 200 psi.

View B
flow is through 200 psi valve

200 psi opens valve B

300 psi opens valve C

A

B

C

Pump

Illustration #255 - Parallel Flow Paths

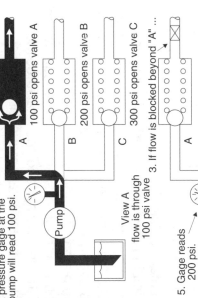

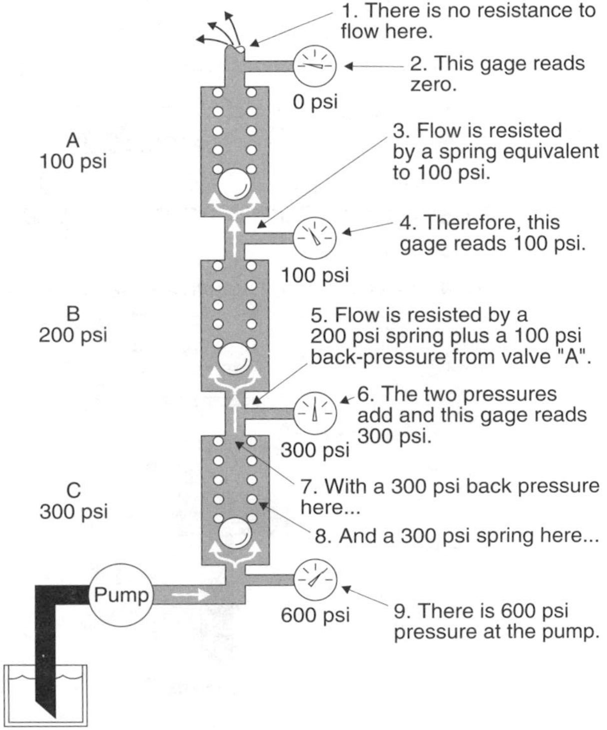

1. There is no resistance to flow here.

2. This gage reads zero.

0 psi

3. Flow is resisted by a spring equivalent to 100 psi.

4. Therefore, this gage reads 100 psi.

100 psi

5. Flow is resisted by a 200 psi spring plus a 100 psi back-pressure from valve "A".

6. The two pressures add and this gage reads 300 psi.

300 psi

7. With a 300 psi back pressure here...

8. And a 300 psi spring here...

9. There is 600 psi pressure at the pump.

600 psi

Pump

A
100 psi

B
200 psi

C
300 psi

Illustration #256 - Series Resistance Adds Pressure

Measuring Fluid Pressure (cont'd)

When flow resistance is connected in series, as shown in illustration #256, the pressures add up. Gages placed in the lines indicate the pressure required to open each valve plus back pressure from the valves downstream. The pump pressure is the sum of the pressures required to open individual valves.

The "force-to-pressure" relationship is fundamental to fluid flow measurements of any pumping system or hydraulic application. For example, the total force, in pounds, applied to the piston rod in illustration #257 will be evenly distributed over the entire face of the piston. The pressure within the cylinder equals the force exerted on one square inch of the piston's surface; the total force must be divided by the total amount of piston surface area. Thus if the total force is 1500 lbs (680 kg) and the area is 20 square inches (129 square centimetres), the pressure within the cylinder, measured at the pressure gage, would be 75 psi (517 kPa).

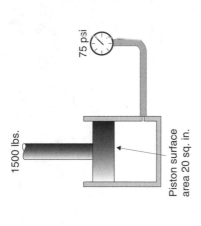

Illustration #257 - Relationship Between Force and Pressure

The "force-to-pressure" relationship shown in illustration #257 can be expressed by the general formula:

Pressure (P) = Force (F)/Area (A)

In this relationship:

P = pressure in psi or kPa

F = force in pounds or kilograms

A = area in square inches or centimetres

Measuring Fluid Pressure (cont'd)

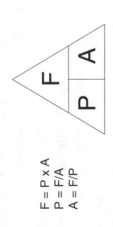

$F = P \times A$
$P = F/A$
$A = F/P$

Illustration #258 - Relationship Between Pressure, Force, and Area

From this can be seen that an increase or decrease in the load or force will result in a proportional increase or decrease in the operating pressure. Pressure is proportional to load, and a pressure gage reading indicates the load at any given moment.

The relationships between pressure, force and area can be shown in illustration #258.

How Pressure Is Created

Pressure results whenever there is a resistance to fluid flow or to a force which attempts to make the fluid flow.

Flow can be supplied by a mechanical pump or may be caused by the weight of the fluid. A mechanical pump is rated to produce a certain amount of flow against a maximum amount of resistance. Measurements are taken to determine whether the pump is producing the correct flow and at what pressure the pump is working against.

Pressure within a fluid may be developed by the weight of the fluid above. A water column (WC) is often used to demonstrate how this works. The term "pressure head" comes from the weight of the fluid.

As shown in illustration #259, a "head" of one foot of water is equivalent to .433 psi, and ten feet would be 4.33. To calculate .433 psi divide the weight of one cubic foot of water (62.4 lbs) by 144 (the number of square inches in a square foot), (62.4 lbs ÷ 144 sq. in. = .433 psi). A one foot head of oil is equivalent to about .400 psi.

Fluid Performance

Measuring Fluid Pressure (cont'd)

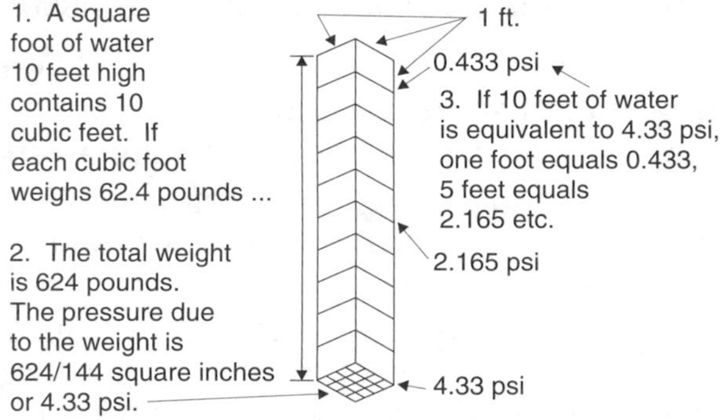

1. A square foot of water 10 feet high contains 10 cubic feet. If each cubic foot weighs 62.4 pounds ...

1 ft.

0.433 psi

3. If 10 feet of water is equivalent to 4.33 psi, one foot equals 0.433, 5 feet equals 2.165 etc.

2.165 psi

2. The total weight is 624 pounds. The pressure due to the weight is 624/144 square inches or 4.33 psi.

4.33 psi

Illustration #259 - Pressure "Head" From The Weight of Fluid

Note: In many industrial applications, the term "head" is used to describe pressure. The term pressure and "head" are sometimes used interchangeably.

Atmospheric Pressure

Atmospheric pressure is the pressure of air in the atmosphere due to its weight. At sea level, a column of air one square inch in cross section and the full height of the atmosphere weighs 14.7 pounds.

Thus the pressure is 14.7 psia. At higher altitudes there is less weight in the column, so the pressure becomes less. Below sea level, atmospheric pressure is more than 14.7 psia.

Any condition where pressure is less than atmospheric pressure is called a vacuum or partial vacuum. A perfect vacuum is the complete absence of pressure or zero psia.

Boyles' Law

A basic physical law governing fluid power equipment, known as Boyles' Law, states: "if the temperature of a confined body of gas is maintained constant, the absolute pressure is inversely proportional to the volume." This simply means that when the volume of a confined gas is reduced by some amount, its absolute pressure will increase by the same amount. It is important to note that this law is in terms of "absolute" pressure, not "gage pressure." Absolute pressure is 14.7 psi more than the reading of a pressure gage.

Boyles Law (cont'd)

The reason for this is that a pressure gage shows zero pounds pressure when it is open to the atmosphere, although 14.7 pounds is actually being exerted upon it.

To convert from psia to psig:

Gage Pressure + 14.7 = Absolute Pressure

Absolute Pressure - 14.7 = Gage Pressure

Bernoulli's Principle

Fluid in a pumping system contains energy in two forms: kinetic energy by virtue of the fluid's weight and velocity; and potential energy in the form of pressure. Both energy forms are necessary in hydraulic systems where hydraulic fluid is used to transmit power to an actuator.

Bernoulli's Principle states, "that the sums of the pressure energy and kinetic energy at various points must be constant if flow rate is constant." For example, when the pipe diameter in illustration #260 changes, the fluid's velocity changes.

Kinetic energy thus either increases or decreases. However, energy can neither be created or destroyed. Therefore the change in kinetic energy must be offset by a decrease or increase in pressure.

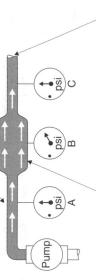

1. In the small section pipe, velocity is maximum. More energy is in the form of motion, so pressure is lower.

2. Velocity decreases in the larger pipe. The kinetic energy loss is made up by an increase in pressure.

3. Ignoring friction losses, the pressure again becomes the same as at "A" when the flow velocity becomes the same as at "A".

Illustration #260 - Constant Flow Rate

Flow Measurement Devices

There are a number of more common methods for determining the amount of flow through a particular section of a fluid flow system. By determining the rate of flow to what the recommended flow rate is supposed to be at that point in the system. This is essential for determining pumping capabilities and efficiencies.

Elbow Taps: A flow measurement using elbow taps depends on the detection of the differential pressure developed by centrifugal force as the direction of fluid flow is changed in a pipe elbow. As shown in illustration #261, taps are located on the inner and outer radius in the plane of the elbow; the diameter which passes through the taps is at either 45 or 22 1/2 degrees from the inlet face of the elbow. Elbow taps are easy to implement because most piping systems already contain elbows.

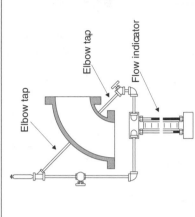

Elbow tap

Elbow tap

Flow indicator

Illustration #261 - Flow Detection with Elbow Tap

Any solids or contaminants can obstruct the taps, therefore they should be periodically purged if the process fluid is not clean.

Note: Elbow taps develop relatively low differential pressures, therefore, they should not be used for measurement of streams with low velocity. The upstream piping is a factor in the installation of elbow taps. It is recommended to provide at least 25 pipe diameters of straight pipe upstream and 10 diameters downstream.

Flow Measurement Devices (cont'd)

Note cont'd: Tap holes should be perpendicular to the surface of the elbow. The tap hole diameter should not exceed 1/8 of the pipe diameter. Elbows should be of the flange type with elbow diameter equal to pipe diameter.

Flow Switches: Are used to determine if the flow rate is above or below a certain value. This value, the setpoint, can be fixed or adjusted. When the setpoint is reached, the response can be the actuation of an electric or pneumatic circuit. When the flow switch is actuated, it stays in that position until the flow rate moves back from the setpoint by some amount. The difference between the setpoint and the reactivation point is called the switch differential.

One type of flow switch is the swinging vane flow switch, as shown in illustration #262.

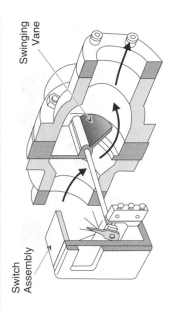

Swinging
Vane

Switch
Assembly

Illustration #262 - Switching Vane Flow Switch

Note: Flow switch reliability is increased by the elimination of moving parts, so that the pipe vibrations or fluid flow pulses will not cause erroneous switch actuation. One of the most popular solid-state designs is the thermal flow switch. All heat activated flow switches sense the movement or stoppage of the process stream by detecting the cooling effect (temperature change) on one or more probes.

Fluid Performance

Flow Measurement Devices (cont'd)

Flowmeters: Probably the most common type of flowmeter is the rotameter, as shown in illustration #263. It consists of a metering float in a calibrated vertical tube.

The metering float is free to move in the tapered glass tube. The fluid flows through the tube from the bottom to top. When no fluid is flowing, the float rests at the bottom of the tapered tube and when flow begins the fluid enters from the bottom and raises the float. The greater the flow rate, the higher the float rises in the tube. The tube is graduated to allow a direct reading of the flow rate.

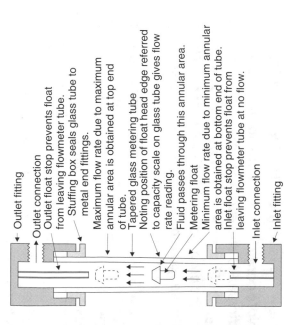

- Outlet fitting
- Outlet connection
- Outlet float stop prevents float from leaving flowmeter tube.
- Stuffing box seals glass tube to metal end fittings.
- Maximum flow rate due to maximum annular area is obtained at top end of tube.
- Tapered glass metering tube
- Noting position of float head edge referred to capacity scale on glass tube gives flow rate reading.
- Fluid passes through this annular area.
- Metering float
- Minimum flow rate due to minimum annular area is obtained at bottom end of tube.
- Inlet float stop prevents float from leaving flowmeter tube at no flow.
- Inlet connection
- Inlet fitting

Illustration #263 - Rotameter (Flow Meter)

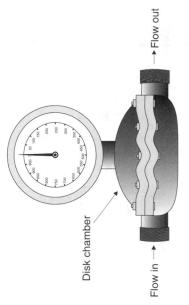

Disk chamber

Flow in →

→ Flow out

Illustration #264 - Flow Meter with Disk Piston

Flow Measurement Devices (cont'd)

Illustration #264 shows another type of flowmeter, which incorporates a disk piston. As the fluid flows through the body, the disk piston develops a rotary motion, which is transmitted through gearing to a pointer on a dial which indicates flow rate.

A schematic drawing of a turbine-type flowmeter is given in illustration #265. This design of flowmeter incorporates a turbine rotor mounted in a housing connected in a pipeline in order to measure the flow rate. The fluid causes the turbine to rotate at a speed that is proportional to the flow rate. The rotation of the turbine generates an electrical impulse every time a turbine blade passes a sensing device. An electronic device connected to the sensor converts the pulse to flow rate information.

Orifice Meters: Illustration #266 shows an orifice plate, which is basically a disk with a hole through which fluid flows, installed in a section of piping. This device is an actual flowmeter when the pressure drop across the orifice is measured, because there is a unique relationship between the pressure drop and flow rate for a given orifice size. Specifically, the greater the flow rate, the greater the pressure drop.

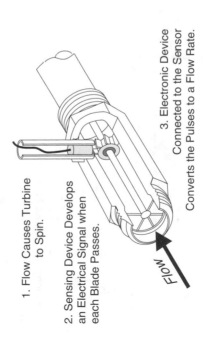

1. Flow Causes Turbine to Spin.

2. Sensing Device Develops an Electrical Signal when each Blade Passes.

3. Electronic Device Connected to the Sensor Converts the Pulses to a Flow Rate.

FLOW

Illustration #265 - Turbine Flowmeter

Flow Measurement Devices (cont'd)

Fluid Performance

Illustration #267 shows the actual fluid flow pattern and the sharp leading edge of the orifice plate. The sharp edge results in an almost pure line contact between the plate and the effective flow, with negligible fluid-to-metal friction drag at this boundary. Any nicks, burrs, or rounding of the sharp edge can result in errors of flow measurement.

Sight Flow Indicators: Are used when a visual inspection of the process is necessary. Illustrations #268A, #268B, and #268C show three designs. The flapper design is used in transparent or slightly opaque solutions and in gas services. Flow direction is either vertical or horizontal. Some indication of flow variations may be made by observing the position of the flapper. Bi-directional flappers are also available. In these designs the flapper is hinged in the center of the pipe. The drip-tube design, shown in illustration #268B, is used where the flow is vertically down and is well suited for intermittent flows.

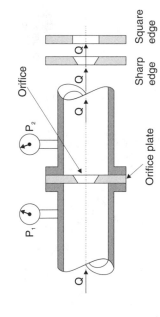

Illustration #266 - Orifice Flowmeter

Illustration #267 - Flow Pattern With Orifice Plate

Flow Measurement Devices (cont'd)

The paddle design, as shown in illustration #268C, is used on dark process fluids since the motion of the paddle can be easily detected. Flow through the paddle design is suited to higher flows, because low flows will not turn the paddle.

Venturi Tubes, Flow Nozzles, Flow Tubes:
Are based on Bernoulli's Principle. In these devices there is continuous contact between the fluid flow and the surface of the primary device. Surface finish of the device can have some effect on the meter coefficient.

The classic venturi tube, as shown in illustration #269, consists of a cylindrical inlet section equal to the pipe diameter; a converging conical section in which the cross-sectional area decreases causing the velocity to increase with a corresponding increase in the velocity head and a decrease in the pressure head; a cylindrical throat section where the velocity is constant so the decreased pressure head can be measured; and a diverging recovery cone where the velocity decreases and almost all of the original pressure head is recovered. The unrecovered pressure head is commonly called "head loss."

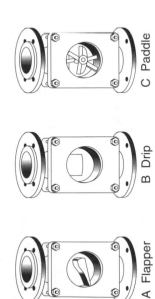

A Flapper   B Drip   C Paddle

Illustration #268 - Sight Flow Meters

Fluid Performance

Flow Measurement Devices (cont'd)

Illustration #270 shows one type of flow tube. This flow tube has a higher ratio of pressure-developed-to-pressure-lost than a venturi tube. This design is more compact than a classical venturi tube.

Illustration #271 shows a typical flow nozzle installation. The most common type of flow nozzle is the flange-type. As in this illustration, differential pressure taps are installed on either side of the flow nozzle.

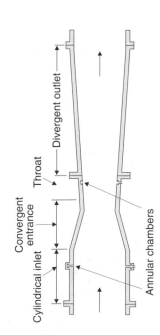

Illustration #269 - Classic Venturi

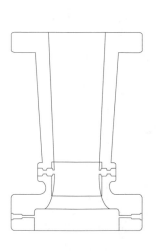

Illustration #270 - Compact Venturi Tube

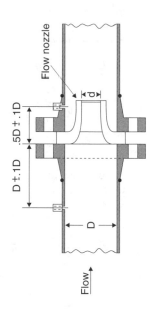

Illustration #271 - Flow Nozzle Installation

Pressure Measurement

Pressure measurement devices are required in process fluid systems to determine performance and efficiency of process equipment such as pumps and actuators. In addition to testing and trouble-shooting, they are used to adjust pressure settings for control and relief pressure purposes.

One of the most common pressure measuring devices is the Bourdon Gage, as shown in illustration #272.

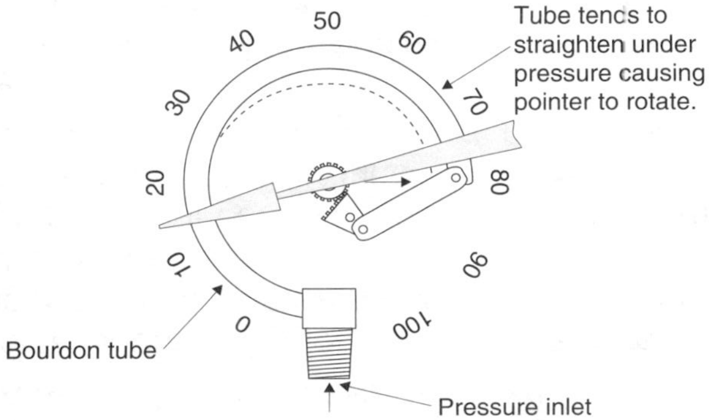

The Bourdon Gage contains a sealed tube formed in the shape of an arc. When pressure is applied at the port opening, the tube starts to straighten somewhat. This activates a linkage-gear system, which moves the pointer to indicate the pressure on the dial. The scale of most Bourdon Gages reads zero when the gage is open to the atmosphere, because the gages are calibrated to read pressure above atmospheric pressure or gage pressure.

Illustration #273 - Fluid Filled Pressure Gage

Tube tencs to straighten under pressure causing pointer to rotate.

Pressure inlet

Bourdon tube

Illustration #272 - Bourdon Gage Operation

Pressure Measurement (cont'd)

Some Bourdon Gages are capable of reading pressures below atmospheric or vacuum (suction) pressures, such as those existing in pump inlet lines. The range for vacuum gages is from 0 to 30 inches (0-76 mm) of mercury, which represents a perfect vacuum.

Illustration #273 identifies a fluid-filled type of Bourdon pressure gage. This type of pressure gage uses fluid to give the pressure gage a high pressure range operation.

Illustration #274 is a similar type of Bourdon Gage, except its called a dry gage, where no fluid is used to dampen the pressure effects to the gage. Both gages have dual measuring scales, in PSI and BAR. (1 BAR equals 14.7 PSI).

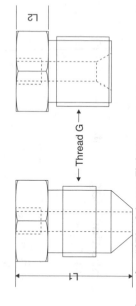

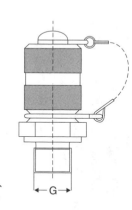

Illustration #274 - Dry-Type Pressure Gage

Illustration #275 - Test Point Fitting

Illustration #276 - Adaptor Fittings

MEASURING PERFORMANCE

Pressure Measurement (cont'd)

In order to install pressure gages in process fluid systems it is essential to have proper test fittings. Illustration #275 shows a special fitting called a test point fitting.

It is installed in the piping system, at preselected points, and is designed to accept a standard "quick connect" fitting on a pressure gage.

Illustrations #276, #277, and #278 show high pressure fittings and hose for attaching pressure gages into the process fluid systems.

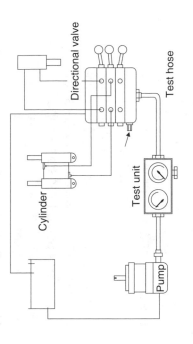

Illustration #279 - Performing a Pump Test

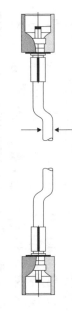

Illustration #277 - High Pressure Hose

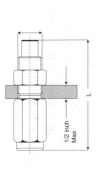

Illustration #278 - Pressure Gage Connector

Fluid Performance

Pressure Measurement (cont'd)

In order to troubleshoot process fluid systems to determine flows, pressures and temperatures, special test kits can be purchased from manufacturers which comprise of a flow indicator, built-in thermometer, and a pressure gage. A kit of this type provides an ideal solution for servicing hydraulic circuits and other fluid flow systems. Illustration #279 shows one example of how a test kit can be used to do a pump test on a hydraulic circuit. Both fluid flow and pressure can be determined this way.

Troubleshooting Fluid Power Circuits

Hydraulic systems and lubrication systems common to rotating equipment depend on proper flow and pressure from the pump to provide necessary performance and reliability. Flow and pressure measurements are two important means of troubleshooting faulty hydraulic and lubrication systems.

The use of flowmeters can determine whether or not the pump is producing proper flow and can also indicate whether or not a particular actuator is receiving the expected flow rate. The flowmeter monitors fluid flow rates to determine pump performance, flow regulator settings, or system performance. Pressure measurements provide an indication of leakage problems and faulty components such as pumps, flow control valves, pressure relief valves, strainers and actuators. Excessive pressure drops in pipelines can also be detected by the use of pressure measurements.

Combination flow-pressure test kits are available to measure both flow and pressure. These test kits are quickly installed in a circuit. It is best if quick-connect/disconnect couplers are located in the circuit. This makes it faster, easier and safer to connect the test-kit into the circuit.

Troubleshooting Fluid Power (cont'd)

When troubleshooting hydraulic and pressure lubrication systems, it should be kept in mind that the pump produces flow of a fluid. However, there must be resistance to flow in order to have pressure and the pump must be able to perform to a set pressure which is usually at or near the pressure relief valve setting.

The following is a list of hydraulic and lubrication system operating problems, and the corresponding probable causes which should be investigated during troubleshooting.

1. Noisy Pump:

- air entering pump inlet
- misalignment of pump and drive unit
- excessive oil viscosity
- dirty inlet strainer
- chattering relief valve
- mechanical fault within pump
- excessive pump speed
- loose or damaged inlet line

2. Low or Erratic Pressure:

- air in the fluid
- pressure relief valve set too low
- pressure relief valve not properly seated
- leak in hydraulic/lube line
- defective or worn pump
- defective or worn actuator

3. No Pressure:

- pump rotating in wrong direction
- ruptured lines
- low oil level in reservoir
- pressure relief valve struck open
- broken pump shaft
- full pump flow bypassed to tank
- defective or worn pump

4. Actuator Fails To Move:

- faulty pump
- directional control valve fails to shift
- system pressure too low
- defective actuator
- pressure relief valve stuck open

Troubleshooting Fluid Power (cont'd)

- actuator load is excessive
- check valve installed backwards
- ruptured lines
- insufficient flow to actuator

5. Slow Or Erratic Motion Of Actuator:

- air in system
- viscosity of fluid too high
- worn or damaged pump
- pump speed too low
- excess leakage through valves/actuator
- faulty/dirty control valves
- blocked air breather in reservoir
- low fluid level in reservoir
- faulty check valve
- defective pressure relief valve

6. Overheating Of Hydraulic/Lube Fluid:

- incorrect fluid
- overloaded system
- poor air movement around system
- undersized components or piping
- too many restrictions
- faulty heat exchanger
- faulty cooler
- continuous operation of pressure relief valve
- dirty fluid
- reservoir too small
- inadequate supply of oil in reservoir
- excessive pump speed
- clogged or inadequate-sized air breather

Temperature Measurements

Temperature is an expression denoting a physical condition of matter, as are mass, dimensions and time. Temperature depicts heat as a form of energy associated with the activity of the molecules of a substance. These minute particles of all matter are assumed to be in continuous motion which is sensed as heat. Temperature is a measure of this heat.

Temperature Measurement (cont'd)

Temperature measurement, just as flow and pressure measurements, is another method for determining both performance and reliability of rotating equipment and hydraulic and lubrication systems.

To standardize the temperature of rotating equipment components and other system machinery under varying conditions, several scales have been devised. The Fahrenheit scale arbitrarily assigns the number "32" to the freezing point of water and the number "212" to the boiling point of water and divides the interval into 180 equal parts. The Centigrade or Celsius scale calls the freezing point of water "0" and its boiling point "100".

In line with the standard definition of temperature, some relation to the point where molecular motion is at a minimum had to be established, and the Kelvin scale, using Centigrade divisions, was drawn.

Zero Kelvin was determined to be -273.15°C. The Rankine scale places zero at -459.61°F using Fahrenheit divisions.

Temperature measurements are used many ways for determining performance and reliability of rotating equipment components, fluids and process systems. Primarily, temperature measurements are used to monitor bearing and lubrication temperatures. They may also be used to determine electrical faults, hotspots, leaks, and internal friction/rubbing problems in a variety of equipment and machinery.

Temperature Measuring Devices

Bimetallic Thermometers: Make use of two fundamental principles: one, metals change volume with temperature; and two, the coefficient of change is not the same for all metals. If two different straight metal strips are bonded together and heated, the resultant strip will tend to bend toward the side of the metal with the lower expansion rate.

Temperature Measuring Devices (cont'd)

Deflection is proportional to the square of the length and the temperature change, and inversely proportional to the thickness.

Temperature Measurement

A bimetallic spring, as shown in illustration #280, can be calibrated to produce a predictable deflection at a preset temperature. This is the basis of operation of many bimetallic temperature sensors and switches common to the monitoring systems of rotating equipment.

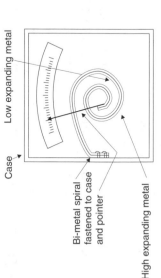

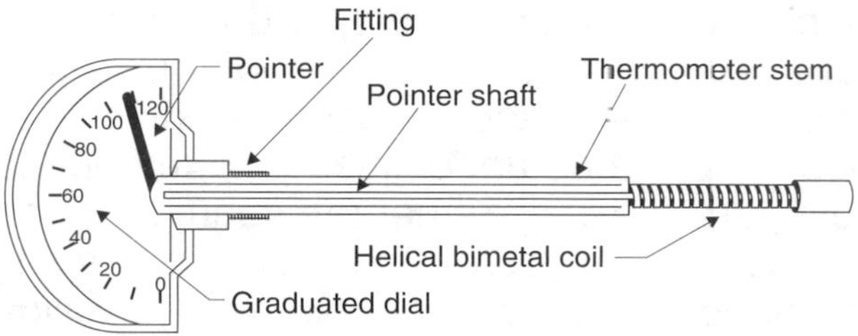

Illustration #281B - Bimetallic Thermometer

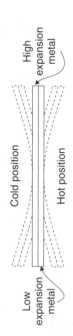

Illustration #280 - Bimetallic Spring

Illustration #281A - Bimetallic Ambient Air Thermometer

Temperature Measuring Devices (cont'd)

Common types of temperature thermometers using the bimetallic principle include those shown in illustrations #281A,B,C. The thermometer is usually back or bottom connected, depending on which orientation allows the operator or the technician better visibility of the dial face. See illustration #282.

Thermocouples: are only as accurate as the wire from which it is made. Most manufacturers offer either standard or special calibrations in which more care goes into selection of wire, handling, and construction. In order to maintain highest accuracy in a thermocouple, an adequate checking and calibration program is necessary. Illustration #283 shows one type of thermocouple. It consists of a terminal block and head, an element (wire) and insulator, and a protecting tube. The protecting tube may also be called a thermowell. See illustration #281C.

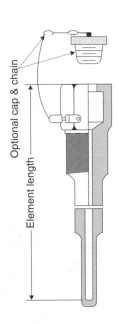

Optional cap & chain

Element length

Illustration #281C - Thermowell

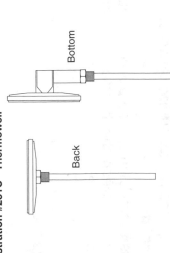

Bottom

Back

Illustration #282 - Back & Bottom Thermometers

Temperature Measuring Devices (cont'd)

It is essential that good physical contact be made between the thermocouple junction and the metallic surface of the inside of the well. The purpose of the thermowell is to protect the thermocouple from mechanical damage and corrosion.

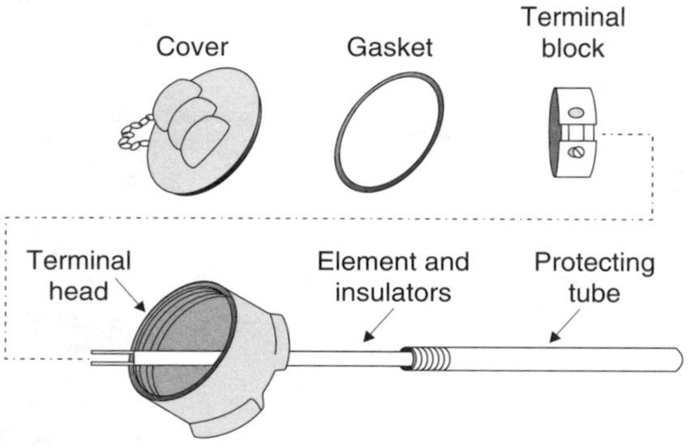

Illustration #284A - Liquid Filled Capillary Tube Thermometer

Illustration #284B - Digital Thermometer

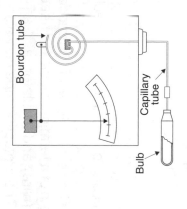

Illustration #283 - Thermocouple Assembly

Temperature Measuring Devices (cont'd)

Temperature Sensitive Bulbs: Come in many sizes and shapes to handle temperature readings for many different applications. It is good practice to use the largest bulbs which will do the job. This reduces ambient temperature errors, and permit smaller spans and longer capillaries. Plain bulbs are used where the process medium is not under pressure and will not harm the bulb material. Using a thermowell protects the bulb from harmful process medium. This will slow down the response time of the bulb. Illustration #284A gives one example of a thermal bulb attached to a capillary tube and Bourdon gage. Illustration #284B shows another style of temperature sensitive bulb. In this example, the bulb is attached to a remote reading digital thermometer.

Contact Pyrometers: Measure the temperature of a bearing's housing. An example is a probe pressed against the housing. The temperature is read out on a dial face. Illustration #285 is an example of a handheld portable pyrometer.

Illustration #285 - Contact Pyrometer

Temperature Measuring Devices (cont'd)

Note: Although the temperature of the bearing housing is not identical to the bearing temperature, the two are related. The housing temperature serves as a point of reference in that an increase in the temperature of the bearing housing reflects an increase in the temperature of the bearing; and an abrupt change in the temperature of the housing would indicate a problem with the bearing. A thermocouple can be installed to read temperatures at the bearing where the operation is critical. The measurement is usually read out on a recorder located at a central monitoring point in the plant.

Thermographic Instruments: With thermographic instruments the technician can "see" infrared radiation. Everything and everyone constantly loses heat to the environment in the form of invisible infrared radiation.

Infrared radiation can be felt but cannot be seen with the naked eye. The technique for detecting this invisible heat is called "thermography."

The thermographic instrument is designed to be held in the hand and up to the eye so that it may be sighted on target. An adjustable focus permits the operation to focus on an image of the source whose temperature is to be determined. The use of the human eye as the detector restricts accuracy somewhat because the eye responds to both color and brightness rather than directly to energy, and no two eyes are exactly the same. However, it is possible to detect both a color and brightness match by adjusting to the difference between known and unknown.

With thermographic instruments one can see and record infrared radiation on a standard television screen. The instrument is capable of storing the temperature data on video tape or floppy disk to be analyzed later.

Temperature Measuring Devices (cont'd)

The instruments are expensive and require some degree of training and practice in order to develop some level of competency when performing any temperature analysis of equipment. Thermographic inspections are proving to be an indispensable predictive maintenance tool in providing positive evidence to help solve heat related problems in various types of equipment and applications. The following list identifies possible applications for thermographic inspections:

- electrical system faults and hotspots
- locate missing or damaged insulation
- identify air leakage energy loss
- identify leaking steam traps, valves, lines and fittings
- predictive maintenance on rotating equipment
- quality control of product
- locate water damage

Illustration #286 shows a type of thermographic instrument which provides a digital readout of temperature at the targeted point. This type of instrument uses a precision laser to accurately aim the instrument at the source.

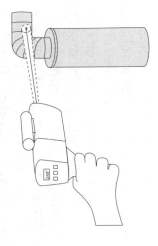

Illustration #286 - Thermographic Instrument

Temperature Measuring Devices (cont'd)

Pocket Digital Thermometers: Are direct reading thermometers which provide a digital readout of temperature. Usually the measurements can be given in either the Fahrenheit or Centigrade scale. Illustration #287 shows one type of pocket digital thermometer. Depending on design, the range can be from -40°F to +300°F (-40°C to +149°C).

Illustration #287 - Pocket Digital Thermometer

Color Indicators and Crayons: A number of temperature-related physical changes have been used to produce simple thermometers.

Temperature Measurement

Crayon marks, for example, on heated work pieces, change from solid to liquid when their melting point is reached. There are several temperature-range crayons available on the market.

Paints and heat-sensitive labels change color and luminescent materials change their brightness. These are examples of temperature sensitive devices where color changes are used as temperature indicators. Color indicators are a class of temperature sensors which have the property of changing their original color when a certain temperature is reached. The change should be distinct, not just an alteration in shade. For example, an indicator may change from yellow to grey, or blue to brown, depending on the temperature range. Temperature is indicated by a chemical reaction, where a molecule of gas, such as ammonia or water vapor, is driven off the basic stock, thus changing its color. The change is usually permanent after the object cools down.

Temperature Measuring Devices (cont'd)

Touch: Touching a bearing housing, with the hand, is the simplest and most often used method for determining temperature. Although this is a crude method, experience enables a technician to know from feeling/touching the housing whether or not it is running too hot. Always be careful, as burning is one of the hazards of this method for determining temperature.

Ultrasonic Detection Devices

With ultrasonic detection it is possible to capture the presence of ultrasounds. Ultrasounds are soundwaves beyond the limit of human hearing. The average human ear is capable of picking up sound waves in the 20 Hz to 20 kHz (20,000 Hz) frequency range, where one Hertz is equal to one cycle per second. All sounds above 20,000 Hz are considered ultrasounds.

Most of the ultrasonic detection devices on the market are pistol grip designs and are relatively simple to use. The handheld listening device comes complete with a frequency tuning and monitoring system. Range of operation is usually between 20 kHz to 100 kHz where the unit transposes the ultrasounds into the audible range for the operator, who listens through attached headphones. Generally, ultrasonic detection devices perform in two modes: scanning mode or contact mode.

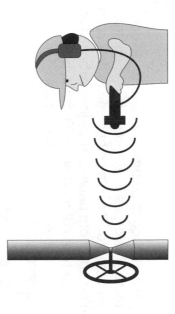

Illustration #288 - Ultrasonic Detection

Ultrasonic Detection Devices (cont'd)

As shown in illustration #288, the scanning mode is being used for leak detection of fluids, gases or vacuum. As the fluid or gas escapes through a small opening, it creates a turbulence noise which consists of ultrasonic wave patterns; the leak causes the ultrasonic detection device's meter to register the emission, accompanied by a significant change in volume heard through the headphones.

Because ultrasounds are short wave signals, they are loudest at their source, enabling the operator to pinpoint the leak with extreme accuracy.

In the contact mode, a metal probe is attached to the end of the scanning device. When the probe is place against the equipment surface, it is stimulated by the ultrasonic sounds occurring on the other side.

This method is commonly used to detect internal leakages that occur in steam traps, valves, etc. It can also be used to detect friction and wear deterioration in gearboxes and other types of rotating equipment, by recording sound levels to form a basis for future comparison.

Tachometers

Both contact and non-contact tachometers are useful instruments for determining the rotational speed of rotating equipment. It is often necessary to know the speed of the equipment in order to determine performance and efficiencies.

Illustration #289 identifies one type of contact tachometer. This unit is handheld and offers a wide speed range, usually from 0.1-25,000 RPM.

MEASURING PERFORMANCE

Tachometers (cont'd)

To use this type of tachometer, carefully make contact to the rotating part with the friction wheel on the shaft end of the unit. Be careful to not contact a key or keyway on a shaft. Once contact is made the digital readout provides a fairly accurate speed.

One example of a non-contact tachometer is the phototachometer. This unit uses an easy-to-aim visible light beam which provides a high resolution measurement of speed without any mechanical contact. This type of tachometer is safe to use and is ideal for measuring a variety of shaft speeds and gear and flywheel speeds. These units are common for industrial and automotive applications. Again, this unit is handheld and offers a speed range anywhere from 5-100,000 RPM. Illustration #290 shows one type of non-contact phototachometer. A digital readout on an optional LED display provides immediate speed readings. Many of these units have memory capabilities.

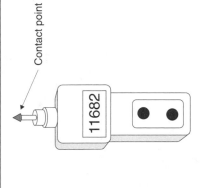

Contact point

Illustration #289 - Contact Tachometer

Illustration #290 - Non-Contact Phototachometer

SECTION EIGHT QUESTIONS

Performance Monitoring

1. Some type of comparative standards must be established to serve as a basis for indicating machinery performance and condition.

   ☐ true   ☐ false

2. Generally, there are two types of comparative standards commonly used in machinery performance and condition monitoring. These are:

   Answer: _____

3. Identify four points to be considered in order to judge the performance and condition of machinery.

   Answer: _____
   _____

4. The ability to make safe and accurate electrical circuit measurements is an integral part of measuring machinery and equipment performance.

   ☐ true   ☐ false

5. When possible, turn the electric circuit off and verify it is off before performing work on the machine.

   ☐ true   ☐ false

6. It is best to discharge stored energy from all components before attempting to do any work on the machine or machine part.

   ☐ true   ☐ false

7. Why is it good practice to never place both hands into an electrical circuit?

   Answer: _____

8. Multimeters are used to measure three electrical units. These are:

   Answer: _____

9. VOM is an acronym for:

   Answer: _____

10. The amount of current flowing in an electrical circuit is dependent upon the value of electrical pressure and the opposition to the flow of current. This statement refers to:

    ☐ Pascal's Law
    ☐ Boyle's Law
    ☐ Ohm's Law
    ☐ Bernoulli's Principle

11. Calculate the current flowing in a circuit having 10 ohms resistance and 120 V of electrical pressure.

Answer: _____

12. Calculate the resistance of a circuit that allows only 6 Amps to flow when a voltage of 240 V is applied.

Answer: _____

13. Calculate the voltage in the circuit when the current flow is 15 Amps and the resistance in the circuit is found to be 8 ohms.

Answer: _____

14. Voltmeters are always connected in series, not parallel, in the electrical circuit.

☐ true   ☐ false

15. A device used to measure current in a circuit is called a/an:

☐ ammeter   ☐ voltmeter
☐ megohmmeter   ☐ wattmeter

16. A/an _____ is always connected into the electrical circuit (series connection).

☐ voltmeter   ☐ ammeter
☐ megohmmeter   ☐ ohmmeter

17. Resistance in an electrical circuit _____ to the flow of current.

☐ is supportive   ☐ is parallel
☐ is in opposition ☐ is in reverse

18. Conductor resistance is not a significant problem when the wires are long and carry high current flow.

☐ true   ☐ false

19. The instrument commonly used to measure resistance is:

☐ ohmmeter   ☐ megohmmeter
☐ wattmeter   ☐ ammeter

20. For a basic analog ohmmeter, when the leads are open, the ohmmeter indicates _____ resistance.

☐ zero   ☐ infinite

21. An ohmmeter has its own power supply and therefore must never be connected into an energized circuit.

☐ true   ☐ false

22. Which testing instrument is recommended for measuring very high resistance values in electrical circuits?

☐ wattmeter   ☐ ammeter

☐ megohmmeter   ☐ ohmmeter

23. Which unit is used for defining power in electrical systems?

☐ amperes   ☐ volts

☐ ohms   ☐ watts

24. Which testing instrument is used to measure true power in an electrical circuit?

☐ wattmeter   ☐ voltmeter

☐ ammeter   ☐ megohmmeter

25. Energy measurement is accomplished by using a watthour meter.

☐ true   ☐ false

26. Fuses and circuit breakers are used to safeguard against: _____

Answer: _____

27. _____ is defined as being the current that is out of its normal path and may be caused by faults in the insulation or by faulty connections.

Answer: _____

28. _____ is defined as being low level faults that are caused by temporary current surges.

Answer: _____

29. Fuses are intentionally weakened circuit components that close when the current reaches a dangerous level.

☐ true   ☐ false

30. When a fuse melts it is said to have "blown." Explain what this means.

Answer: _____

31. Circuit breakers are able to open a circuit by "tripping."

☐ true   ☐ false

32. Generally, circuit breakers use:

☐ single wire element which melts and breaks

☐ a special bimetallic strip

Section 8   Performance Monitoring   Page Q8-3

33. A bimetallic strip is made up of two different metal alloys, each having:

☐ similar expansion qualities
☐ different coefficient of expansion
☐ similar magnetic qualities
☐ opposite conductor characteristics

34. "Pressure applied on a confined fluid is transmitted undiminished in all directions, and acts with equal force on equal areas, and at right angles to the surface." This statement is referred to as _____.

☐ Ohm's Law　　　　　☐ Pascal's Law
☐ Bernoulli's Principle　☐ Boyle's Law

35. Pressure results in any fluid system whenever the flow of a fluid is resisted.

☐ true　　　　　☐ false

36. An inherent characteristic of fluids is that they always will take the path of _____ resistance.

☐ least　　　　　☐ greatest

37. Force (F) in fluid systems is equal to:

☐ Pressure/Area (P)/(A)
☐ Pressure x Area (P)x(A)

38. Pressure (P) in fluid systems is equal to:

☐ Force x Area (F)x(A)
☐ Force/Area (F)/(A)

39. Fluid flow in fluid systems is commonly supplied two ways. These are:

Answer: _____

40. A mechanical pump in fluid systems is normally rated to produce a certain amount of flow against a maximum amount of resistance.

☐ true　　　　　☐ false

41. Measurements are commonly taken to determine whether a pump is operating efficiently. Two common measurements are:

Answer: _____

42. At sea level, a column of air one square inch in cross section and the full height of the atmosphere weighs _____.

☐ 62.4 pounds　　☐ 4.33 pounds
☐ 14.7 pounds　　☐ zero pounds

43. Below sea level, atmospheric pressure is more than at levels well above sea level.

☐ true ☐ false

44. Absolute pressure is 14.7 psi more than the reading of a pressure gage.

☐ true ☐ false

45. Gage Pressure plus 14.7 = _____.

Answer: _____

46. Fluid in a pumping system contains energy in two forms:

Answer: _____

47. List six devices used to measure fluid flow rates through particular sections of fluid flow systems:

Answer: _____

48. Bourdon Gages are commonly used to measure:

☐ rate of fluid and gas flow
☐ fluid and gas pressure
☐ temperature
☐ vibration

49. Why are some Bourdon Gages filled with fluids?

Answer: _____

50. Can pressure measurements in a fluid system be used to determine leakage problems?

☐ yes ☐ no

51. Which type of device would be most useful for setting a pressure relief valve in a hydraulic system?

☐ flowmeter ☐ vacuum gage
☐ tachometer ☐ pressure gage

52. One cause of having a noisy hydraulic pump would be:

☐ air entering pump inlet
☐ excessive oil viscosity
☐ dirty inlet strainer
☐ all of the above

53. List several causes for low or erratic pressure results in a hydraulic pumping system:

Answer: _____

54. If the pressure relief valve was stuck open, the hydraulic actuator would probably fail to move.

☐ true ☐ false

55. If the viscosity of the hydraulic fluid were too high, there probably would be slow or erratic movement of the actuator.

☐ true ☐ false

56. Continuous operation of the pressure relief valve will typically not cause the hydraulic fluid to overheat.

☐ true ☐ false

57. Primarily, temperature measurements are used to monitor _____ and _____ temperatures on rotating equipment.

Answer: _____

58. List eight methods used for measuring temperature in and around rotating equipment:

Answer: _____

59. Ultrasonic Detection Devices are useful for performing "leak detection" on rotating equipment.

☐ true ☐ false

60. Is it necessary to know the speed of the equipment in order to determine performance and efficiencies?

☐ yes ☐ no

61. What precaution must be taken into consideration when using a contact tachometer?

Answer: _____

62. A Phototachometer is one example of a non-contact tachometer.

☐ true ☐ false

SECTION NINE

EQUIPMENT LOCKOUT AND TAGOUT

Introduction

Many industrial accidents are caused by the uncontrollable release of hazardous energy. The unexpected activation of machinery or process equipment during regular maintenance and servicing operations can have tragic results. That's why the first step in any lockout or tagout procedure is to be aware of the types of energy sources and hazards which need to be controlled.

Provincial, State, and Federal governments in Canada and United States have comprehensive standards for the control of hazardous energy sources for industry. The information used to write the standards has been gathered from industry, along with governmental regulatory agencies, including occupational health and safety groups, workers compensation boards, the National Institute of Occupational Health and Safety (NIOSH), and the American National Standards Institute (ANSI).

Introduction/Lockout/Tagout

Standards for lockout and tagout are designed to protect employees involved in service and maintenance activities against an unexpected start-up of machines or equipment, or the release of stored energy that could cause injuries. The laws concerning lockout and tagout are generally flexible enough to allow each employer to develop a suitable lockout and tagout program with procedures designed to meet specific needs for the type of machinery and equipment being serviced and maintained by the employees.

Lockout and Tagout

Lockout: This is a method of keeping equipment from being set in motion and endangering employees. Lockout is the use of locks to positively secure the control device(s) used to control the hazardous energy. In lockout a disconnect switch, valve, or other energy isolating mechanism is put in the safe or off position.

Lockout and Tagout (cont'd)

A lock is attached so that the equipment cannot be energized as shown in illustration #291.

Tagout: In tagout, the energy isolating device(s) is placed in the safe or off position. An approved tag with "Danger" clearly written on it and "Do Not Remove This Tag", and other specific warnings, is attached to it. Illustration #292 shows an example of a tag attached to a lockout device.

Illustration #292 - Typical Lockout and Tagout

Note: Its common practice, and in many cases law, that all lockout and tagout materials and devices be supplied by the employer.

Each device must be: durable; withstand wear; substantial, so it won't come off easily; and recognizable, so the person who applied it can be identified. Many companies issue each employee authorization to apply their own locks and tags.

Illustration #291 - Typical Lockout

Lockout and Tagout (cont'd)

An "assigned lock" is a lock that the employee is personally responsible and accountable for. They control the key.

Application of Lockout or Tagout

Procedures for lockout and tagout are necessary whenever performing service and maintenance to any machinery or equipment where there could be injury from:

- Unexpected start-up of the machine or equipment, and/or
- A sudden release of stored or restrained energy.

Two common situations tradespeople and operators are most likely required to have lockout and tagout procedures are:

1. When any part of a person's body could be caught by moving machinery parts.

2. When any equipment guard or safety device must be removed from a machine or piece of equipment.

Lockout/Tagout/Hazardous Energy

Some common jobs and activities for which lockout and tagout are used include:

- Repairing or testing electrical circuits.
- Cleaning or lubricating machinery where there are moving parts.
- Inspecting or testing machine parts.
- Clearing debris or product from the machine or process equipment.
- Freeing up jammed parts or mechanisms.

Hazardous Energy Sources

Energy of some sort is always present in any type of powered machinery or equipment. There is always a chance that something can move, by being released suddenly or slowly.

Energy can come from many sources, but it is always one of two classifications:

- Kinetic Energy: the force caused by the motion of the object or part.
- Potential Energy: the force stored in an object or part that remains inactive, but can be either slowly or suddenly released.

Types of Energy Sources

Electrical Energy: There are two types of electrical energy sources: generated electric power and static electricity.

Generated electric power is found at the main source of electricity to the machine, as well as within the various circuitry of the machinery and equipment. Generated electric power is the energy required to perform work or to produce an action.

Note: Generated electric power can also be stored energy, such as in batteries or capacitors.

Static electricity is an energy source that is fixed on the surface of an object. An example of this can be found in an electrostatic precipitator. These are commonly used for dust collection in various industrial processes and environmental management installations.

Mechanical Energy: Mechanical energy is usually expressed as either transitional (linear) or rotational motion.

Transitional motion is usually a linear movement from one fixed point to another. Examples of this would include gates which swing or slide, doors on hinges, and conveyor belts and rollers.

Rotational motion is a common form of mechanical energy when working in and around rotating equipment. Rotational energy refers to objects/parts which revolve, such as flywheels, pulleys, gears, shafts, couplings, and rollers.

There can be tremendous amounts of stored energy waiting to be released as rotating energy in any one of these examples. It is imperative that proper blocking and securing procedures are followed in order to protect against rotating energy sources.

Thermal Energy: This is one type of energy few people consider when working in and around machinery and equipment.

Energy Sources (cont'd)

Typically, thermal energy cannot be just turned off or eliminated; one can usually only control it or cause it to dissipate slowly. Several examples include: the heat from a furnace in a foundry; the heat around the kiln in a cement plant; and the frost and cold in large industrial freezers and coolers.   The power sources to these can be turned off, but the thermal energy remains, and there is a waiting period before the thermal energy dissipates.

Note: Heat is considered as being an energy source. Cold is an absence of heat and not considered an energy source

In addition to thermal energy generated by process equipment and certain machinery, certain amounts of thermal energy can be created by chemical reactions.

Hazardous Energy Sources

Chemical reactions can be either exothermic or endothermic. *Exothermic* reactions raise temperatures and *endothermic* reactions lower temperatures. Controlling thermal energy from chemical reactions can be as dangerous, or more dangerous, than either electrical or mechanical energy hazards.

Chemical reactions can be quite complex to identify and control. The methods for isolating and controlling the thermal effects of chemical energy must be written specifically for those chemical processes specific to that location and work area.

Note: Exposure limits are: 110 degrees F (43 degrees C) maximum and 34 degrees F (1 degree C) minimum. At either of these extremes tissue damage begins. Proper personal protective equipment must be worn when working in conditions beyond these temperatures.

Energy Sources (cont'd)

Whether the thermal energy comes from a furnace, kiln, freezer or cooler, it has to be dissipated. In addition, if the thermal energy source is from a chemical reaction, either eliminate the chemical(s) to prevent any reaction or control the reaction to where the thermal energy created can be safely tolerated.

Potential Energy: Potential energy sources, like thermal energy sources, can be difficult to simply turn off, therefore, one may have to dissipate the potential energy source or control it somehow. Types of potential energy sources within machines and process equipment include: pressurized fluids and gases; springs and linkages, and gravity.

Several common types of pressure sources are used extensively around machinery and equipment. These are: hydraulic fluids, compressed gases, and vacuums.

Hydraulic pressure refers to forces being applied to a contained fluid and as the forces on the fluid increase so does the fluid's pressure. The fluid pressure within the container will be equal in all directions and if the pressurized fluid were to be suddenly released, the energy transmitted would be sudden and have tremendous force which could cause severe injury to people or damage to equipment. Hydraulic energy sources are not limited to hydraulic systems, but to any system where fluids are either stored or transmitted under pressure.

Compressed gases are at pressures high enough to be safely stored in tanks or cylinders and are commonly transmitted in piping systems or held in lines by valves. There are many types of compressed gases common to industrial and process equipment and machinery: compressed air, nitrogen, oxygen, carbon dioxide, freon, acetylene, hydrogen and helium are only a small sample of the more common ones.

Energy Sources (cont'd)

Similar to hydraulic energy sources, compressed gases remain stable when stored under constant pressure within an appropriate confined space or container. If there is any chance that the gases are released from the confined area, the release can be uncontrolled and sudden. The seriousness of this can never be stated strongly enough. Always dissipate or control pressurized gases first from any type of machine or process equipment before any type of maintenance or service work is to be undertaken.

Note: Be sure to know what compressed gases are in the system before dissipating them into the atmosphere, as the gases could be toxic and/or lethal. Always check first and wear the required protective equipment.

Vacuum sources of energy are another form of pressure, only it is a pressure that is below atmospheric pressure.

Hazardous Energy Sources

There are several industrial examples where extreme caution must be taken to prevent injury from vacuum sources. Vacuum systems are used in special presses for vacuum forming, in certain packaging applications in both manufacturing and food processing, and in other services such as intake ducts and exhaust systems where fans or blowers remove gases and solids with vacuum. Some compressor and pump applications have high vacuum regions on their intake and suction piping and valves as well.

The real danger with most vacuum energy sources is not only with being drawn into a duct or pipe, but lies in machines or equipment which use vacuum as an energy source to activate something on the machine or within the process. Never forget to lockout or tagout a vacuum control energy source.

Springs are another source of potential energy. The energy potential of springs varies with their size and application.

Energy Sources (cont'd)

Many serious mishaps have been documented which demonstrate how springs have caused serious injury and damage. Springs, when not in any form of tension, either in a stretched or compressed position, pose no real danger. If the spring is stretched or compressed, depending on its design, and held in that position, stored energy is present and if released there is a chance that serious injury and/or damage would result.

Springs and the mechanisms they're attached to can be found throughout many industrial applications. Coil and leaf springs are the most common springs. When working on or near springs always relieve and control the tension first. Ensure that the tension cannot return because of something done on the machine or at another part on an associated machine.

Gravity is another source of potential energy. For any machine or piece of equipment being worked on, whether it is operated by electrics, hydraulics, with pneumatics, or even by hand, and with the energy source under control, certain parts or devices may still have to "come to rest", and it is gravity that causes this to happen. It may be that by removing one of the operating energy sources, the weight of some part shifts and due to gravity there is a subsequent reaction or movement of another part. "What goes up must come down", if there is nothing in place to secure it.

Examples of gravity energy sources which have to be controlled include: counterweights, eccentric drives, camshafts, gates, hydraulic and pneumatic cylinder rods, and conveyors such as bucket elevators and vertical and sloped chain conveyors.

Energy Sources (cont'd)

In any one of these examples there is a chance that something can reverse or come down suddenly if there is nothing in place to secure it. Normally there are devices such as brakes and anti-rotation devices (back-stops) used to prevent coasting or reversing. Blocks, wedges, dogs, and pins are used to secure or prop a unit or part from moving when there is a chance that gravitational forces are possible.

Unintentional Operation

In many industries throughout Canada and United States the frequency and severity of on-the-job accidents and injuries have been increasing despite the more comprehensive and stricter occupational health and safety controls and regulations. This may be partly due to an increase in both the complexity and advancement in technology of machinery, equipment and associated processes.

Accidents and injuries may also be partly attributed to pressure to speed up a job and take shortcuts while performing service and maintenance work. None of these factors should ever cause one to overlook using some common sense before starting the job. Lockout and tagout procedures are there to be used by everyone and never should be overlooked. It takes a little extra time to go through the procedures, but there is no time so well spent as the time one takes to properly lockout and tagout the energy sources of the machinery and equipment that will be worked on.

Most organizations have policies and procedures in place to protect workers from accidents caused by unintentional start-up of equipment. Safe lockout and tagout practices provide a system for rendering a piece of equipment inoperable and powerless so that authorized personnel can perform the required work safely.

Unintentional Operation (cont'd)

Several common ways workers can be injured on machines and equipment which is unintentionally started up include:

- Entanglement in belts, chains, ropes or conveyors.
- Crushing, cuts, or amputations when working on presses, shears or in cylinders or crankcases of engines, pumps or compressors.
- Burns from hot materials and fires and explosions.
- Scalding from steam/vapors, hot fluids, solids and fines.
- Falls and immersion into tanks, vessels, and other containers which hold fluids, slurries or semi-solids.
- Asphyxiation in vessels, bins, silos, tanks or other types of confined spaces.

Unintentionally operated equipment can also cause severe and costly damage to equipment. Often there is a "chain effect" when one piece of equipment unintentionally moves and subsequent equipment is either impacted by the first or it shifts in position and presents another problem.

Another reason for lockout and tagout procedures is to prevent injury to users of the equipment. A tradesperson may be required to adjust or repair a machine and sometimes when spare parts are unavailable, etc., the equipment is not repaired for a prolonged period of time. In that interim period, should the equipment be used inadvertently by the operator, serious damage and injury could occur. This is one more reason why locks and tags have to be used.

What Should a Lockout Program Include?

A typical equipment lockout program should consist of at least the following components:

- Safety Lockout Policy
- Lockout Procedures
- Lockout Equipment and Resources
- Methods for Enforcing the Procedures
- Employee Training
- Updating and Follow-up Procedures

The equipment lockout policy is usually a series of short statements which clearly state the following:

- Why equipment lockout is necessary?
- When is equipment lockout required?
- Who is responsible?
- What are the consequences for non-compliance?
- What training is required prior to doing the job?

Lockout Program

The equipment lockout procedures should clearly describe the approved methods and practices employees must follow prior to beginning work on any machine or piece of equipment.

Typical lockout procedures would be similar to these:

- Guarding equipment against mechanical movement.
- Identifying all energy sources to the machine.
- Elimination of stored energy.
- Identifying valves, switches, and controls.
- Determine approved methods for locking out each device.
- Shutdown practices for specific machines and equipment.
- Closing off auxiliary lines, controls, and support equipment.

Lockout Program (cont'd)

- Tagging procedures for valves, switches and controls.
- Application of approved equipment lockout devices.
- Using locks and tags.
- Describe color scheme for tags.
- Reporting procedures prior to starting the job.
- Attempt start-up prior to starting the job, after lockout is done.
- Checking that all tools, equipment and parts are accounted for prior to official start-up.
- Ensuring that all work related personnel are accounted for prior to official start-up.
- Carrying out approved lock and tag removal procedures prior to official start-up.

Note: Equipment lockout policies and procedures must be complied with whenever conducting maintenance, repair, installation and service activities. Failure to comply can put the employee(s) in danger because of the potential hazards associated with the energy sources at or near the machinery and equipment.

Note: Performing maintenance or testing on an operating machine, process equipment, or within the system is not permitted when there is danger to the health and safety of any employee.

In those special cases where it is necessary that the machine, process equipment or part of the system must remain in operation during maintenance and testing work, it is general practice that written safe work permits/procedures be developed in each of these instances.

Equipment Lockout Procedures

As a general rule, equipment lockout is the preferred method in most companies for ensuring that machinery and process equipment is properly secured against any unintentional start-up while people are performing maintenance and service functions.

Equipment lockout procedures have certain advantages over tagout procedures according to the following:

- Locks are difficult to bypass, as it would require a major effort to compromise a quality lock. Tags can be easily removed.
- Tags can be easily damaged by environmental or physical conditions.
- Tags only serve as a warning and are not to be considered a "safety device", whereas locks are.
- Locks, once applied to a switch, control or valve speak everyone's language.

Equipment Lockout Procedures

Locks cannot be easily misunderstood, whereas tags can be if people are speaking a different language or cannot read well. There is no question what a lock means when it is installed on a power switch for example.

Lockout is the preferred method when the energy isolation device is capable of being locked out, but there are certain situations where tagout systems are acceptable on their own. For example:

- When the equipment cannot be physically locked out. Some types of machines or equipment may not be easily locked out without significant modification or redesign, therefore, they are considered to be incapable of being locked out.
- There are instances when tagout systems are used very effectively and safely and are considered to be an approved alternative to lockout.

Equipment Lockout Procedures (cont'd)

Some machinery or process equipment in complex systems that are controlled through a series of computer systems may be difficult or not even feasible to employ a total lockout system. Appropriate tagout procedures are developed and employed instead.

When tagout is selected over lockout, it must provide the employees with the same level of safety and protection an approved lockout procedure would. If possible, consider implementing additional measures such as:

- Isolating a portion of a circuit.
- Disconnecting a switch.
- Removing or covering a valve handwheel.
- Taking an electrical plug apart.
- Doing that something extra that gives an edge in personnel safety.

Once the company has determined what procedures are to be used for equipment lockout and tagout, there has to be assurance that the locks and tags meet specific standards in order to be in compliance with the regulations and policy. There are several basic performance requirements for selecting approved lockout equipment:

1. Must be identifiable. The lock and/or tag should be recognized as being the standard type used throughout the organization. No one should be confused by a mixed assortment of locks, tags, and lockout device clips.

2. Locks and tags must never be used for purposes which are not associated with lockout and tagout procedures and functions.

3. Locks and tags must be durable enough to withstand the harsh physical and environmental exposures they are often placed in. Types of exposures considered are: chemicals, extreme temperatures, weather conditions, wet, dusty and abrasive environments. Tags must remain legible throughout their exposure to these types of conditions. A soggy, illegible tag is like having no tag at all.

Equipment Lockout Procedures (cont'd)

4. Locks and tags must be substantial. This means that the locks and tags are secure enough to prevent unauthorized removal through the inadvertent or accidental actions of fellow workers.

5. Locks and tags must be standardized in color, shape, and size. These standards must be adhered to by all employees, departments and outside contractors who are working on site.

6. Locks and tags must be easily recognized by any employee. They should easily recognize, the lock, tag or both, and know who is working on the machine or equipment. If a lock and tag is in place, and that person is not around, co-workers will know who to look for when the job is complete, or, if work is still in progress, confirm that the worker is safe.

7. By identifying the people who own the locks and tags the supervisor and safety officer can determine who is and who is not in

Procedures/Controls

compliance with the equipment lockout and tagout procedures. Action on any non-compliance should be undertaken immediately.

8. The individual is both responsible and accountable for the lock and tag. Locks and tags should have the owner's name on them, and in some cases, the owner's photograph may be required. Remember, each individual is responsible for the correct application of his locks and tags and ensuring full compliance with the company's equipment lockout and tagout procedures.

Applying Energy Controls

Energy isolation and lockout/tagout procedures are to be applied only by trained and authorized employees. While certain procedures will vary because of the diversity of machinery, equipment, and processes, there are basic rules and requirements that are common to most organizations.

Applying Energy Controls (cont'd)

When applying energy controls consideration should be given to the following points:

Purpose: Convey the message why there are procedures for ensuring lockout and tagout of energy isolating devices for machinery and equipment and why these must be followed whenever maintenance or servicing is performed. It must be clear that full compliance by everyone is mandatory and any violation with these procedures is neither permissible or acceptable.

Preparation For Shutdown: Before any machinery or equipment is shut off to lock or tag it out, the following must be known:

- What type(s) of energy sources are present?

- What amount of energy is present?

- What hazards do the energy sources present?

- What method(s) are used to control the energy source(s)?

Equipment Shutdown: The equipment must be shutdown using the appropriate operating and process controls. There must be an orderly procedure in place for preparing the machine or equipment for the application of locks and/or tags. When preparing to shutdown any equipment consider the following:

- Notification must be given to all personnel affected by the shutdown and that lockout and/or tagout procedures will be applied. One cannot simply shutdown a piece of equipment or any part of the process when it could effect other parts of the system. A sudden shutdown could jeopardize someone's safety.

- Shutdown the equipment using normal procedures for each specific piece of equipment so that nobody gets injured during the shutdown.

Applying Energy Controls (cont'd)

- Isolation involves the activation of all energy isolation devices from the equipment so there is complete isolation from all energy sources.

Application of Lockout and Tagout: The lockout and tagout devices are applied only by authorized personnel who are doing the work. Only standard lockout and tagout devices supplied by the employer are to be used. A lockout device clip should be used if the lock(s) cannot be placed directly on the energy control. Every employee performing work on the equipment must attach their own personal lock and/or tag. Always remember to provide all the necessary information as requested by the tag.

Control of Stored Energy: Consider the following points when guarding against the possibility of stored energy located within the machinery or process equipment:

Energy Controls

- Inspect the system to make sure all parts have stopped moving.
- If required, install ground wires.
- Release any tension on springs or linkages and block/restrain the movement of spring loaded parts.
- Attach warning tags to the pins and clamps of any spring mechanisms and linkages and restrict the release or access to only those personnel who are authorized to do so.
- Block or brace parts that could fall because of gravity.
- Block parts in hydraulic and pneumatic systems that could move because of a loss in pressure.
- Bleed hydraulic and pneumatic lines and leave vents or drains open.

Applying Energy Controls (cont'd)

- Drain process piping systems and close valves to prevent the flow of hazardous materials.
- If a line must be blocked where there is no valve, use a blank flange.
- Purge lines, tanks, piping cylinders and casings with proper purging gases or fluids.
- Dissipate extreme cold or heat and wear approved personal protective equipment when working in hazardous material areas.
- If any stored energy can accumulate, monitor for this in order to keep it below hazardous levels.

Equipment Isolation Verification: This is the last step taken before actual maintenance or service work begins. There are several ways to verify isolation:

- Attempt start-up, but first insure that all personnel are clear. Press all start buttons and other activation controls.
- Use test equipment, such as a voltmeter, to determine if there is any electrical energy source at the machine. Other types of test equipment should be made available in order to verify the presence of other energy sources.
- Visually inspect the machine to ensure that any other activation controls and switches are off and that locks and tags are securely in place in all the proper locations.

Disconnecting Energy Controls

Once the maintenance and servicing work has been completed proper procedures must be taken to disconnect the energy controls before start-up commences. Several steps to consider include:

- Remove all tools from the work area.

Applying Energy Controls (cont'd)

- Ensure that the machine and equipment is fully assembled.
- Do a head count to make sure everyone is accounted for and clear of the machinery and equipment.
- Notify everyone who works in the area that lockout/tagout is being removed and start-up is to commence shortly.
- Remove the lockout and tagout devices. Except in emergencies, each device must be removed by the person who put it on.
- In some workplaces the last person to remove their lock is responsible for removing the lockout device clip, taking the tag off and signing it before turning it in to the control room or giving it to a supervisor.
- In some companies, the supervisor removes their lock last.
- Follow a checklist of required steps and procedures to re-energize the machinery or process equipment. In some companies only a qualified electrician can

Energy Controls/Testing

re-energize the electric energy sources.

Testing/Positioning During Lockout

There are times when the machinery or process equipment must be either tested or re-positioned before any further service or maintenance work is undertaken. In order to safely do this, consider the following steps:

- Make sure that all non-essential equipment, tools, parts, and test instruments are removed from the work area.
- Make sure that equipment guards, safety restraints, blocking, rigging, and parts have been either removed or adequately secured.
- Make sure that non-essential personnel are clear of the machine or equipment.
- Remove the lockout and tagout devices, remembering that only the workers who applied them should remove them.

Testing/Positioning During Lockout (cont'd)

- Re-energize the equipment and proceed to start the machinery or process equipment which is required in order to perform either the tests or re-positioning.

- De-energize and reapply the energy control devices in accordance with the standard lockout and tagout procedures.

Note: When maintenance and servicing work lasts more than one work shift, the lockout and tagout protection must not be interrupted.

At many workplaces employees who are leaving work at the end of their shift do not remove their locks or tags until the job is completed. The job may last several days or weeks. In some cases, an employee cannot remove their lock or tag until people arriving for the next shift are ready to put their locks and tags on in the appropriate locations.

Outside Contractors

When contractors or other outside personnel are performing maintenance or service on machinery and process equipment they too must comply with the company's lockout and tagout policy and procedures. It is imperative that the outside contractor be completely informed about how the lockout and tagout procedures work. The contractor's employees who are on site are required to fully comply with the rules and procedures as stated by the company's energy control program.

Lockout and Tagout Training

Without proper training, the employee may error in performing equipment lockout and tagout. They may work on the equipment in an unsafe manner. In order to have an effective and safe lockout and tagout system, training (and occasional refresher) programs should be prepared and presented to the company's employees.

Training (cont'd)

The training program should include:

- Purpose of the lockout and tagout policy and procedures.
- Hazardous energy recognition.
- Identify different types of energy sources.
- Locate points of energy control.
- Application of locks and tags.
- Wearing personal protective equipment.
- Re-energizing procedures.
- Enforcement and discipline.

The training program must ensure that personnel are familiar with all procedures and know where to obtain further information regarding the company's equipment lockout and tagout policy and procedures.

Refresher training should be repeated semi-annually and complete training must be provided for all new employees and contractors.

Enforcement and Discipline

The company should include the means for enforcing full compliance to their equipment lockout and tagout policy and procedures. The company should take disciplinary action when there is non-compliance to the policy and procedures.

Periodic inspection of lockout and tagout procedures should be undertaken by someone qualified to do so. The purpose of the inspection is to locate any non-compliance, and to make appropriate corrections before any further work is completed.

SECTION NINE QUESTIONS
Equipment Lockout and Tagout

1. Many industrial accidents are caused by the uncontrollable release of hazardous energy.

   ☐ true   ☐ false

2. Identify the first step in any lockout or tagout procedure.

   Answer: _____

3. _____ is a method of keeping equipment from being set in motion and endangering employees.

   Answer: _____

4. In lockout, a disconnect switch, valve, or other energy isolating mechanism is put in the safe or off position.

   ☐ true   ☐ false

5. It is common practice, and in many cases law, that all lockout and tagout materials and devices be supplied by the employer.

   ☐ true   ☐ false

6. Procedures for lockout and tagout are necessary whenever performing service and maintenance to any machinery or equipment where there could be injury from:

   Answer: _____

7. List five common jobs and activities for which lockout and tagout are used:

   Answer: _____

8. Hazardous energy can come from many sources, but it is always one of two classifications. These are:

   Answer: _____

9. _____ is the force caused by the motion of the object or part.

   ☐ kinetic energy   ☐ potential energy
   ☐ transitional energy   ☐ fluid energy

10. _____ is the force stored in an object or part that remains inactive, but can be either slowly or suddenly released.

    ☐ kinetic energy   ☐ potential energy
    ☐ transitional energy   ☐ fluid energy

11. Identify two types of electrical energy sources common to rotating equipment and associated machinery. Provide a brief explanation of each type.

Answer: _____

12. Typically, thermal energy cannot be just turned off or eliminated; one can usually only control it.

☐ true   ☐ false

13. "Cold" is considered to be an energy source.

☐ true   ☐ false

14. "Heat" is considered to be an energy source.

☐ true   ☐ false

15. Exothermic chemical reactions:

☐ raise temperatures   ☐ lower temperatures

16. Endothermic chemical reactions:

☐ raise temperatures   ☐ lower temperatures

17. Thermal energy sources can be difficult to simply turn off.

☐ true   ☐ false

18. List three types of common potential energy sources found in rotating equipment and associated machinery:

Answer: _____

19. Explain why hydraulic fluid under pressure can prove to be very dangerous.

Answer: _____

20. Compressed gases remain _____ when stored under constant pressure and temperature within an appropriate container.

☐ inert
☐ dynamic
☐ stable

21. What is one of the real dangers with vacuum energy sources?

Answer: _____

22. A spring, either stretched or compressed depending on its design, contains stored energy. What must be done before any work is done?

Answer: _____

23. Gravity may cause machines and their parts to "come to rest." Explain what this statement means.

Answer: _____

24. List examples of gravity energy sources which have to be controlled.

Answer: _____

25. "It takes a little extra time to go through the procedures, but there is no time so well spent as the time taken to properly lockout and tagout the energy sources of machinery and equipment that will be worked on."
Explain the importance of this statement.

Answer: _____

26. Several common ways workers can be injured on machinery and equipment which is unintentionally started up include:

Answer: _____

27. Often there is a _____ when one piece of equipment unintentionally moves and subsequent equipment is either impacted by the first or shifts position and presents another problem.

Answer: _____

28. A typical equipment lockout program should consist of several main components. These are:

Answer: _____

29. A typical lockout procedure would be closing off auxiliary lines, controls, and support equipment.
☐ true   ☐ false

30. When would written safe work permits/procedures be required?

Answer: _____

31. Tags only serve as a warning and are not to be considered a "safety device", whereas locks are.
☐ true   ☐ false

32. Before any machinery or equipment is shut off to lock or tag out, several things must be known. List four factors which must be known first.

Answer: _____

Equipment Lockout and Tagout

33. Why can't one simply just shutdown a piece of equipment or any part of the process?

Answer: _____

34. It is not important that every employee performing work on the equipment must attach their own personal lock and/or tag.

☐ true   ☐ false

35. One method for controlling stored energy is to bleed hydraulic and pneumatic lines and to leave vents or drains open.

☐ true   ☐ false

36. List three methods for verifying that equipment isolation has occurred:

Answer: _____

37. To remove the lockout and tagout devices, except in emergencies, each device must be removed by:

☐ the supervisor
☐ the person who put it on
☐ anyone who performed work on the machine

38. Are the contractor's employees who are on site required to fully comply with the rules and procedures of the company's stated energy control program? Explain the answer.

☐ yes   ☐ no

Provide an explanation to your response.

Answer: _____

39. In order to have an effective and safe lockout and tagout system, training and occasional refresher programs should be prepared and presented to the employees. The training program should include several main features:

Answer: _____

40. The company should include the means for enforcing full compliance to their equipment lockout and tagout policy and procedures.

☐ true   ☐ false

SECTION TEN

FORMULAS AND CONVERSIONS

Length

1 metre (m)	= 100 cm	= 1000 mm
1 micron (μm)	= 1 mm x 10^{-3}	= 1m x 10^{-6}
1 inch	= 25.4 mm	= 0.0254 m
1 foot	= 304.8 mm	= 0.3048 m
0.001 inch	= 0.0254 mm	= 25.4 μm

Force

1 newton (N)	= 10^5 dynes	
	= 0.2248 lb-force	
1 kilogram-force	= 9.807 N	
1 lb-force	= 4.448 N	

Mass /Weight

1 kilogram (kg)	= 1000 grams (g)	
	= 9.8 newtons	
1 pound (lb)	= 16 ounces (oz)	
1 kg	= 2.2 lb	
1 lb	= 0.4545 kg	
1 oz	= 28.35 g	

Density

1 kg/m^3	= 10^{-3} g/cm^3
1 oz/in^3	= 1.73 g/cm^3
1 oz/in^3	= 0.00173 g/mm3

Area

1 m^2	= 10^4 cm^2
	= 10^6 mm^2
1 in^2	= 6.4516 cm2
1 ft^2	= 929.03 cm2

Note: The kilogram is a unit of mass and exerts a force of 9.8 Newtons due to gravity at sea level. A force of one Newton will accelerate a one kilogram mass 1 metre/sec^2

FORMULAS AND CONVERSIONS

Acceleration

Note: Beware of confusing the imperial term for the acceleration due to gravity "g" with the metric term for gram (g). In metric the acceleration due to gravity is 9.807 m/s²

1 g (acceleration)	= 32.2 ft/sec²
	= 9.807 m/s²
1 ft/sec	= 0.3048 m/s
1 m/s	= 3.2808 ft/sec

Energy

1 joule (J)	= 1 Nm	= 1 Watt second
1 ft lb-force	= 1.356 J	
1 calorie (international)	= 4.1868 J	
1 calorie (dietetic)	= 4.1855 kJ	
1 Btu	= 778 ft lb	= 1.055 kJ
1 kilowatt hour	= 3.6 MJ	

Power

1 Watt (W)	= 1 J/s	= 1 Nm/s
1 HP	= 746 W	= 550 ft lb/sec
	= 0.707 Btu/sec	
1 kW	= 1.340 HP	

Pressure

1 pascal	= 1 N/m²	
1 kilopascal (kPa)		= 0.145 psi
1 psi	= 6.895 kPa	
1 atmosphere	= 14.7 psi	= 101.325 kPa
Absolute press.		
	= gage press. + atmospheric press.	
1 bar	= 100 kPa	= 14.5 psi
Pressure (psi)	= Force(lb) / Area(in²)	
Pressure (kPa)	= Force(N) / Area(m²) x 10^{-3}	
Head pressure (H_2O)	= Height (ft) x 0.433 psi	
Head pressure (H_2O)	= Height (m) x 9.8 kPa	

496 FORMULAS AND CONVERSIONS

Electrical

W = Watts (power)	V = Volts or EMF
I = Amperes	R = Resistance (Ω)
V = I x R;	I = V/R;	R = V/I
W = I² R	W = V² /R
1 Hertz = 60 CPM	

Viscosity

Absolute (dynamic) viscosity measurement units are the centipoise (cP) and the millipascal second (mPa·s)

Kinematic viscosity measurement units are m²/s or mm²/s. The latter is referred to as the centistoke (cSt) and is commonly used in the petroleum industry.

Relative viscosity is usually measured in Saybolt Universal Seconds.

Saybolt Universal Seconds (SUS) to Centistokes (cSt)

 32 to 100 SUS

cSt = 0.2253 x SUS - (194.4/SUS)

 100 to 240 SUS

cSt = 0.2193 x SUS - (134.6/SUS)

 Over 240 SUS

cSt = SUS/4.635

Centipoise (cP) = Centistoke (cSt) x density
 [(kg/m³) x 10⁻³]

Thermal Expansion

ΔL = change in length

L = original length

α = coefficient of thermal linear expansion

ΔT = change in temperature (Co) or (Fo)

(°C and °F refers to Celsius and Fahrenheit degrees respectively)

ΔL = α x L x ΔT

FORMULAS AND CONVERSIONS

Material	α per °C	α per °F
Aluminum	22.3×10^{-6}	12.4×10^{-6}
Brass	18.0×10^{-6}	10.0×10^{-6}
Concrete	12.0×10^{-6}	6.7×10^{-6}
Copper	16.2×10^{-6}	9.0×10^{-6}
Iron	11.9×10^{-6}	6.6×10^{-6}
Carbon steel	11.3×10^{-6}	6.3×10^{-6}
Lead	29.3×10^{-6}	16.3×10^{-6}

Temperature

Kelvin temp.(K)
= Celsius temp.(°C) + 273.150

$100°C = 373.15 K$

Rankine temp.(R)
= Fahrenheit temp.(°F) + 459.70

Celsius temp.(°C)
= (Fahrenheit temp.(°F) - 32) x 5/9

Fahrenheit temp.(°F)
= (Celsius temp.(°C) x 9/5) + 32

Fluid flow

1 US gallon	= 0.83267 Imp. gallon
1 Imp. gallon	= 1.20095 US gallon
1 US gallon/min.	= 231 in^3/min.
1 Imp. gallon/min.	= 277.42 in^3/min.
1 US gallon/min.	= 3.785 litres/min.
1 US gallon/min.	= 3785 cm^3/min.
1 litre	= 1000 cm^3
Velocity(ft/sec)	= (0.3208 x flow rate(gpm))/ID area (in^2)
Velocity (m/s)	= flow rate (m^3/s)/area(m^2)
Velocity (m/s)	= (flow rate (litres/s) x 10^{-3}) /area (m^2)

Unbalance (weight x radius)

From	To	Multiplier
oz-in	gram-mm	720
gram-mm	oz-in	0.00139
oz-in	gram-in	28.35
gram-in	oz-in	0.0353
gram-in	gram-mm	25.4
gram-mm	gram-in	0.03937
gram-mm	gram-metres	0.001
gram-metres	gram-mm	1000

Formulae

Exitation force

= Stiffness (K) + Mass (m) + Damping (C)

Where:

Stiffness is in lbs/in or kg/cm

Mass is in $lb.sec^2/in$ or $kg.sec^2/cm$

Damping is in lb.sec/in or kg.sec/cm

Displacement, Velocity and Acceleration

Imperial Units:

D = Displacement (mils peak to peak)

V = Velocity (inches/second peak)

A = Acceleration (g peak)

F = Frequency of the vibration in CPM

$D = 19.10 \times 10^3 \times (V)/(F)$

$D = 70.40 \times 10^6 \times (A)/(F)^2$

$V = 52.36 \times 10^{-6} \times (D) \times (F)$

$V = 3.87 \times 10^3 \times (A)/(F)$

$A = 14.20 \times 10^{-9} \times (D) \times (F)^2$

$A = 0.27 \times 10^{-3} \times (V) \times (F)$

Displacement, Velocity and Acceleration (cont'd)

Metric Units:

D = Displacement (μm peak to peak)

V = Velocity (mm/second peak)

A = Acceleration (g peak)

F = Frequency of the vibration in CPM

$D = 19.10 \times 10^{3} \ (V)/(F)$

$D = 1.79 \times 10^{9} \ (A)/(F)^{2}$

$V = 52.36 \times 10^{-6} \ (D) \times (F)$

$V = 93.58 \times 10^{3} \ (A)/(F)$

$A = 0.56 \times 10^{-9} \ (D) \ (F)^{2}$

$A = 10.69 \times 10^{-6} \ (V) \ (F)$

Force generated by an out of balance weight.

Using Imperial Units:

$F = 1.77 \times R \times W \times (RPM/1000)^{2}$

Where

F = The force generated in pounds

R = Radius of the out of balance weight in inches

W = Weight of the out of balance in ounces

Using Metric Units:

$F = 0.011 \times R \times M \times RPM^{2}$

Where

F = The force generated in Newtons

R = Radius of the out of balance weight in metres

M = Mass of the out of balance in kilograms

500   FORMULAS AND CONVERSIONS

Using Gram-Inch Units:

$F = 0.0625 \times R \times W \times (RPM/1000)^2$

Where

F = The force generated in pounds

R = Radius of the out of balance weight in inches

W = Weight of the out of balance in grams

Residual Unbalance Tolerances

1. Max. residual unbalance

$U_{max} = 56347 \ W/N^2$

2. Max. residual unbalance

$U_{max} = 4 \ W/N$

Where

W = Journal static load in pounds

N = Maximum continuous speed in RPM

The metric eqivalent of the above is:

1. Max. residual unbalance

$U_{max} = 89 \times 10^6 \ W/N_2$

2. Max. residual unbalance

$U_{max} = 6350 \ W/N$

Where

W = Journal static load in kilograms

N = Maximum continuous speed in RPM

The first equation, gives an unbalance force approximately equal to 10% cf the journal load.

When rotating speeds are low, the second equation will result in lower unbalance tolerances. As speeds are increased, the first equation will provide the lowest tolerances.